# HOW TO
# *heal*
# A BAD BIRTH
## MAKING SENSE, MAKING PEACE, & MOVING ON

By Melissa Bruijn and Debby Gould

## Dedication

*For mothers who have been impacted by birth, their partners, their families, and those who support them.*

Photography by Jen Shipston from The He{ART} of Motherhood
Cover design by Jesse Richardson

First published 2016
Reprinted 2017

National Library of Australia Cataloguing-in-Publication entry

Bruijn, Melissa J., 1968- author.
How to heal a bad birth : making sense, making peace and moving on
/ Melissa Bruijn & Debby Gould.

ISBN: 9780992351601 (paperback)

Childbirth--Psychological aspects.
Labor (Obstetrics)--Complications--Psychological aspects.
Delivery (Obstetrics)--Psychological aspects.
Post-traumatic stress disorder--Treatment.
Psychic trauma--Treatment.

Gould, Debby A., 1971- author.

618.76

---

# Contents

## PART TWO: HOW DO YOU FEEL RIGHT NOW?

## PART THREE: TOOLS FOR YOUR HEALING JOURNEY

## PART FOUR: THE CONTINUING JOURNEY

## APPENDICES

# ABOUT US

Melissa Bruijn and Debby Gould founded Birthtalk.org in 2002. As sisters-in-law they have seen first-hand how a traumatic birth can impact upon the early months and years of parenting, and were inspired to create Birthtalk.org with the desire that no other family should experience such isolation, desperation and confusion after a birth.

**Debby Gould** Debby originally trained and worked as a midwife, and is now a childbirth educator, doula and mother of two children. Debby is the primary facilitator of Birthtalk's Healing From Birth meetings, as well as Birthtalk's popular empowering birth education courses. She also works as a Private Birth Consultant, Childbirth Educator, and doula offering individualised support for women and men after a traumatic birth, or for those working towards an empowering birth. As a Director of Birthtalk, Debby has presented at the Australian College of Midwives Queensland State Conference, and spoken as a guest lecturer to Bachelor of Midwifery students at Griffith University and the University of Queensland. She has given presentations for The Australian Doula College and Australian Breastfeeding Association counsellor conferences, plus provides Professional Development workshops for hospital midwives and doulas on the topic of Birth Trauma and how to support women to heal and have better births. Debby has appeared in the media including radio, newspaper, birth and parenting magazines and podcasts, offering an experienced heath professional's voice to the issue of traumatic birth.

**Melissa Bruijn** Melissa had a diverse career before becoming a mother, including Music Director for many of South Bank Parkland's family festivals and Music Licensing Supervisor at EMI Music/Virgin Records in Sydney, Australia. After her first birth, a traumatic experience that ended in a caesarean, Melissa slowly realized that she was not 'ok'…and found that few people understood what she was going through. She embarked upon a roller-coaster ride of reading, researching, and soul-searching and was supported on this journey by Debby, who shared ideas and information that gave the healing she was experiencing new meaning and depth. Melissa has gone on to have two more babies, both empowering and positive experiences. Melissa is responsible for the creation and management of Birthtalk's website and social media plus their blog, Birth Trauma Truths, aiming to spread awareness, understanding and hope to women who have been impacted by their births.

# ABOUT BIRTHTALK.ORG

Birthtalk is a unique support and education organization founded in 2002. Birthtalk specialises in recovering from a traumatic birth, and working towards an empowering birth in any scenario. A cornerstone of Birthtalk's services are free "Healing from Birth" meetings that form the basis for the material shared in this book. Since 2002, these meetings have been attended by women, men, support people, student midwives and health professionals wanting to further their understanding about the impact of traumatic birth and discover ways to heal and move on. Birthtalk also runs empowering antenatal education courses, including a VBAC (Vaginal Birth After Caesarean) course. Birthtalk increases awareness within the wider community by guest-speaking at community events, seminars and conferences, guest-lecturing at university for student midwives, and providing in-service education for health professionals in hospital settings. Birthtalk is based in Brisbane, Australia, and offers support to women worldwide.

# A SPECIAL THANK YOU BEFORE WE START

We have seen many, many women and men work through these ideas and emerge more fully 'present', more able to feel a depth of love for their children, and move on, whether it is to another birth (often using our tools in preparation for a much better experience), or just moving forward with peace in their heart.

Their stories are scattered throughout the pages of this book, and on our website, blog, and Facebook page, as they offer their experiences to inspire and support others.

We thank all of them for giving us permission to share their journeys to support and inspire others and we honour you, the reader, as you undertake your own journey.

Thank you, and enormous hugs from us both.

*Melissa and Deb*

# PART ONE: BEGINNING YOUR HEALING JOURNEY

# Welcome

## ONE NIGHT AT A BIRTHTALK MEETING

There was no way that Sophie was going to talk. She had told Deb as much, when she rang to RSVP for that evening's 'Healing From Birth' meeting. Deb reassured Sophie over the phone that it was absolutely fine for her to not say anything, and later, when Sophie arrived, Deb whispered to Melissa, "Sophie just wants to listen." A common situation. Melissa nodded, made a note, and the meeting began.

Eleven women and one man introduced themselves to the circle, telling us how old their children were, and a bit about why they had come. When we got to Sophie, she gave her name, but as soon as she tried to say why she was there it got too much. She sat quietly crying, overwhelmed with emotion, tears running down her cheeks, and shook her head, motioning for us to move on. We gave her a minute, and then went to the next person, indicating that Sophie could talk at any time if she wanted to. When the circle came around to Melissa, Deb suggested she begin a more in-depth explanation of her own birth, the feelings surrounding it, and the massive fall out afterwards.

As Melissa spoke, many heads were nodding, some people could only look at their hands, and there were some quiet sniffles and searching for tissues as aspects of her experience resonated with some of those attending. As Melissa finished, she said, "I won't talk about some aspects of my healing journey now, as they will come out as we work through some of your birth stories tonight." At this Sophie could contain herself no longer. She blurted out, "But … how do I heal?"

We let her know that was a really good question, and that the answer was not the same for everyone. We shared that even though there were many steps, the order that people addressed their issues depended on various things. "Well," Sophie said, and her whole story spilled out.

It became very clear why she had not wanted to speak in the beginning, and very clear why she was struggling to deal with her birth. As we discussed her situation, you could see the understanding and clarity she received brighten her whole face, and change her entire posture. She left that meeting with a completely different understanding about birth, and about herself and the way forward.

**And that's why we have written this book.**

We have seen so many women undergo this transformation, whether in one meeting or over a number of months. Now we want to offer you this opportunity too, so you can feel a similar relief, and gain clarity and understanding, and find a new way forward.

Thank you for considering taking the healing journey with us – and welcome to Birthtalk.

# HOW TO USE THIS BOOK

This book is intended as a compass for healing a bad birth, leading you in new directions, yet always towards healing for you and your family.

We understand that, as a parent, you get very little time to yourself. That is why we have organised particular sections of this book in short, easy-to-read grabs, to make it as simple as possible to begin the healing process. Other sections have longer explanations, for when you have more space to deepen your understanding and further your healing.

You may find some things repeated in different parts of the book; that's just because we are assuming that you may not have time to read the whole book at once, so we will repeat things, if they are important to the healing process, and may help you at that moment.

But before you jump in and look for answers to the burning questions that led you to purchase this book in the first place, we ask that you stop and do this first:

Read the chapter titled *The foundations of your healing journey* (p37).

We know you want answers, and we know you are likely hurting, and need some relief *now*. Yet without an understanding of the essential information within this chapter, you won't get very far down the healing track. This is the reason you are here – because birth trauma is not understood in our culture, which is why it's hard to get support, and hard to recognise what's happening to you.

In this chapter you will find vital information in sections such as:

- *What is a traumatic or bad birth anyway?* (p42): This section sets you up to be able to understand the rest of the book. (Even if you already know your birth was bad).
- *Birthtalk Breakdown – a new tool* (p47): This special tool may change the way you think about your birth, and give you important clues for your healing journey.

After this, we suggest you also read *How do I heal?* (p61) in the chapter titled *Healing – the big questions.*

This section will give you further understanding of how your journey may unfold and explains more about how to use this book to support yourself.

Before you can make peace and move on, you need to make sense of your experience. A number of chapters are designed to provide this clarity and equip you with ideas to enhance your understanding of the rest of the book. Reading *The foundations of your healing journey* (p37) will likely involve some 'light bulb moments', some huge sighs of relief, and possibly some tears as you learn more about what's going on – and that there is a way out. So we encourage you to 'go there' and explore this chapter first.

After you have read *The foundations of your healing journey*, and *How do I heal?*, you may find it helpful to read *Sharing your story – finally being heard* (p111). This chapter is representative of what is experienced by the women who attend our 'Healing From Birth' meetings when they tell their story to us for the first time. And while we may not be able to meet with you in person, this chapter can offer you a glimpse into our meetings, and the process that enables women's fears to be turned into hope for healing.

Then, when you have read these sections of the book just jump right in! Turn to whichever section you think will best meet your current needs. Some women use the tools and ideas in this book in conjunction with a counsellor or a supportive midwife. Some explore the sections with their partner or a trusted friend. Most importantly, be gentle with yourself. You are amazing and courageous to just to get through your experience and to make it to the point where you are able to embrace the idea of healing.

We stand with you as you walk forward on this new path.

# WHY WOMEN COME TO BIRTHTALK MEETINGS

One of the most important initial steps on the healing journey from a bad birth can be the validation that comes from hearing other women's stories, and often hearing them express similar emotions and responses to those that you are experiencing. At the start of each Birthtalk meeting, we invite those attending to share what has brought them to the session. Following are some insights from previous Birthtalk attendees:

> *The days that followed the birth were full of anxiety. I had flashbacks of the experience the entire first three nights and didn't sleep a wink. I felt an incredible sense of failure surrounding the second 'pushing' stage of the birth and I started the whole process of motherhood from a place of extreme vulnerability, which shook me deeply.* **Christy**

> *In the days after the birth, my wife sometimes cried without warning or apparent cause. I can see now that she was in the grip of strong feelings that weren't being acknowledged by those around her, and which she couldn't put into words herself. Trying to talk about it made her cry, and she didn't know why.* **Ben**

> *I could not stop thinking about the birth and replaying it over and over. I could not stop the emotion coming out when I had quiet moments to myself. I would often cry in the shower or at night when I was trying to fall asleep, but I couldn't sleep because I kept replaying his birth in my mind. This was crazy when I was sleep deprived already from getting up to the baby. Why wouldn't my mind just be quiet and forget?* **Kerri**

> *I felt guilty, ashamed, upset, let down (by myself) and like I hadn't 'finished the job' – physically, emotionally and mentally. I was continually told to 'get over it' or 'forget about it' because I had a beautiful, healthy boy. This made me feel even more guilty. Why couldn't I get past this horrible birth experience when I was so lucky to have my beautiful boy? Why couldn't I just let it go?* **Sue Ellen**

> *I knew I was in trouble (mentally). I was not coping with basics: driving, getting out of the house. My confidence was shot with anything and everything; I wasn't eating properly, and was having nightmares and flashbacks about the birth.* **Neve**

*I just wanted to get my life back in order. I was suffering panic attacks and my newfound naturopath suggested I go to Birthtalk for a debrief. I also had not started my periods again and for some reason I believed that it was due to mental blocking rather than a physical reason.* **Tina**

*I suffered from separation anxiety with my daughter and checked on her constantly throughout the day and night while she slept. I was hypervigilant, much more so than the other first time mums.* **Sharona**

*Although I don't classify myself as deeply 'traumatised' by my birth, I had a great deal of self-criticism during and since the birth. I thought I should regard myself as 'lucky' to have the birth I did (it was very fast) and any negative feelings about it should be glossed over. I found myself negatively comparing myself with my mother who appeared as a 'superwoman' figure in her attitude to birth and I was very upset when she commented about the length of my labour. I felt that she considered it was almost inconsequential, whereas to me, it had been overwhelmingly frightening and unbearable. I feel I didn't connect with my baby until we came home.* **Anna**

*The birth of my second baby was a successful vaginal birth after caesarean (VBAC) and initially I felt euphoric that I'd succeeded to birth my baby vaginally. However, in the postpartum period I kept reliving the final twenty minutes of my birth and experienced a lot of distress. I couldn't understand why I couldn't be happy with my birth and wondered what was wrong with me that had led me to feel so dissatisfied with my experience.* **Sally**

*When I arrived home with my newborn son I was so happy and relieved to be out of hospital. But over the coming weeks I started to feel more and more like a failure. I had trouble breastfeeding, trouble bonding with my baby. I was having panic attacks when trying to get out of the house. I was hypervigilant, checking in on him two or three times while he was napping. I just felt like a failure. My husband could not understand what was going on; I also had this feeling that something wasn't quite right with my body – I kept getting infections and it felt like my body kept letting me down.* **Trudy**

*I was **so** affected by this birth. Postnatal Depression (PND), Post-Traumatic Stress Disorder (PTSD), nightmares, going over and over the birth. I had no confidence, almost rechecking everything I did. I was unable to do normal things and felt that I was failing or doing a bad job of everything. I was overprotective of my son, not to mention I had an injury that required surgery to repair. In regards to relationships, it almost cost us our marriage. Luckily I had previously been depressed when my mother died, so I knew I was in trouble and got professional help. But if I hadn't, I could be dead by now. I was so emotionally low, so lost and felt so betrayed, abused, raped and so abandoned by the people who are supposed to look after you. I had months of thoughts that were not healthy. If I was driving by myself, I would be thinking, "If I just wandered over the line, that truck would hit me and, bang I would be dead. It couldn't possibly hurt as much as the birth; it would only happen once – not over and over like the contractions and pain". I have been in car accidents and they were not as bad as the birth. It's almost like the contractions and pain kept going after the birth; mentally, they didn't stop – so driving off the road, or into a wall, or truck looked like a good option. The only things that stopped me were that my little man needed me and that I didn't want to hurt anyone else.* **Natalia**

*I just hated my body and was angry at myself for not being able to birth my son or breastfeed him.* **Kerri**

*I think if I had been able to summon enough energy, I would have hated myself in that first year. I felt like a failure and became really bitter. I lost all confidence in myself and my anxiety took over without a fight. I lost all my sexual confidence. I was ashamed about how I felt about my daughter and confused because I didn't feel as maternal as I had been all my life before; I loved my nieces much more than I did her. I cut off all my hair. I withdrew from most people, especially anybody that knew me well. I began to distrust the universe intensely. I almost hated my own daughter but couldn't bear the thought of anyone else except David (and not even him sometimes) holding her – especially my mother-in-law, who was calling Alya 'her' baby. I reacted with lots of venom to this and told her that unless she could remember pushing her out of her body or being cut open, then she had no claim to her as her baby.* **Thea**

*I was a busy mum of three, with a hubby who worked long hours. I was running on overdrive. I didn't have time in the earlier months to deal with how I was feeling about my birth. I knew I had issues when people asked me about my labour; I had practiced saying, "It was a one hour birth, no pain relief, no stitches, all fine," and couldn't talk about it any further or I would get emotional and feel silly.* **Sophie**

*I started to have panic attacks. My baby would cry all day, she didn't sleep and I could not seem to comfort her. Mark would come home in the afternoon, take her, give her a bottle, talk to her, she'd smile, coo, talk to him and then she'd go to sleep. I honestly felt like she hated me. I was riddled with anxiety; I was probably very depressed but couldn't see past the misery of my life to notice.* **Jana**

*I sometimes found myself thinking about the birth and I have forgotten to breathe. In the first year, I would cry a lot. Every time I heard about someone else's natural birth or even caesarean birth, all the feelings would flood back. I would push my feelings down, just to put a smile on my face to get through the day. I didn't have anyone to talk to. My husband was very supportive but I just didn't feel like he could say anything right to me. The other mums did not understand at all; everyone just kept saying to me that it was okay because our daughter was healthy and happy and I was okay.* **Sharona**

All of these Birthtalk attendees have since done a great deal of healing work. They have discovered benefits for themselves and their families as a result of taking the healing journey, improving relationships, increasing self-awareness, self-confidence and adopting a kinder attitude towards themselves. All of them have moved on, and gone back to their families more complete and at peace. And all of those who have birthed again have gone on to experience an empowered, positive birth.

# A NOTE TO PARTNERS, HEALTH WORKERS AND GRANDPARENTS
## (AND OTHERS WHO WANT TO HELP BUT DON'T KNOW HOW)

### Firstly, we want to say thank you.

Thank you for picking this book up and opening it. In doing so, you are opening up opportunities for a woman to heal, to grow, to process, and to move on, and become the mother she always wanted to be. That is invaluable, and we are grateful to you for taking that step.

It can be so hard to support a woman after a traumatic birth, for so many reasons.

One of the biggest problems is a lack of understanding in our general culture of the issues surrounding birth trauma. Even the woman herself may not understand what is happening to her, so she cannot clearly articulate this to you, and it can become extremely confusing.

That is the purpose of this book – to bridge that gap between what most people generally 'know' about traumatic birth, and the truth. Gaining this knowledge will make a huge difference to how you support a woman, and how she tackles the healing process.

Often, the worst thing a woman can be told is to, 'just get over it'.

Why?

Because it's not that easy.

Neither should you tell her she should be grateful, that other women have had worse births or that this is just the way birth is.

These comments are not helpful and can be quite damaging to a woman who has been impacted negatively by her birth. (You'll find out why later in the book!)

### So what can you do?

The best thing you can do is to *read this book*, and then *listen*.

Start by reading the chapter of the book titled *The foundations of your healing journey* (p37). We invite you to bring all your questions and doubts and current knowledge to the table while you explore this information.

And then, just open the book to any section you feel might be relevant to the woman you want to support, and explore the information within. You will find personal accounts from other women and men, which will give you further insight into how people respond to similar situations, and discover *Tools for your healing journey* (p403) to support her along the way.

Once you have expanded your understanding of what comprises a good birth versus a bad birth – of how women can feel and respond to a traumatic birthing situation, how women heal from bad births, of the benefits for the entire family when women are supported in taking the healing journey, and of the possibilities for healing, then you will be ready to really *listen*.

The greatest gifts you can give her are *understanding* and *validation*. It is difficult to validate her experience without an understanding of why women can feel the way they do, so reading the sections of the book we have recommended will provide a greater knowledge, which will enable you to offer genuine validation – and hopefully she will feel heard, and gather her courage to continue on this journey.

Again, thank you. You may be about to change the life of an entire family – and maybe that family is your own. We wish you strength and courage as you move forward.

(NB There is another note to you at the end of the book, which you might find helpful after you have read other sections that are relevant to you!)

# MELISSA'S OWN STORY OF BIRTH TRAUMA AND HEALING

**The silent women: why birth trauma remains unspoken, and why we must keep talking about it.**

## Day three

I knew something wasn't right. Day three after the birth of my first child and I felt I was in some sort of surreal 'other world', where everyone seemed to be ignoring the trauma of the birth. Inside my head I was screaming, "*What just happened to me?! Am I okay? Am I okay?!*" And outside my head, I was waiting for someone – anyone – to acknowledge what a horrific thing I'd just been through.

But no one did. Everyone just went about their work at the hospital, trying to latch on my baby who had hidden razor blades in his gums, who was himself drugged and confused. I was fed, washed, had pads matter-of-factly changed, and my fresh caesarean scar checked. Everyone wanted me to walk. And to wee. But my feet were like puffer fish, and weeing just seemed too hard. And anyway, why wasn't anyone asking me how I was? Not just a, "How are you today?" but a sincere direct reference to the birth, like, "Gee, thirty hours – that was a long haul. How are you feeling about it all?"

But no one asked. I was quite confused – where was my support now? I had been abandoned by the birth centre midwives long before this. (I understand now that this was not their fault). But surely someone was concerned about my emotional wellbeing. I certainly was.

But I had a baby to feed and to docilely watch while my husband changed him and bathed him. I was merely the boob machine, whose nipples were held by strangers and shoved roughly into my poor baby's tired little mouth.

Everyone was so matter-of-fact, and I felt a real air of, "Well you're a mum now, your needs don't come first anymore, honey," whenever I would venture to suggest that I was maybe finding it all quite hard. It felt like I was again on a timeline, that they needed me to be independent and walking and caring for my child, so they could tick off my notes, kick me out, and call out, "Next!"

## Pulling the rug out from under me

The first couple of days after the birth, I was so very grateful for my husband's presence. He slept on a foldout bed in my private room, which was a godsend. He could help me sit up, change and bathe our baby and, most importantly, get my baby out of the plastic cot. There is such a feeling of helplessness when your baby is crying in the cot; because I was recovering from major abdominal surgery, I couldn't even pick him up. It was a reinforcement of the failure I was beginning to feel – not only had I failed the birth centre, and failed natural birth, I was failing at breastfeeding, and I was truly failing at mothering, as I couldn't even pick up my child to comfort him.

I was just rising over that hump when the hospital staff pulled the rug out from under my feet. On day three, I was told they were re-tiling the bathroom in my bedroom so I needed to go into a shared room and, as a result, my husband could not stay the night. This was a huge blow; he was my lifeline, the only person constantly there who knew me, and who was able to care for me and our baby at all times. At this stage I was only tentatively walking, and very wobbly. He had also been helping me remember everything the midwives were telling me about breastfeeding. I just couldn't take it in – I guess due to the shock I was in and the sleep deprivation. My head was swirling with the thought of facing this all without him there.

I bravely went into the shared room. I remember attempting to breastfeed that night in front of an old friend of ours, and breaking down into tears when it just wasn't working, and knowing my husband was about to go home. My baby howled and howled most of the night.

## A dark, dark place

I sat in the vinyl chair in the middle of the night, feeling helpless, crazy with sleep deprivation with my hormones making the baby's cries go right through me. I was in a very, very dark place. Terrible thoughts went through my mind and I was terrified that I was even thinking such things. The worst thing was that I was too scared to ever admit these feelings to anyone, in case they took my baby away. My nipples were in excruciating pain, my baby wanted to feed again, and I began a soft, snuffly cry, not wanting to wake the woman behind the curtain in the next bed.

The next minute I heard her padding out of bed, and coming towards me. Her baby, her second child, had only been born a couple of hours earlier. I felt like a complete moron, that here I was, on day three, and I was being comforted by someone who had just birthed. She stayed with me and patted my arm.

I wailed that it was so hard, and I wasn't sure if I could keep breastfeeding, and she just listened. It was a very dark night that left me shaking. When daylight came I was so glad that I had made it through. That day my mum visited, and I asked her to just hold my son while we both slept. I crashed, exhausted, and quite a few hours later I woke up, and she was still sitting there, holding him, still looking at him with such love and wonderment. I was so grateful for her presence, and still feel teary when I think about what that meant to me – that she would just sit and hold my child when I was in such a state, emotionally and physically.

When my husband arrived that day, I begged him to please, please get a private room again. He could see the desperation in my eyes, and he returned triumphant a short while later to say he had negotiated for us to get a private room so he could stay. To our surprise, we were put right back into the room we had vacated, so that 'tiling' could be done. But no tiling had been done. I began to suspect that the midwives were trying to 'throw me in the deep end', to get me to care for my baby without my husband as backup. This just added to my feeling of being abandoned and misunderstood.

## Didn't anyone care?

Another night, my baby was screaming all night again. I visited the nurses' station and asked for help. I think I was told something like, "It's just because he can smell your milk". So I began to walk. I walked and walked through the wards, rocking and cradling my son as he cried, singing him the lullabies I had imagined crooning to a dozy baby. There is something very isolating about walking the hospital corridors in the middle of the night, feeling abandoned by the midwives, like my heart – and body – was broken.

Sure, my dear sister-in-law Deb, a student midwife at the time, and my poor husband had reassured me that the birth *had* been 'that bad'. But it wasn't until the last day – day seven – that someone from the hospital finally acknowledged that maybe the birth might leave some sort of emotional mark. And it was the physiotherapist. She looked at my notes and clucked, and said something small like, "Gee, you've been through the mill, haven't you?"

That was it – my first, and only, acknowledgement of the internal turmoil I was facing. Of course, I burst into tears, feeling at last they would see that I really, truly, was not okay. But they didn't understand. And I didn't understand. And it would be three years until it all began to make sense.

So why didn't anyone approach me to discuss the possible emotional fall out from the birth? I was there a full week, and had countless midwives checking me, chatting with me, advising me. There were plenty of opportunities to see that I was reeling from the experience. But because no one asked, it truly felt like no one cared.

## The motions of mothering

I just felt, well, shell-shocked. Like everything and everyone else was muted and at a distance, and I was in the middle of swirling, whirling fears and thoughts and feelings and physical pain. And no one could see that I was drowning and, as a result, I began to shut down.

I ended up assuming this must be how everybody feels after birth, and other mums must just all be putting on a great big act. So I did the same. I knew what 'good mothering' looked like, so I robotically went through the motions, all the while feeling as though someone would recognise that I was an impostor. This was not how I had imagined life with my new baby would be.

Of course, I blamed myself. Naturally. It was all my fault. This is extremely common among women traumatised by their birth, and I followed the same path. What a travesty. Now I know that I was as little to blame for my trauma as my baby was. So, whose fault was it really?

## Just who or what was to blame?

As I undertook my journey to healing emotionally from my experience, my answer to that question underwent some radical changes. If it was not my fault, then was it the midwife caring for me? And if not her, then was it the obstetrician who did my caesarean? And if not her, was it the hospital system I was in? And if not that, was it the actual caesarean? And if not that, was it the culture I have been raised in? And if not that – then what??? It was confusing and frustrating at times, but each time I explored a new avenue, I unravelled a bit more of the big picture of birth trauma, and why it is misunderstood and even ignored.

My baby was born after thirty hours of labour, via caesarean. Twenty-two hours were in a birth centre (in Sydney), the rest in the regular labour ward with an epidural, then finally Syntocinon*, and then the operating theatre when I was

---

*Syntocinon is a brand name for synthetic oxytocin, known in some countries as Pitocin

nine to nine-and-a-half centimetres with a cervical lip, and a posterior baby.
I saw around five midwives in that time, and no one from the birth centre
transferred with me. Once out of their zone, I was on my own.

## Ripple effect

The ripple effect of that birth on my postnatal life, for months afterwards,
was dramatic. It affected my social confidence, my parenting confidence, my
relationship with my husband (oh yes – another person I blamed) and even
my relationship with myself. I dissociated from my body, disgusted that it had
failed Birthing 101, and I felt like a shell of the bright, happy person I had been
previously.

As I had no idea of the nature of birth trauma, I set about trying to 'fix' things,
which meant I had to look for where things were 'broken'. As I began to express
my displeasure with the birth, the natural assumption from others was that
I had simply "set my sights too high". Apparently, all I was doing was grumbling
about having a caesarean when I had wanted a natural birth. I knew that wasn't
it, but I had no other answer, so I went with that explanation. It must be just
because I was a driven person, who prided herself on setting goals and reaching
them. And because you can't control birth, then I was setting myself up for a fall,
and lovey, did I get it. I had a healthy baby, so just what was my problem?

But, as my sister-in-law Deb (who was a midwife) said to me much, much later
– why shouldn't women work towards a natural birth? It is usually the safest,
most straightforward way to get a baby out. However, at the time, I began to
condemn myself for what I saw as my flawed personality traits: my aim for
'the best' and my unrealistic expectations of 'birth as a positive experience'.
I was placing the blame for the turmoil I found myself in squarely on my own
shoulders, which is a hard burden to bear when you can see your whole life,
including your child, paying the price.

## Feeling helpless and useless

I stayed in this holding pattern for a good year or so, trying hard to change
my notion of wanting 'the best'. I saw that as the start of this whole wretched
business. I had a baby who didn't sleep and screamed most of the night. I felt
helpless and useless and 'not really a mother'. When I saw the health nurse at
the local pharmacy, I asked for a Postnatal Depression (PND) questionnaire,
desperate for some support. But even as I filled out the form, I knew the

profile didn't fit. I begged the Riverton Centre (a local baby sleep centre) to take me, but I had to get a doctor's referral, and I couldn't put into words what I was feeling.

According to Sheila Kitzinger, a renowned author and social anthropologist specialising in pregnancy and childbirth, "PTSD is distinct from post-natal depression. PTSD is essentially a state of panic – and while it can include depression, that is not its primary state".[1] This, I know now, is why I couldn't pigeonhole myself as having PND. I contacted the local PND chapter, and enquired about their methods of treatment, but I knew that drugs weren't what I needed… so just what was? Why couldn't someone ask me the right questions, so I could get to the bottom of this?

A year after the birth I was seeing a wonderful, caring counsellor and had only just begun to explore the possibility that the reason I was feeling so bad was because of the birth. This came from me, not from her, as she readily acknowledged later that she had no idea the birth had impacted on me so fully. It was not until I told her my full birth story with my husband at my side, that she came and hugged me and apologised for not realising how it had affected me. She was the one who suggested I might have PTSD from the birth and, at the time, it was an incredible relief, although I struggled to accept it at first.

We charted a course to recovery together, with both of us deciding that traditional methods of dealing with PTSD were not what I needed. It took many months – actually a couple of years – of researching, talking with trusted midwives and doctors, journaling, debriefing on chat lists, using birth art, having healing bodywork and using other tools to emerge with a new appreciation of the gifts I had received from the journey to healing. Gifts from my son.

## How birth should be

I now know that I was not traumatised because I set my sights too high. I was also not traumatised merely because I ended up with a caesarean. I was traumatised because of the set of circumstances that resulted in me feeling confused, frightened, abandoned and unacknowledged, and fearful for my own life.

1    Kitzinger, Sheila in Hilpern, K. (2003, June 5). The Unspeakable Trauma of Childbirth. Sydney Morning Herald, *www.smh.com.au/articles/2003/06/05/1054700311400.html* accessed January 2014.

Just check out that list of feelings. Is that how I imagined this peak experience of womanhood to feel? Absolutely not. Is this how we would want any of our loved ones to feel at a huge milestone of their lives? Of course not. Then why is this set of feelings seen vastly as being 'normal' in a birthing scenario?

I often have referred to the birth as being 'like a car crash'. That is the only analogy I have found that comes close. My body felt jarred and violated, my senses were severely jangled and confused and my system was on a constant state of high alert, waiting for the next 'emergency'. Fact is, if I *had* been in a car crash, I would have received better support. There is just so little acknowledgement from anyone that our experience of birth could ever impact so completely on everything that follows. A car crash is not normal – it is expected that we might feel confused, afraid, alarmed and helpless. These feelings are usually acknowledged and addressed.

But does a 'normal' birth need to include these feelings? I know now, from personal experience, that it doesn't. There is no place for feeling out-of-control, abandoned or frightened in birth. Those feelings are not 'birth'. However this is not what we have been taught from our culture's films, books, stories and myths passed down through generations of women. These feelings are generally seen as part of 'the burden we must bear'. And usually we connect those feelings to the fact that birth is painful. So if we take away the pain, it'll be okay, right? Um, no. After my epidural, there was no pain. But my mind was still working, and I can tell you that although the pain had stopped, those feelings just kept right on going.

## Where the trauma lay

I ended up discovering that experiencing all these feelings during the birth was where the trauma lay. The trauma was not just in 'having a long labour', not just in 'having a caesarean', but in having these things while feeling vulnerable, frightened, confused, unable to ask questions and abandoned. It was the fall out from these feelings that were having an impact on my life afterwards.

I used to believe that a traumatic birth was one where there was overt physical or emotional trauma to the mother or child, beyond those usually expected. I assumed that trauma must be something apparent or tangible. It's quite easy to see how a massive haemorrhage or a premature birth might be considered traumatic. These are outside 'the norm', so it can be easier to offer commiserations, support and understanding, which of course a woman in these situations definitely needs.

But I had no idea that there was this hidden web of feelings underlying each aspect of a birth, which seems to drive the response postnatally. It now made sense that I was so damaged emotionally. Put it this way: if someone came to me and told me they felt frightened, confused, out-of-control, unable to ask questions about what was happening to them and unsafe – in any situation, whether it be a girl on her first date, or a man being threatened by a gang, or a child on their first day of school – I would expect there to be some emotional fall out. Why do we not expect this when it occurs in birth? Is getting a healthy baby supposed to wipe the slate clean?

## Birthtalk

Now, I facilitate Birthtalk's 'Healing from Birth' support group with Deb. An interesting thing occurs at Birthtalk when we acknowledge these feelings as being of vital importance to understanding and healing: women can see their birth reflected outside of 'what happened', and explore 'how they felt'. Once women understand that their feelings during the birth need acknowledging and exploring, rather than just acknowledging 'what happened', a floodgate often opens, as Birthtalk mums share here:

> "When I first met Melissa and Debby at Birthtalk I had no idea of the depth of my grief. I was absolutely shocked at the words and feelings and great big sobs that emerged from me that first meeting."

> "It was like a big smack in the face – 'Healing from birth: dealing with a traumatic birth'. I had never thought of my birth as traumatic! I went onto the website and realised that this is how I had been feeling. I was astonished to realise the depth of feelings about the birth and how let down I had felt."

When we began Birthtalk's 'Healing From Birth' support group, I really wanted it to be a 'Healing from Caesarean' group. That's what I felt I had so desperately needed in the early days, and what I wanted other women to have access, too. But Deb insisted that the group be open to all women, regardless of how they had birthed. I was sceptical, finding it hard to imagine that a vaginal birth could ever be as traumatic as an emergency caesarean like mine had been. Let's just say I have eaten a whole truckload of humble pie since then!

After we started to meet women deeply traumatised by their vaginal birth, I began to understand what Deb had known all along – that a traumatic birth is not defined by 'what happened' in the birth so much as 'how the woman felt' during and afterwards.

Deb herself has commented that she, too, has been humbled. Although she knew it was the women's feelings that needed acknowledging, she was not initially aware of the breadth and depth of a traumatic birth and just how fully it can impact on so many areas of a woman's life. The women of Birthtalk, with all their individual stories and amazing courage and strength, have given and taught us so much.

So is there one way to support different women, with all their different experiences, which resonates for all of them? The simple answer is, 'Yes' and the reason is also simple because we have found all women coming to Birthtalk whose birth was traumatic share similar feelings during, and after, the birth, regardless of the mode of birth, the place of birth, the type of health professional, or the personality of the woman birthing. Without this information, it can be so confusing not just for women, but also for health carers wanting to support them. This has also been, for us, the key to supporting women as they move on and heal. And of course, the key to my own journey of reclaiming the birth and moving on.

## Discovering how much birth matters

I have birthed twice since that story – both vaginal birth after caesareans (VBACs), with my last birth being a waterbirth just after my forty-third birthday. I know now that birth can be amazing and beautiful, with feelings of safety, nurturing and of being acknowledged. I also know now, from my experiences with some courageous Birthtalk mums, that a caesarean birth can have positive feelings just as surely as a vaginal birth can.

I know that my 'bad birth' was not my fault. I also know I cannot rest the blame fully on the midwife who abandoned me, or the obstetrician who manipulated me into agreeing to a caesarean. I eventually saw our maternal health system as being highly dysfunctional and our culture as fuelling the misconceptions about birth that I bought into.

But the overriding factor in all of this was just that I didn't know how much birth matters.

So, what do I wish someone had said to me or asked me in those first horrific days after the birth of my son? Jenny Gamble, an eminent researcher in the field of birth trauma, lecturer, midwife and a significant player in my own recovery, once asked me the same question in front of a group of midwifery students. I have been mulling the answer over ever since, and I am still searching for exactly the right one; however, I'll give it a go.

I wish someone had 'read between the lines' of the birth notes hanging on the end of my hospital bed. I wish someone had known I may have been feeling fear, helplessness, confusion or horror. And I wish they had known that this could lead to problems postnatally. Most of all, I wish they had just said, "That must have been a pretty full-on experience". That could have been an opening for me to, firstly, allow myself to admit how I was feeling and, secondly, acknowledge that it would be a normal response to such a situation. And my journey to healing could have begun straight away, rather than being stopped inside me until my son was well past his second birthday.

In a nutshell, I wish someone had whispered to me that birth matters, and that we don't just leave our feelings from the birth at the hospital when we go home. Now I am shouting it from the rooftops, and Deb, my sister-in-law who began Birthtalk with me all those years ago, is standing alongside me, shouting just as loud. Birth truly does matter. The only thing is, she knew it before I did.

# A GUIDE FOR BIRTH WORKERS AND OTHER HEALTH PROFESSIONALS

Thank you so much for supporting women in the work you do. While this book is written primarily for the women who need it, and their partners, the material is highly relevant for health professionals as well.

This book was created as a means to support, inform, empower, give insights and understanding, and provide a safe path to healing. We envisage that most of these aims are directly aligned with what many of you are also doing for women, so our goal is to provide you with a valuable, easy-to-use resource to complement your current practice, particularly in the area of traumatic birth.

The insights contained within this book are highly applicable for birth workers and other health professionals from a patient-care perspective, for those working with women and supporting them in a variety of settings: antenatally, during birth, postnatally, in special care or intensive care, or in the community over the longer term.

## Getting personal

You may also find the information and individual women's stories shared here resonate with you on a personal level, which we find often occurs when birth workers attend our 'Healing From Birth' meetings. Sometimes this resonance is a result of being a mother yourself and recognising your experiences and emotions from your own birthing history. This experience can open the door for some profound and new healing to take place, as well as increase your ability to support women you encounter in your professional life.

Or you may find, that as a health carer, you have witnessed and even perhaps been involved in some traumatic birthing scenarios – sometimes they may even have been traumatic for you rather than the woman involved. These experiences are important and worthy of acknowledgement and processing; we have held debriefs with student midwives, doulas and other birth workers who are struggling to make sense of things they have witnessed or been ordered to do in another woman's birth.

We encourage you to go gently with yourself if you are finding the book is connecting with your personal experiences. Taking the time to explore this aspect can only deepen your compassion and ability to connect with those you support.

## How to use this book

Our suggestions for health professionals using this book with the aim of further supporting those in your care is very similar to the suggestions we give to mothers. Although it is tempting to 'dive right in' and flick to the parts you are interested in, we invite you first to read Part One of the book , including the chapters *The foundations of your healing journey* (p37), *Healing – the big questions* (p61), *Do I Need a Diagnosis and Sharing your story – finally being heard* (p111).

This will give you a better understanding of the basis for our philosophy, and the framework that underpins the later parts of the book. It will also give you insights that could support the women and families you encounter in your work, especially if they are struggling with the issues we explain here.

## Creating a roadmap to healing with your clients

In Part Two titled *How do you feel right now?* (p121) you will find each chapter is named for common issues and emotions that we find women experience after a traumatic birth. These chapter headings are indicative of women's experiences that we have encountered over the past ten years, and illustrate the prevailing themes we've found for those healing from a traumatic birth.

If you have a client who is expressing a particular concern or challenge in her journey to healing, you may find a section within these chapters that mirrors her current issue. If you are supporting a client who is struggling to identify why she is feeling so bad, you could even show her the section topics and ask if any of them resonate with 'where she is right now'.

There may be an opportunity to explore the relevant chapters in this part of the book together with your client. This exploration could be more useful to her if your client also has a clear understanding of the issues surrounding traumatic birth. She will likely benefit from accessing the early chapters of this book such as *The foundations of your healing journey* (p37).

Each section in *How do you feel right now* concludes with guidance for particular exercises and activities to further the healing. These exercises and activities are found in *Part Three: Tools for your healing journey* (p403). As you explore with your client, you can discover the tools she can use to extend her understanding and make peace with her experience.

You may find the principles and tools for healing in this book can be applied or adapted to other disappointing, difficult or traumatic life experiences that require some healing or closure. Women do not birth in a vacuum – they often bring their life experiences with them, so it may be possible to explore these issues alongside their healing journey from birth.

Together you can create a roadmap to healing – one that is individual for each woman you work with – and provide quality support for her journey.

## Using this knowledge in your practice

If your daily work involves caring for women preparing for birth, or birthing, you can use the information in this book to consider what will make their experience optimal, in terms of their emotional safety. What one small change could you make to your interactions with the women you support that could further enhance their experience with you? (Don't answer that yet – wait until you have delved into the book first!)

Or, if you are interacting daily with women postnatally, you may find this book enables you to 'read between the lines' as they make a comment about their birth, or about how they are coping now. You will hopefully gain insights into the emotional hurdles they may be facing, and provide them with understanding and validation of the 'normality' of their response, which can be the first steps of their healing journey.

## Your own journey

Another way to use this book in your own practice is as a tool for your own self-awareness: to simply read, and be aware of what comes up.

Does the information and the women's and men's stories presented make you feel angry, inspired, helpless, overwhelmed, proactive or questioning? What steps can you take to explore this response further? Why does it bring up particular emotions? How can the answer to this question support you in understanding your own practice, and perhaps help you make any adjustments to enhance the way you or others support women and their families?

## With gratitude

We are so grateful that you have considered taking the time to read our book, to be willing to explore the ideas presented and to listen to the voices of the women and men impacted. Their stories are peppered throughout these pages and offer a rich insight into the impact of traumatic birth.

You have the opportunity to completely alter the life of a family with every encounter you have with a woman traumatised by her birth, and enable them to find their way to healing and new-found strength. We thank you for taking this responsibility seriously, and for working to support women as they make sense of, make peace with and move on from their births.

# The foundations of your healing journey

## WHAT MAKES A BIRTH GOOD OR BAD?

Understanding this section can be a turning point in:

- understanding why you feel so bad
- making sense of what happened
- how to explain 'what's happening' to other people
- how to make it better next time (if you are birthing again).

### What is a bad birth?

Firstly, look at these stories. Can you tell which stories are 'good' and which are 'bad'?

> *Naomi's* waters broke nine days before her estimated due date. She went into immediate labour, met her husband at home, they went to the hospital and three hours later her first child was born vaginally with help from a ventouse. Her husband was told to lean on her leg during the birth and, as a result, her hip ligaments were

damaged. The baby was born with a low Apgar score* and a large bump on his head from the ventouse. He was very jaundiced and he also had two ventricular septal defects (VSDs) – holes in the wall that separates the right and left ventricles of the heart and an undescended testicle. By the time they left hospital he was doing well, although still jaundiced and with a bump on his head.

***Dana*** began her labour by using castor oil to kickstart things, as the hospital considered her to be overdue at forty-one weeks and five days. She laboured for twenty-nine hours without pain relief, first at home, then, when the hot water ran out, at the birth centre. Her baby was not engaged, there was slow progress, and her waters were broken. The baby came down in a posterior position, there was meconium, and her contractions had dropped off to ten minutes apart and lost their strength. She transferred out of the birth centre, had a continual monitor attached and Syntocinon‡ and an epidural were activated. She eventually pushed her daughter out with the anaesthetist at the door ready to take her for a caesarean. The total length of the birth was thirty-two hours.

***Melanie*** planned an active, natural birth. She transferred to the birth centre when in well-established labour and worked hard for twenty-two hours. The baby turned posterior. She then had an epidural, Syntocinon‡ and finally a caesarean after a thirty-hour labour.

***Vanessa*** experiences a phenomenon known as 'silent labour' – she did not feel her contractions until she was in transition or close to pushing the baby out. Vanessa went to hospital knowing she was in labour, yet she was without any pain. She was aware that, due to family history, she may be having a silent labour. She was put in a general waiting room for some time before being taken to a room. She was still not experiencing pain with her contractions. She eventually had a foetal/contraction monitor put on and was administered a Syntocinon drip. Very bad pain started in one of her hips only during the peak of contractions, as the baby was posterior, but turning. Vanessa was otherwise still without pain. She was continually offered pain relief. She was administered pethidine via a drip. After four hours she birthed her baby

---

*Apgar score: a measure of the physical condition of a newborn infant.

‡Syntocinon is a brand name for synthetic oxytocin, known in some countries as Pitocin

vaginally. A vacuum was used; her baby was turned slightly, and came straight out. Her baby was healthy with no signs of foetal distress at any time.

*Kathryn* was planning a natural, active birth with her first child. However, at her 37-week appointment, her baby was transverse (lying sideways instead of lengthways), so it was decided she would have an external cephalic version (ECV). Her baby was still transverse after three attempts to turn him. At her thirty-eight week appointment, it was decided she would have a caesarean that afternoon. Without being able to go home and collect their things, Kathryn and her husband went into the operating theatre and emerged with a healthy son.

*Danielle* was planning a gentle vaginal birth after caesarean (VBAC), attending Birthtalk's VBAC course after a disempowering first birth that ended in caesarean. She says, "I was determined to get a VBAC, come hell or high water. I wasn't really considering anything else. We even switched carers!" As part of her preparation, she attended Birthtalk's VBAC course. When she was thirty-four weeks, it was found that her baby had inter-uterine growth restriction (IUGR), and would have to be born immediately. A caesarean was performed and her son was born. The baby spent three weeks in special care, and Danielle had a number of complications post-birth.

Some of these stories seem obviously bad. With others, it's hard to tell. We can tell you that three of them were bad experiences and that the other three were empowering, wonderful births that took these women into motherhood with many gifts.

So… which was which? Why can't we tell for sure? Because we are missing a vital piece of information about each birth.

Once you have this information, there is no mistaking how each woman experienced her birth.

We'll tell you which were which shortly. But first…

# WHY DOES IT MATTER? AND ISN'T A LIVE BIRTH A GOOD BIRTH?

Every woman is working towards having a live baby. Yet emerging with a live baby does *not* mean the birth was good. And it matters because birth has an impact.

We don't just leave our birth at the hospital – it comes home with us. Why?

The *process of birth is meant to give us gifts for parenthood,* which makes sense from an evolutionary point of view. Nature needs attentive mothers who act on instinct and make decisions feeling strong and confident. Women could obtain these abilities and others from birthing, which means our species is more likely to survive. But, if your birth was bad, you are probably thinking, "Gifts from birth? Yeah right!"

But when all her hormones are working beautifully, and the right emotional support is there, a woman *can* emerge from *any* birth feeling wonderful. However, to feel wonderful *afterwards* she needs to feel certain things *during* the birth. And this leads to our new definition of a good birth.

# WHAT IS A GOOD BIRTH?

## Good birth: a new definition

### During a good birth, a woman needs to feel:

- empowered (central to the experience and 'doing' birth, not having birth 'done' to her)
- safe
- supported by those around her and supported by her knowledge base
- respected
- nurtured
- able to ask questions
- that her expert knowledge about herself and her baby is acknowledged and respected.

**If she feels these things, there is a high chance, in our experience, that afterwards she will feel:**

- a sense of completeness and fulfillment
- high levels of confidence with mothering and a sense that she is the most capable person to make decisions for her baby
- feelings of strength and capability
- an increased connection with her partner
- a fulfilling and bonded relationship with her baby.

There are a couple of important things to note here.

Firstly, this definition applies to the partner and their feelings as well.

Secondly, we've talked here about birth, but really it's about how a woman feels during her entire pregnancy, the birth and the postnatal period.

It all makes sense. If you feel safe, cared for, respected and supported during a major life experience, chances are you will take that experience and move forward with confidence.

If, during your childhood, you mostly felt safe and supported, cared for and nurtured, respected and empowered, then chances are you would have found the transition to adulthood largely exciting, manageable and positive. So your experience during childhood has an impact on how you move forward.

Similarly, we can use the example of your early sexual experiences, which involves the extra intimacy and vulnerability of our sexuality, not dissimilar to that of birth.

If, as a younger female, you felt safe, nurtured and in control during your initial sexual experiences, you likely moved forward confidently into other sexual relationships. But, if your first experiences were negative, and you felt forced, frightened or violated, then you might suffer trauma and experience a long-term impact, including shying away from intimacy, having relationship difficulties or a lack of confidence around your sexuality.

So, with these examples in mind, let's look at a new definition of a 'bad birth'.

# WHAT IS A TRAUMATIC OR BAD BIRTH ANYWAY?

In our culture, the words 'traumatic birth' and 'bad birth' are increasingly being used to describe a wide range of birth experiences.

At Birthtalk, we see 'traumatic' or 'bad' birth as a definition for a spectrum of experiences and responses, and we find that most women we meet use the term in that way.

The spectrum of responses to a traumatic or bad birth can range from feeling empty and numb, to disappointment and general uneasy feelings, to anger and confusion, to feeling shell-shocked and damaged, to showing symptoms of Post-Traumatic Stress Disorder (PTSD) or even, in very rare cases, psychotic symptoms*. Wherever you lie along this spectrum, it is important for you to receive the validation and support you need for healing.

In our work, and throughout this book, we use the terms 'bad' or 'traumatic' birth to describe any birth that leaves you feeling less-than-great and like you might need some support to process the experience and move forward.

## How bad is 'bad'?

Most people think that a traumatic birth or a bad birth is one where there is overt physical or emotional trauma to the mother or child.

Most of us assume that trauma must be something apparent or tangible.

It might be easy to see how a massive haemorrhage or a premature birth might be traumatic (even though women who have these experiences often still do not receive appropriate emotional support).

These experiences are outside 'the norm' so it can sometimes be easier to offer initial commiserations, support and understanding, which of course a woman in these situations definitely needs (yet doesn't usually get, and we have ideas on how she can move through these experiences in other chapters).

---

* Of course, no matter where you feel you fit on the spectrum, if at any time you are feeling desperate, or that you might be a danger to yourself or your children, please seek immediate help from a trusted friend or health professional. There are some 24-hour helplines for various countries listed in *Appendix A*

However, a traumatic birth doesn't have to be one that is unusual or obviously life-threatening or dangerous. A traumatic birth can appear completely 'normal' to an outsider[†]. This is where it gets tricky for many people to acknowledge a birth as being 'traumatic'. Why?

Because most people, including many health professionals, have no idea that there is a hidden web of feelings underlying each aspect of a birth that drives a woman's response postnatally. That is, how she felt *during and after the birth* can affect her response in the weeks and mont–hs afterwards. It is how she experienced the birth and her response to it that indicates if a birth is traumatic, rather than just what appears to be happening on the surface.

This leads to our definition of a bad birth.

## Bad birth: a new definition

### During a bad birth, women may feel:

- powerless
- confused
- fearful
- isolated or abandoned
- unacknowledged or unheard
- that her innate knowledge about her body and her baby are being disregarded.

**If a woman feels like this during a birth, there is a high chance, in our experience, that afterwards she may experience any of the following:**

- disappointment or emptiness – a feeling that there was something missing from the birth
- a lack of confidence with mothering and an unawareness or rejection of her mothering instincts
- hypervigilant in the care of her baby
- feelings of failure, which can impact on her general confidence in life
- anger with her partner, especially if she felt they should have rescued her, whether or not they really could
- feeling so constricted by the trauma of the birth that she cannot fully express her love for her baby.

---

† If you want to read research and comments from health professionals that support this new definition of a 'good birth' and a 'bad birth', see the sections *Can you get PTSD after childbirth?* (p83) and *Common 'hidden factors' that can make a birth traumatic* (p99).

These feelings of powerlessness, confusion, fear and isolation can occur during pregnancy, during the birth, and even postnatally. Whether you experience these feelings is dependent on what occurred for you during these phases and can potentially impact on you or others. For example, you might have felt fine during the birth, but disempowered in your hospital stay, and this can still affect how you feel afterwards.

This emotional and physical response has significant consequences for both the mother and the baby postnatally. Once you know this, it can help you understand why someone can be so damaged emotionally from a birth, even when the birth seems so 'normal' to an outsider. Cheryl Beck, a professor at the University of Connecticut who specialises in birth trauma research, says, "Birth trauma lies in the eye of the beholder."[2] In her research paper titled "Birth Trauma: in the eye of the beholder" she comments, "What a mother perceives as birth trauma may be seen quite differently through the eyes of obstetric care providers, who may view it as a routine delivery and just another day at the hospital."[3] This may be because many clinicians are largely unaware of the web of feelings that underpin a birth and its potential impact on the postnatal experience.

Put it this way: if someone came to you and told you they felt frightened, confused, out-of-control, unable to ask questions about what was happening to them and unsafe, in any situation, whether it be a girl on her first date, or a man being threatened by a gang, or a child on their first day of school, you would expect there to be some emotional fall out.

Why do we not expect this when it occurs in birth? Is the healthy baby supposed to wipe the slate clean? We know that it *doesn't*. Another way of saying this is that birth *has an impact and a ripple effect*.

This concept goes against everything we are taught in our culture about birth, so it can take some getting used to. However, this concept is so important that we are going to show it to you again alongside our new definition of a good birth.

---

2  Beck, C. (2004a). Birth trauma: in the eye of the beholder. Nursing Research, 53(1), 28–35. *www.tabs.org.nz/pdfdocs/eyebeholder.pdf.*

3  ibid.

| Type of feelings during birth | Results for parents postnatally and beyond |
| --- | --- |
| Empowered, safe, supported, respected, nurtured, and able to ask questions. | Positive, confident, strong, instinctive, able to cope, good bonding. |
| Powerless, confused, fearful, isolated or abandoned, unacknowledged or unheard, knowledge about baby disregarded. | Difficult to move forward, panic attacks, vivid flashbacks, hypervigilance, feelings of emptiness, a struggle with mothering or life in general (can impact all areas of life), disappointment, emptiness, feeling like something is missing from the birth, lack of confidence, feelings of failure, anger etc. |

So, you can see that *it matters* how we feel during birth and in the immediate postnatal period, because we can then take those feelings and their consequences into our wider life afterwards.

If we feel *good feelings*, we take them and their happy consequences into parenthood. If we feel *bad feelings*, then we take all those negative consequences into our new life. The saddest thing of all is that many people think that the bad feelings are *just part of birth*. But we know from our own births, and from the many women we work with, that *none of those bad feelings need to be part of birth*. And none of those bad consequences need to be part of the postnatal period.

*Any* birth can be good – that is, any birth can have the feelings of being empowered, involved, nurtured and respected, even if the birth goes differently to expected. Even if there were complications. Even if there are challenging outcomes. It is still possible to be well-supported through these experiences. But that doesn't mean that if it wasn't good that it was your fault. It doesn't mean that you were feeling the 'wrong' feelings.

It means that you were in a situation where the events that unfolded, the care you received, the support you had, the environment surrounding you, and the quality of information or antenatal education all possibly did not enable you to have what you needed to feel those good feelings.

What we mean is, any path to birth can be good, if you are in a position where you have the right information and support so that you can experience those good feelings†. Not many women know this. Not many health professionals know this. So how could you?

We will give you information about having a good birth after a traumatic birth in *How to have a better birth next time* (p507), and you can get more ideas about birth in other sections including *Why wouldn't my body work in labour?* (p230).

But first we invite you to read the next section *Birthtalk Breakdown – a new tool* (p47) to discover the 'missing information' that most women unintentionally omit when sharing their birth stories. Now you know our new definition of a good and bad birth, understanding this information can give you a whole host of insights about your experience and guide your path to healing.

---

† You might not feel safe if you are, for example, extremely unwell during or after the birth, but if you have great support and carers who answer your questions, give you useful information, listen to your concerns, and acknowledge your fears for your safety with understanding and ideas to help you regain your sense of safety, then you will likely feel empowered, cared for and supported, rather than emotionally damaged and isolated as you recover and take stock of your experience.

# BIRTHTALK BREAKDOWN – A NEW TOOL

So, what's an easy way to access more information about your birth so you can identify just why you feel so bad about it, with or without a diagnosis? This is where the Birthtalk Breakdown comes into play. Remember the six stories we introduced at the beginning of this chapter?

Could you identify which of those births were traumatic, and which were empowering? If you couldn't, you're not alone. It's actually not possible to determine from the information we gave you. We told you exactly 'what happened' in each woman's birth. But sharing in this way does not reveal the true impact of a birth on a woman. So, what was the missing information? We did not reveal how each woman felt during this process. That is, 'what happened' was evident. Yet 'how she felt' was not. This information is the vital clue into understanding your own birth.

To explain things, let's draw up a table. The left hand column is headed 'What happened'.

| What happened | |
| --- | --- |
| If we write the actual path of a birth, we get a story much like the ones we outlined earlier. This is how many women describe their births – a series of steps beginning in early labour, and resulting in the birth. | |

However, what if we create a second column titled 'How I felt'?

| What happened | How I felt |
| --- | --- |
| | We ask women to write down their feelings at each of those steps. A new picture of their birth emerges. |

*This is the missing information.* And it can be the key to understanding why you might be feeling bad.

This table is our Birthtalk Breakdown tool. Shortly, we are going to invite you to write your own story in this way. But first, let's revisit the stories from the start of this chapter, this time using a Birthtalk Breakdown for them to give us more insights into whether these were good or bad births.

## Naomi's Birthtalk Breakdown

| What happened | How I felt |
|---|---|
| Naomi's waters broke nine days before her estimated due date. | I felt nervous and panicky, and not yet ready. I had felt my husband's support waning over previous weeks, and felt neglected even before labour. |
| She went into immediate labour, met her husband at home, they went to the hospital and three hours later her first child was born vaginally with help from a ventouse. | It all was happening so fast. No one told me things were okay. I couldn't hear anyone and I didn't know if I was okay or not. I was terrified. My husband had not rung my other support person so I felt alone and isolated and helpless to change things. I felt, "Everything hurts; this is wrong, it's all wrong!" |
| Her husband was told to lean on her leg during the birth and, as a result, her hip ligaments were damaged. | No one listened when I screamed at the pain of my hip being damaged. I was completely vulnerable, exposed and powerless. |
| The baby was born with a low Apgar and a large bump on his head from the ventouse. He was very jaundiced and he also had two VSDs and an undescended testicle. By the time they left hospital he was doing well, although still jaundiced and with a bump on his head. | My baby was doing okay by the time we left hospital, but I was so NOT fine. I had an anxiety attack when we went to leave the hospital. There was another baby leaving that day who looked so perfect and in one piece, and not yellow. We ended up in counselling for an hour or two before going home as I couldn't stop crying. I was still in shock. I was feeling very broken and like my baby had been ripped out of me. I felt I had really bashed my baby up because of my failure. I felt I had damaged my child by somehow being responsible for his speedy and horrible entry. I had trouble sleeping, I had nightmares and flashbacks. I felt like my marriage was over and completely lost my confidence for months afterwards. And I had ongoing symptoms from the damage to my hip. |

## Dana's Birthtalk Breakdown

| What happened | How I felt |
|---|---|
| Dana began her labour by using castor oil to kickstart things, as the hospital considered her to be overdue at forty-one weeks and five days. | I was excited and really looking forward to getting the show on the road after the pressure on me to go into labour. I also felt relieved that I was going to be able to go to the birth centre after all. |
| She laboured for twenty-nine hours without pain relief, first at home, then, when the hot water ran out, at the birth centre. | I felt tired, but really strong and surrounded by people who love me. I felt listened-to by my midwife, who I had spent time getting to know in my pregnancy. All the decisions that were made were in consultation with me and my support team (husband and friend). My midwife knew what was important to me and did everything possible to make sure I felt safe and involved. |
| Her baby was not engaged, there was slow progress, and her waters were broken. The baby came down in a posterior position, there was meconium, and her contractions had dropped off to ten minutes apart and lost their strength. | I felt a bit frustrated by the various challenges that arose, but I felt supported, strong and part of the team with my midwife in deciding what to do and where to go next. |
| She transferred out of the birth centre, had a continual monitor attached and Syntocinon and an epidural were administered. She eventually pushed her daughter out, with the anaesthetist at the door ready to take her for a caesarean. The total length of the birth was thirty-two hours. | Afterwards I felt amazing, empowered and capable of anything that was thrown my way. A lot was thrown my way postnatally, but because of the strength I gained from the birth, I coped well in really difficult circumstances in the weeks after my baby was born. |

## Melanie's Birthtalk Breakdown

| What happened | How I felt |
|---|---|
| Melanie planned an active, natural birth. She transferred to the birth centre when in well-established labour, and worked hard for twenty-two hours. | I felt excited and confident that I would be able to 'do this'. |
| The baby turned posterior. | I felt confident and strong until a new midwife came on. She was blunt and didn't try to get to know me. She wasn't with me when I needed her. When the pain got unbearable, she wasn't there. I didn't know if I was okay. I felt out-of-control, helpless, terrified and teetering on a precipice. No member of the staff acknowledged my emotional situation. |
| She then had an epidural, Syntocinon and finally a caesarean after a thirty-hour labour. | I hated the epidural and felt even more vulnerable stuck on a bed. The caesarean was horrible – I could feel the pulling and tugging, and struggled with the idea of being cut open while I was awake. I had symptoms of PTSD for two-and-a-half years before I found help and understanding. It played havoc with my relationship with my son, my partner, my friends and me. |

## Vanessa's Birthtalk Breakdown

| What happened | How I felt |
|---|---|
| Vanessa experienced a phenomenon known as 'silent labour' – she did not feel her contractions until she was in transition or close to pushing the baby out. | I knew I was in labour, but because it was my first baby, I wasn't sure what I should do. |
| Vanessa went to hospital knowing she was in labour, yet she was without any pain. She was aware that, due to family history, she may be having a silent labour.<br><br>She was put in a general waiting room for some time before being taken to a room. | I had to insist on going in to the hospital. No one would believe that I was going to have my baby soon, but I felt it was close. I felt foolish when they said to call back later and stay at home, like, "What would I know about my own body?" I also felt no one was listening to me and acknowledging what I knew was happening. |
| She was still not experiencing pain with her contractions.<br><br>She eventually had a foetal/ contraction monitor put on and was administered a Syntocinon drip. | It was personally invasive, physically uncomfortable and I was stuck on the bed on my back. They still didn't believe me as I was not yet in any pain. I was frustrated at not being able to turn over or walk around. I doubted myself because I felt like they thought my body was not working properly. I really wanted to leave, pull all the straps off and the drips out. |
| Very bad pain started in one of her hips during the peak of contractions, as the baby was posterior, but turning. | Again being ignored, I realised my partner did not know what to do or how to help, or what I was trying to say.<br>I felt alone. |

## Vanessa's Birthtalk Breakdown (continued)

| What happened (cont'd) | How I felt (cont'd) |
|---|---|
| Vanessa was otherwise still without pain.<br><br>She was continually offered pain relief.<br><br>She was administered pethidine by a drip. | I felt annoyed, frustrated, tired and not listened to again. I did not want the pain relief. I didn't feel it was right or that it would fix the pain. I didn't know what to say or how to say that I needed something else.<br><br>The pethidine was administered without my awareness or consent. I found out about it after the birth and was extremely angry. |
| After four hours she birthed her baby vaginally.<br><br>A Ventouse was used; her baby was turned slightly, and came straight out. | I was angry. I felt like I had to follow some timeline so they could go home.<br><br>Before I agreed to the vacuum, I was being threatened with a forceps delivery.<br><br>As a result, I did not want to go back to the hospital, or obstetricians. I felt scared, vulnerable, and unable to ask questions. It was very disempowering.<br><br>I felt like I had missed something important.<br><br>I felt foolish – why should I complain? My labour was so short and relatively pain-free compared to many, especially for a posterior baby. I wasn't happy with the experience at all.<br><br>I ended up not trusting hospitals or obstetricians to do what is best for me as an individual. |
| Her baby was healthy with no signs of foetal distress at any time. | I felt bullied and manipulated by unnecessary threats.<br><br>I found out that my partner had been threatened that I would need a caesarean as I was taking too long for them and their guidelines. I was angry; I wasn't treated as an individual. They wanted me to 'fit' their timetables and guidelines. |

## Kathryn's Birthtalk Breakdown

| What happened | How I felt |
| --- | --- |
| Kathryn was planning a natural, active birth with her first child. | I was excited and full of anticipation, armed with the knowledge I learned at Birthtalk classes. |
| At her thirty-seven week appointment her baby was transverse (sideways), so it was decided she would have an external cephalic version (ECV). | I was concerned, but well informed as we knew what questions to ask using the BRAN technique (Benefits, Risks, Alternatives and do Nothing – see more on this decision-making tool in *The pitfalls of going with the flow in birth* (p513)). |
| Her baby was still transverse after three attempts to turn him. | The specialist got him to about a forty-five degree angle, but something was stopping him. We didn't know what, but still, while concerned about the situation, we knew we were in good hands and again used the BRAN technique when talking to the specialist. He referred us back to our obstetrician. |
| At her thirty-eight week appointment, it was decided she would have a caesarean that afternoon. | The following day was the thirty-eight week appointment. Because of the distance we lived from the hospital (a forty-five minute drive) the obstetrician recommended a caesarean. After again going through the BRAN options with him, we agreed that while it wasn't my preferred method, we really wanted to make sure our baby arrived safe and sound. |
| Without being able to go home and collect their things, Kathryn and her husband went into the operating theatre and emerged with a healthy son. | Even though my birth didn't go as planned (it wasn't the first preference in our birth plan) I had a very fulfilling experience as I was very much a part of the process, not just the 'lump of meat giving birth'. The birth was a most fulfilling experience for both of us. Because of the confidence I gained through the birthing process, I am confident as a mother that I will be able to handle whatever challenges may come along and know what questions to ask in relation to medical issues. |

## Danielle's Birthtalk Breakdown

| What happened | How I felt |
|---|---|
| Danielle was planning a gentle VBAC, after a disempowering first birth that ended in caesarean. She says, "I was determined to get a VBAC come hell or high water. I wasn't really considering anything else. We even switched carers!" As part of her preparation, she attended Birthtalk's VBAC course. | I felt emotional – I didn't want a repeat performance of last time! |
| When she was thirty-four weeks, it was found that her baby had IUGR, and would have to be born immediately. | Physically, I knew something was wrong. I wanted to get bub out as fast as possible. |
| A caesarean was performed, and their son was born. | I felt supported and able to make my own decisions. I was the one who opted for intervention. I was scared, but even with a very terrifying situation it was actually very stress free! |
| The baby spent three weeks in special care, and Danielle had a number of complications post-birth. | Even though we have faced an incredible amount of trials, I now understand what Birthtalk means by it being about the experience and not 'how' the baby comes. We have been floating on happy hormones for the past few months and our little family is going from strength to strength. Ethan James weighed in at 1.7 kilograms. He spent a total of three weeks in the special care nursery but was healthy and thriving from birth, surprising all. I can't thank you enough. This experience has completely changed my outlook on motherhood and life. It has been the most hectic and scary journey ever but I would not change a single thing. |

## Danielle's Birthtalk Breakdown (continued)

| What happened (cont'd) | How I felt (cont'd) |
|---|---|
| | For the first time since I had my first child three years ago, I feel like a strong woman and a real mother to both of them, not like I am just watching anymore. |

As you can see from reading the 'How I felt' columns, *how we feel in birth* can affect *how we feel afterwards*. The women who felt the *good feelings* felt good postnatally and beyond. The women who felt the *bad feelings* suffered huge repercussions that rippled out into their whole lives.

You can see from Vanessa's story that a largely pain-free labour does not make a good birth. You can see from Naomi's story that a short birth does not make a good birth. You can see that a healthy baby is not enough to make a birth positive, and that the definition of 'healthy mother' needs to include 'emotionally healthy'.

No one except you can tell you whether your birth was bad or not, because no one except you experienced the feelings you did. Not even your partner. The good news is that the *good feelings* are possible in just about any birth scenario. Your next birth can be filled with those good feelings. You can see that from Danielle's story that she had a very unwell baby and a very uncertain period of his early life, yet she still feels empowered. However, this takes a certain sort of information and understanding, which we will share in later parts of the book, including *Why wouldn't my body work in labour?* (p230) and *Birthing again* (p507).

For now, we just want you to know that it never has to be that bad again.

Ever.

# BENEFITS OF A BIRTHTALK BREAKDOWN

Here are what other women have said about their experience of completing a Birthtalk Breakdown, and the new understanding that emerged about their birth:

> *[Before doing a Birthtalk Breakdown] I hadn't understood the feelings I was having to deal with. But there was fear (I didn't know what the obstetrician was doing); trauma (he was rough, pinning me down and yelling, the emotional shock of which had a lasting effect); confusion (no one explained to me what was happening or why my baby had stopped breathing); shock (my adrenaline was still running too high from the quick labour); powerlessness (they told my support person to leave).* **Sophie**

> *I was so shut down for such a long time that it was only a month or so before I went to Birthtalk that I even started to tell my story and it certainly didn't have the clarity it does now. I don't think I ever really talked about how my story felt, just the 'what happened'; I'm sure people could see and hear the anger and sadness, but I didn't necessarily articulate that.* **Leonie**

> *I had no break between contractions. The placenta came away and I haemorrhaged. I was rushed into an emergency caesarean with very little time to save both of our lives. My husband thought we were going to die. The midwives monitored the baby incorrectly. But now I know the real reason for having a bad birthing experience. What I learnt from Birthtalk was that every one of those things could have happened BUT didn't need to leave me with the terrible experience. If only my husband and I weren't left alone for so long not knowing what to do. If only we were told what was happening. If only we weren't surrounded by panic. If only we didn't feel scared and in the way. If only the midwife hadn't wheeled me naked through the maternity ward with little care for my dignity. If only my husband didn't learn of the severity of the situation due to the nurses swearing and yelling in panic when he went to the toilet. If only we felt cared for, supported, informed and the centre of what was happening without the panic. I realised that the nurses could not control what medically happened to me but they could certainly have changed the way they treated us that night.* **Sue-Ellen**

## Your own Birthtalk Breakdown

So, are you ready to try looking at your own story in this way?

We have provided you with a blank Birthtalk Breakdown sheet (see next page). Many women attending Birthtalk use these at the beginning of their healing journey, to get a clear picture of what happened and how they felt throughout their experience. To complete your Birthtalk Breakdown, you need to find a time when you will not be interrupted and you need to set up a situation where you feel safe. Some women do their Birthtalk Breakdowns sitting up in bed after everyone else is asleep, or when the kids have an afternoon nap. You may even find that you need to do this step with the support of a counsellor.

The most important thing is for you to feel you are in a safe space to do this, physically and emotionally.

## How to use a Birthtalk Breakdown sheet

Use the left-hand column to list everything that you remember happening in the birth, in the order it happened – as much as you know. It doesn't matter if you can't remember exactly.

You can also include what happened prior to labour and the postnatal period too, as we consider that to be part of your birth experience.

Then use the right-hand column to begin to think about how you felt at each of these stages. You don't have to show anybody, so just let it all hang out.

If you are not sure how you felt, try asking yourself these questions about each stage of the labour:

Was I scared? Did I feel out of control? Did I feel safe? Did I feel supported? Did I feel alone? Did I feel helpless? Did I feel overwhelmed? Was I afraid for my life? Or my baby's life?

Did I trust my caregiver? Did I feel comfortable with them around? Did I feel I was treated unkindly? Did I feel judged? Did I feel like everyone was doing things to me or watching me? Did I feel cared for as a person? Did I have to support my partner as well as try and deal with my own stuff?

Was I confused about the situation? Did I feel I was an important part of what was going on? Did I feel I could ask questions? Did I feel like I was being given all the information or did I feel dismissed? Was my expert knowledge about me and my baby acknowledged?

## Your Birthtalk Breakdown

| What happened | How I felt |
|---|---|
|  |  |
|  |  |
|  |  |
|  |  |
|  |  |
|  |  |

From *How to Heal a Bad Birth : making sense, making peace and moving on* by Melissa Bruijn and Debby Gould ©Birthtalk.org 2016

## After you have completed your Birthtalk Breakdown

After you have completed your Birthtalk Breakdown, sit back and look at the feelings you have listed down the right-hand side. Do they give you more information about your experience? Do any of the feelings you have listed seem similar to any of the feelings we have identified in our definition of a bad birth? (See our definition in *What is a traumatic or bad birth anyway?* (p42)).

If you feel a bit separated from what you see on the page, try this exercise. Imagine that you have a teenage daughter, and she comes to you after her first date, and confides that she felt all those feelings you described about your birth. How would you react? What do you think she might need? Or imagine that your young son tells you he felt all these feelings on his first day at school after you left. What would you do?

Wouldn't you take them in your arms and tell them you are so sorry that happened, that it is *not* okay, and that it is *not* supposed to be this way? Wouldn't you hold them while they weep? And can you imagine that they might feel loved, and listened to, and as though their feelings are important?

Our question to you is: don't you deserve this kind of acknowledgement and support and love too? We want to tell you that what happened to you is *not* okay – we are so sorry that it happened. Birth is not supposed to be that way.

And if we could give you a hug right now, we would.

# Healing – the big questions

## HOW DO I HEAL?

Remember Sophie, whose story we introduced at the beginning of this book? She asked this question, "How do I heal?" as a heartfelt plea, as have many other women who have contacted Birthtalk.

So, what's the answer? Well, it comes in two parts.

### Part 1: the healing onion

The first part is that we have found the healing process is like peeling the layers off an onion.

Once you have discovered Birthtalk's philosophy, and understand a bit more about how much birth matters, you might peel off a couple of layers. You might do a bit of crying and grieving, and develop a new understanding. That might be all you need, or all you can cope with for a while.

Then something new might come up. You may see a birth on television, or a friend will have a baby, or you might become pregnant, or the birth notes that you sent away for arrive in the mail, and the time is ripe for some more layers to peel off.

While it may be intense and raw (and make you cry), in this process there are gifts and new emotions, and new connections to be made, and relationships can become more healed. It can feel like there is a bit more sunshine in your life.

Then another layer needs peeling!

But the good thing about this process is that you never need face any more than you feel comfortable with.

## Part 2: healing journeys take a zig-zag path

Every woman has her own path to healing. While many women land at the same points along that path, the order in which they arrive at these points is often very different. So, how will you know which order you will follow?

We find that a woman usually knows what she needs to address at each point along the way, once she has support and understands the process. We have had women attend Birthtalk in utter hopelessness; unclear about what – if anything – can be done to help them feel better. And by the end of their first session, they often realise that there's so much they can do, and that they themselves are the best guide for which direction to go next.

Usually, it comes down to answering this question; "What is bothering me the most right now?" or "How do I feel right now?"

It might be that you are so angry with your partner for not rescuing you that you can't even look at them, or that you feel so devastated about the hours when you were separated from your child after the birth, or that you just need to know why you had a caesarean.

The things that are standing out the most are your clues, and your gifts. They are your signposts for 'what needs to be explored next'.

And a great way to explore is to use this book! As we've said earlier, our hope is that this book can act as a compass, leading you in new directions, yet always towards healing, for you and your family. Once you have read *The foundations of your healing journey* (p37), and *How do I heal?* (p61) we invite you to just keep asking yourself, 'How do I feel right now?' Then look up an appropriate chapter for ideas and further understanding that will help you heal.

(To see how a healing journey might look, see pp66-67.)

## The gift of time

It is important to remember that there is no set timeframe for healing. Dr Lynn Madsen, author of *Rebounding from Childbirth*, believes that the gift of time is valuable. She notes, "Healing happens as a woman is open and ready to do the work involved",[4] and cautions that frustration and a sense of failure at not yet being finished will result from trying to hurry things along. She reminds women to honour every new step in the journey, saying, "Every time a piece of insight or resolution is found or another layer of fear is released, relief is experienced and is real. At each of those moments, pause and take satisfaction in the accomplishment".[5]

Dr Madsen also highlights the importance of taking a break from the healing journey[6], something Melissa from Birthtalk definitely found to be true for her own experience. Taking a break now and then might renew your energy levels, and give you space for new insights to emerge so that you can move your healing forward.

Most importantly, go gently with yourself and take the time that is needed for this very important journey.

## Pregnant now?

We also know that for a woman who is pregnant again, it can feel very much as though time is of the essence and there can be an urgency to heal fully before the next birth. However, there will come a time in the pregnancy when it is appropriate to shift your focus to the upcoming birth. By exploring this new birth within the context of working towards an empowering birth (see our *definition of a good birth* (p40)), you will have opportunities to find clarity about what happened in your previous experience and be able to use those insights in preparation for this upcoming birth. (See *How to have a better birth next time* (p507) and *The pitfalls of going with the flow in birth* (p513).)

---

4      Madsen, L. (1994). *Rebounding From Childbirth: Toward Emotional Recovery.* Westport, Connecticut: Bergin and Garvey. p.132

5      ibid.

6      ibid. p.127

## A journal for the journey

We recommend beginning your own *healing journal* as a tool in your healing process. A journal can provide space to air any frustrations, grief, heartache or other intense feelings. It will also document your journey and illustrate your progress as you move towards healing. For some, the initial act of purchasing a journal can be a useful physical step to symbolise your commitment to the healing process, signifying that the first step has been taken, and the healing journey has a place to unfold. Your healing journal can be anything from a pretty book with a nice design and blank pages, to a plain spiral-bound notebook. In fact, some women have found they prefer a plain book, as a pretty book can feel 'too special' to write in. It can help to think of your journal less as a 'keepsake' and more of a processing tool that you may or may not keep for the future.

We agree with childbirth educator and author of *The Well-Rounded Mama* blog, Pamela Vireday, who reminds women that their journal is their space alone, and not a place to worry about spelling, grammar, or even writing in a way that others would understand.[7] Melissa from Birthtalk says, "I had a journal that was fat and messy from everything I wrote and drew in there, but it helped me pinpoint areas of pain and missing information and little rays of sunshine too".

7    Vireday, Pamela, *Emotional Recovery From a Caesarean*.
     Retrieved from *www.plus-size-pregnancy.org/CSANDVBAC/csemotionalrecov.htm* accessed August 2014.

## A healing journey might look like this:

You feel angry with your health carer

Write a *'Shifting from anger'* letter. Share this with your partner. Access your birth notes. Release some intensity and anger. Feel lighter and more able to focus on your child. Gain a wider understanding of 'what happened'

Now you have begun to explore how birth can be, and released some anger, you feel more sadness about what you and your child missed out on.

You explore these feelings in the chapter *'I feel sad'*, and gain clarity and feel more at peace as you discover tools to support the grieving process.

You work more on your feelings of grief, and learn how to reclaim some of what you and your child missed out on. You begin to feel a reduction in intensity in the relationship with your child and find a more relaxed way of interacting as you both reap the benefits of the emotional work you are undertaking.

You
feel frustration with
your partner, who wants you to
just 'get over it'. You explore the chapter
*'Issues with your Partner'* to find ways to
express the importance of the process you
are undertaking. Your partner begins to
express what the birth was like for them,
and you discover a new closeness as
you realise what each of you
went through.

You
realise you are angry
with your body, for what you
saw as it 'letting you down'. You
explore ways to reconnect with your body,
and honour the job it was doing, and develop
a new understanding about birth hormones
and how our bodies are designed to work
in birth. You begin to forgive your body
and realise it was doing the best
it could in extenuating
circumstances.

You
realise you are feeling
better, more often than not. You
are beginning to lose the rage and
panic and extreme anxiety as you explore
and process different aspects of the birth. You
can see a time where the birth does not play
such a large role in your life, and you just
begin to enjoy your child and family
life right now. It is all going
to be okay.

# DO I NEED TO HAVE ANOTHER BABY TO HEAL THE PREVIOUS BIRTH?

The answer to this is definitely "No!" In fact, we advise against it. That is, we don't advise against having another baby, but we do strongly caution against planning a birth in an effort to heal or 're-do' the previous one. There can be an overwhelming urge to 'go back again' and have a do-over. We understand why this is so tempting (and Melissa has experienced that desire herself, early on in her healing). We know many women who feel that way, and it is a natural urge, although we believe it is one that needs to be addressed and understood, rather than followed through. If part of your plan is to have this child's birth be the salve for the earlier birth, then it could feel like this decision avoids the need to process the previous birth.

We completely understand this.

It can be daunting to consider taking the healing journey. Knowing that the journey can invite hard questions about yourself, your birth, your relationships, and require you to recall possibly the worst day of your life as you process and heal, it is understandable that there might be a desire to bypass it. It would be wonderful if that processing could be avoided by getting pregnant, and having a 'good' birth. But we advise against it. Why? Because there is often fall out in attempting to have another baby's birth heal the previous one.

## Pressure on the baby

At the very least, attempting to have another baby's birth heal the previous one places a truckload of pressure on this new child's arrival to heal your emotional wounds. This child now carries the responsibility of your emotional wellbeing, a heavy weight placed unfairly on tiny shoulders.

Accordingly, it can make the upcoming birth less about the new baby and more about the previous baby's birth. It risks becoming less about the celebration of a new little life, and more about a desperate (and entirely understandable) attempt to get the good things missed out on last time.

There are some important questions that need to be answered when making decisions about another baby, which may mean you are side-stepping the healing journey.

## Another bad birth?

Firstly, there is the question of, "What if this birth starts going the same way the last one did?" Taking the healing journey often involves an exploration of 'what happened' last time. This can result in gathering new information about birth, about yourself, and about the situation.

This new information could support you, if your next birth begins taking a similar path to the previous one, and guide you towards still making this birth empowering and positive. However, if you have not 'gone there', you risk feeling helpless and frightened if the same scenario unfolds, or your fear about it occurring again could stall your labour and create other problems.

Another question is, "What if this birth doesn't go to plan and is traumatic for different reasons to last time?" Understanding what can make a birth traumatic and what is important to reduce the likelihood of a woman being negatively impacted by her birth is part of the healing journey. You will discover ideas that support you in working towards an empowering birth in any scenario, so you and your partner can deal with unexpected situations with knowledge about how to maintain emotional health.

The healing journey also offers insights about yourself and what you need as a birthing woman. You will likely learn more about how to get these needs met, and how to communicate your new-found needs to your support people, which empowers them to be able to 'be there' for you. All of this supports you in having an empowered pregnancy, and an empowered birth, whichever way it unfolds.

## Difficult questions

Something else to ponder is, if your next birth is traumatic too, could you then find yourself in a situation where you are still not healed from the first birth, and then also traumatised by your second birth? Does this then mean that you would be struggling with feelings of wanting to try for another baby, to heal the previous two births? Then there is the question, "Why are we having this child?" If the child's purpose is to 'clear the slate' from the bad birth, and another traumatic birth is experienced, has that child then failed in their purpose?

Will this child still be welcomed, even if the birth was less-than-great?

These are hard questions that are important to face when considering another baby.

## Even if it's a better birth...

Even if it's a better birth, keep in mind that we have some women attending Birthtalk who have recently had a positive birth, but are there to heal a previous birth. They may have had a good experience with their youngest child, which then brings up a whole host of issues surrounding unprocessed grief and anger as they realise even more about what they missed out on the previous time. So, even having a good experience does not necessarily put the traumatic birth 'to rest'. The more that a traumatic birth can be explored and processed, the less 'residue' there will likely be after the positive birth. Or, if issues from the previous birth do crop up, the more skills you will have to process whatever arises due to having already faced the healing journey.

## It never needs to be that bad again

Keep in mind that we do not believe the next birth *ever* needs to be as bad as the previous one. The best chance of having a more positive experience involves taking the healing journey, unravelling the previous birth and gaining insights from this, and exploring new information that can lead towards an empowering birth in any scenario.

> Someone said to me early in my healing journey that you need to have a vaginal birth after caesarean to fully heal from a traumatic caesarean. I did not think it was true then, and I certainly *do not* think it is true now. I did not want my next child's purpose to be to 'save' me. I did not want my next baby to have to bear the burden of having a good birth and be responsible for all this healing. I wanted to be healed before we had this baby, so they could follow their own path to meeting us. And I did not want the pressure of having to have a good birth to heal. Birth is, to some extent, unpredictable. But I knew that however I birthed, I could have an empowering experience, which released me from having to have the 'perfect' birth. **Melissa,** in a speech given at National Caesarean Awareness Day, 2006.

So, our best advice would be to acknowledge the urge to 'go back and do it over'. But know that to do this is potentially robbing yourself of the chance to emotionally recover, to know yourself more deeply, to fall in love with your previous child even more, to address any relationship issues with your partner, and to gain insights to prepare for the empowering birth you, and your baby, deserve.

Note: If you are already pregnant, and became pregnant partly in order to have another birth to heal the previous one, you are not alone, and there is still plenty of time to move to a different mindset, and gather different information. The first thing is to acknowledge your hopes for this birth, maybe grieve the fact that it is not easy, and begin to tackle the healing process. If you are heavily pregnant, you may want to focus more on the upcoming birth. However, if you are in the headspace of wanting to heal and release this new birth to its own path, without it needing to heal your last birth, then you are on the right track. We suggest starting with reading *The foundations of your healing journey* (p37), and then perhaps *The pitfalls of 'going with the flow' in birth*, to get some ideas about empowered birth, which will be a part of the healing journey anyway. Then, just explore the areas that you feel need dealing with, as well as identifying concerns and questions you have from last time, and work to get them answered before birthing again. This may involve finding a trustworthy health professional who can answer your questions. (See *Appendix A* for information that may guide you towards appropriate support.)

# MY BIRTH WAS QUITE A WHILE AGO – IS IT TOO LATE TO HEAL?

The simple answer is: it is never too late to heal.

We've had women attend Birthtalk with newborns and we've had women attend Birthtalk who have toddlers, primary school children, even teenagers. We've also have women attend Birthtalk whose children are in their thirties. We've even talked to women debriefing their births who were in their eighties. We have found that women often don't seek support for a traumatic birth straight away. This can be due to a number of factors, all of which can result in women not accessing support in the initial few months, or even years after the birth.

## The halo effect

In the first weeks after a birth, women, and partners too, are usually simply grateful for their child's survival, and their own survival. According to midwifery lecturer, Patricia Larkin, this 'halo effect', "where women experience euphoria and relief after having a live, healthy baby, means that women are less likely to be negative about their childbirth experiences or criticise their care".[8] They feel gratitude to their health carers, often despite poor management or care, as they are in the throes of early parenthood, and may see the experience through rose-coloured glasses. They might recognise they are affected by the birth, yet shrug it off, hope it goes away and focus on their baby. They might not realise their experience was lacking, or that they are impacted by the birth, and may simply relate any struggles to being a new parent, or recovering from the birth.

## The numbing effect

One consequence of a traumatic birth (and a symptom of PTSD) can be a numbing of emotions.[9] We have seen this emotional numbing functioning as a survival skill, allowing a woman to function as best as possible at a superficial level to meet the requirements of her newborn, without having to face the deep and painful emotions brought about by the birth.

---

8    Larkin, P. (2013). Midwifery Matters – Childbirth: Issues, contexts, outcomes. *WIN, 21*(1), 50. Accessed January 2014.

9    Gamble, J., & Creedy, D. (2013). *Mothers need better care to reduce post-traumatic stress after childbirth.* Retrieved from *https://theconversation.com/mothers-need-better-care-to-reduce-post-traumatic-stress-after-childbirth-12272*, accessed January 2014.

This numbing or disconnection, while fulfilling an important task, can also mean there is little access to the emotions that might indicate a need for support, such as strong feelings of grief or anger.

In addition, women often have little understanding or awareness about birth trauma, so any symptoms will often not be recognised as such. For example, hypervigilance in caring for the baby may be explained away as the mother being 'too controlling', without realising that it is a normal response to a traumatic birth.

As Professor Debra Creedy and her colleagues note, "Continuing avoidance symptoms may indicate attempts to keep strong feelings and memories at bay. This could impair a woman's ability to talk about and process the trauma associated with childbirth, lead to social isolation, and hamper access to appropriate health services and support."[10]

So, some symptoms of the traumatic birth itself, as well as a lack of knowledge about what these symptoms are, can delay a woman's ability to acknowledge that the birth was actually traumatic, and delay her reaching out.

## Survival mode

Another stumbling block in discovering there are issues about the birth that need processing can be purely the nature of caring for a newborn. The early weeks and months can be very intense, especially if a traumatic birth has left a woman struggling to connect with her own mothering instincts.

Life can become a never-ending cycle of feeding, laundry, sleeping (or trying to), changing nappies and placating a baby. The learning curve is steep, and the hours are relentless: hardly the environment for reflection on a less-than-great birth experience.

We have often found that once the first year is over, a woman 'surfaces' and realises that she actually does have issues about the birth. This reflection and analysis can lead to taking steps towards finding support.

---

10      Creedy, D. K., Shochet, I. M., & Horsfall, J. (2000). Childbirth and the development of acute trauma symptoms: Incidence and contributing factors. *Birth, 27*, 104–111.

## Milestones raise issues

Often the instigation that inspires a woman to begin the healing journey is a life event, or milestone, which requires her to address the issue of the birth. First birthdays, or second birthdays (or beyond) can push memories of the birth into her awareness, and raise a discomfort that requires action. Another pregnancy is also a common instigator – it is a reminder with a time limit. A woman realises she must face her previous birth now, before she faces birthing again.

We have had older women, whose grown children are now birthing; attend Birthtalk to face their own births in order to fully support their daughters. They have found great relief and insight from the experience, enabling them to embrace the honour of being present at their grandchild's birth with joy and confidence.

## The perfect time to heal is: when you are ready

We have had women tell us they avoided attending Birthtalk's 'Healing From Birth' meetings, month after month, until finally they were in the headspace and the mindset to begin the journey. Melissa from Birthtalk did not begin her own healing journey until her son was two-and-a-half years old.

Some women come to Birthtalk for the first time in their final weeks of their next pregnancy – finally ready to take steps to clear a space for the upcoming birth. Even in this intense time, they can debrief and process aspects of their previous birth, discovering insights and tools to support them in their healing journey while they prepare to meet their new babies.

We usually find that, if a woman has access to appropriate and helpful support, she will take these steps towards healing when she is ready. There is no 'right' time for that – only YOU will know.

Regardless of how long ago your birth was, it is never too late to heal.

# WHAT IF I'VE FINISHED MY FAMILY? CAN I STILL HEAL?

The answer to this question is a resounding "Yes!" This is really important to know, as you may hear women talk about their empowering subsequent births after trauma, and all the gifts they received, and you may wonder if it's too late for you.

The healing journey is not at all dependent on birthing again.

We often have women attending Birthtalk who do not plan to have more children, and they, too, take incredibly powerful healing journeys. In fact, we strongly caution women against planning another child as part of the healing process – you can read why in *Do I need to have another baby to heal the previous birth?* (p68).

Your healing journey is about making sense of what has already happened. It is about pulling your experience apart and using tools to process and understand what you find. Then it is about making peace with your previous experience when you have more information and insights about the event and your response to it. None of these steps require another pregnancy or birth to be meaningful and effective. The final step is moving on, which can look different for every woman. Some might already be pregnant, and use this new information to plan for an empowering experience. Some might only now be able to even consider another child. And some might simply move back to their family, feeling more complete, more present and more resilient to life.

# WHY TAKE THE HEALING JOURNEY?

*I have had quite a few women say to me, "What's the use?
It happened. It's done. I can't go back and change things, so why
bother?"* **Deb from Birthtalk**

## What you need to know

You are completely right – you can't change anything. Yet that doesn't mean you can't make peace with your experience. It doesn't mean you can't reduce the level of intensity you feel when you think or talk about your birth. It doesn't mean you can't reduce any anxiety you are feeling on a daily basis. All of these things are possible by going back and processing what happened.

Importantly, 'going back' does not mean 'dwelling on the past'. It means exploring your experience; unpacking it and pulling it apart so you can better understand what happened to you, in order to *move on*.

## Shutting down

Some women use the coping mechanism of 'shutting down', 'blocking off' or 'closing up'. This is actually a survival skill that is probably very useful in those early days when you need to learn how to care for a small baby. There is often no room for heavy emotions, especially if you feel you will fall apart if you dare let some feelings in. Many women describe themselves as feeling numb. However, this state of being is not comfortable in the long term. It becomes very hard to keep those emotions down, especially when the baby gets a bit older, and you begin to find 'space' in your day to reflect.

## Why would I 'go there'?

It might feel easier to continue to bury the emotions surrounding your experience and continue to feel blocked and operate on a surface level. It might feel scary to contemplate moving forward, and we completely understand. However, 'going there' and addressing your birth can provide an opportunity to learn, to grow, to reconnect and to heal. If you do 'go there', it will not be to *change* what happened, because that's simply not possible. But 'going there' can change your *now*. The act of processing and exploring your birth has the potential to greatly improve your current emotional status.

We have seen hundreds of women take the plunge and acknowledge that, while they can't change the circumstances of their birth, they have a great deal of power and say in how they experience their lives in the present moment, and this is greatly enhanced by taking the healing journey. We are with you all the way.

## Is it worth it to 'go there'?

We hear from Birthtalk families all the time about how 'worth it' the journey is, how much more connected and empowered women and men feel, how their relationships with their partners, their children and themselves are enhanced and renewed from addressing the issues surrounding their births. We thought we'd let some Birthtalk women and their partners share the benefits they gained from gathering the courage and strength to process their births.

> *Being able to express what was happening for me had an impact on my healing, because the more I have been able to validate my birth as being traumatic, the easier it has been to move through the issues. Clarity is a great tool.* **Leonie**

> *I took onboard Birthtalk's ideas and then acted on them. I got my notes from the hospital, and I did a Birthtalk Breakdown. After coming to Birthtalk (and taking healing steps) I could talk about my birth without feeling teary. I don't get upset and I can understand my feelings. I feel comfortable with my emotions towards birth, as Birthtalk gave me the answers I needed to heal.* **Sophie**

> *Birthtalk helped me by validating and acknowledging the feelings I had. It is okay to feel sad for not giving birth through my birth canal. Through healing classes and reflection, I realised that there were things that I was looking forward to in Levi's birth that I just totally missed. Like seeing my placenta, holding a gooey baby and smelling him! The process is ongoing because it's not always at the forefront of my mind anymore. And so sometimes issues come up and I get sad and grieve for that birth. But now I know how to work through the sadness and that there is a group of women there to support me and a husband who understands me.* **Skye**

*Birthtalk empowered me to acknowledge that things were rough; I could admit that I wasn't superhuman and [the birth] had affected me. Once I became used to talking about it at Birthtalk meetings, I have found the experience easier to communicate with others.* **Tina**

*I remember going to my first 'Healing From Birth' meeting [at Birthtalk]. I just let my story roll out uncensored, without holding back. It was like I had permission to say anything, so I did. It was amazing because it was the first time someone acknowledged what a hard journey my first birth was and how well I had done. It was amazing to hear someone praise me for how well I had done when I always thought I had failed. It really started to turn my thinking around from self-blame to breaking down why it felt like such a bad experience.* **Kerri**

*I knew I was getting better when I felt free of the torment of what I could have or should have done differently to have prevented what happened at my daughter's birth; when I no longer questioned how I could have gone so wrong.* **Sally**

*Expressing myself and feeling validated really started me down the track to feeling better and thinking about the birth less. Hearing the other women's stories made me realise the circumstances might be different, but the emotion is the same. It made me realise birth is a massive emotional journey, not just physical, and if you are unsupported, that is what can make it a bad experience. I could start to take the blame off myself and realise I was having a normal reaction to a bad experience. It was a revelation to even realise I had been traumatised and needed to work through the experience and the emotion.* **Kerri**

*It was tough for Angie and me, processing the trauma of the birth. It was a long road but we wouldn't give up. It has brought us closer together searching for answers. I recommend Birthtalk to anyone, especially when I see guys who have felt as powerless as I did to prevent the caesarean in our first child's birth.* **Dale**

*I felt supported by Birthtalk in a number of ways: receiving validation that my feelings of loss were valid and real; having Deb interpret my hospital notes for me and explain the reasons why the hospital system does certain things; receiving understanding from others mums and dads who have experienced a birth they were unhappy with. This kind of support has enabled me to work through my first birth. It has encouraged me to look forward to, and work towards, a better birth experience next time. It has shown me what real support is, which has caused me to seek real support in other areas of my life. I have learnt to not just 'settle for and accept' bad situations in life, and that it is okay to desire and work towards better situations.* **Angie**

*After a traumatic birth experience, it can be so confusing. You feel things you don't understand and don't understand why you are so upset or unravelled. Intuitively, you know it should have been better than that! But you are not alone and many birthing women feel the same way. For me, it was a blame game on myself and my health carers. I have now learnt that sometimes you need to stick up for yourself and be more proactive; sometimes it's no one's fault and just plain bad luck, and sometimes you need to give yourself a pat on the back for getting through birth whatever way it went! My feelings of failure have given way to immense pride and inner strength, something I would never have thought possible. Thanks Birthtalk!* **Kerri**

*The benefits of processing my traumatic first birth have been far-reaching, and such a gift for my whole family. I see the difference every single day in how I parent, how I relate to my husband, how I interact with the world, and how I feel about myself. It has been so hard, but so worth it.* **Melissa**

# *Do I need a diagnosis?*

When we began Birthtalk, one of our stipulations for attendees was that they do not need to fit any particular set of criteria to attend – they do not need any diagnosis, or even a suspected diagnosis. They do not have to fill out forms or 'prove' that their birth was 'bad enough' to be attending. All they need is to feel as though they want to attend, even if they don't really know why.

Of course, there are definitions and labels that can describe a woman's experience postnatally, and these can be important or helpful, if only for a sense of validation that what they are experiencing is real. But they do not fit all women. It can be really damaging for women who feel they don't fit the description, yet are still confused and desperate for support. It is important to know that a diagnosis is not a part of everyone's healing journey. That is, you do not need a diagnosis to begin to heal.

However, in our experience, you may find it really helpful to understand birth trauma, PTSD, Postnatal Depression (PND) and the possible complications, as defined by health professionals. It can give you ideas on where you may need to focus your healing, and help to validate any feelings or behaviours that are confusing for you or those around you.

So, we want to offer you a brief overview. However, we do not want to focus on diagnosis, as beginning your own healing journey is not dependent on getting a 'green light' from any diagnosis.

It can be helpful for you to investigate the possible ways your response to your birth can be identified, categorised and labelled by health professionals, and then to use those insights in chartering your own course, perhaps with the support of health professionals of your choice.

And maybe what matters is not which term is used to describe your birth, whether it feels like it was traumatic, or bad, or disappointing, or challenging, or devastating or any other descriptive term. As we have mentioned, what matters is that you feel you have the support you need to process any aspect of your experience, regardless of how 'bad' it was. If it feels like it needs to be looked at, dealt with and explored for you to feel a sense of peace and to move on more fully into your life, then that is a 'green light' to begin your healing journey.

## An important reminder

Just to recap, we want to be clear that a diagnosis is not a pre-requisite for healing. And that being unable to obtain a diagnosis does not mean you are 'fine'. There can be benefits from understanding more about aspects of PTSD and birth trauma that can support your healing as you learn more about yourself and realise what a normal response you are having to this situation. The following section, *Can you get Post-Traumatic Stress Disorder after childbirth?* explains more.

# CAN YOU GET POST-TRAUMATIC STRESS DISORDER AFTER CHILDBIRTH?

*There is now no doubt that some women can develop PTSD [post traumatic stress disorder] in relation to a traumatic birth experience.*[11] **Bailham and Joseph, 2003**

*Mothers with post-traumatic stress disorder attributable to childbirth struggle to survive each day while battling terrifying nightmares and flashbacks of the birth, anger, anxiety, depression, and painful isolation from the world of motherhood.*[12] **Beck, 2004**

## What is Post-Traumatic Stress Disorder?

The Birth Trauma Association (UK) describes PTSD as "the term for a set of normal reactions to a traumatic, scary or bad experience."[13] When a life-threatening event has been experienced or witnessed, PTSD can occur following the event. These life-threatening events have traditionally been recognised as things like "military combat, natural disasters, terrorist incidents, serious accidents, or violent personal assaults like rape. However, a traumatic experience can be any experience involving the threat of death or serious injury to an individual or another person close to them (e.g. their baby) so it is now understood that Post-Traumatic Stress Disorder can be a consequence of a traumatic birth."[14]

PTSD can only be diagnosed once more than a month has passed since the trauma.[15] Michele Rosenthal (a PTSD survivor and now a certified professional PTSD coach) puts it this way: "In the immediate aftermath of trauma – say, the first month or so – many people suffer from acute stress, which includes the following symptoms: anxiety, behavioral disturbance, dissociation, hyperarousal,

---

11   Bailham, D., & Joseph, S. (2003). Post-traumatic stress following childbirth: a review of the emerging literature and directions for research and practice. *Psychology, Health, and Medicine, 8*(2), 159–168.

12   Beck, C. (2004b). Post-traumatic stress due to childbirth: the aftermath. *Nursing Research, 53*(4), 216–224.

13   Birth Trauma Association, UK. *What is Birth Trauma?*
     Retrieved from *www.birthtraumaassociation.org.uk/what_is_trauma.htm* accessed January 2014.

14   ibid.

15   American Psychiatric Association. (2013). *Diagnostic and statistical manual of mental disorders* (5th ed.). Washington, DC: Author. p.272

avoidance of memories related to the trauma, flashbacks and nightmares. All of these symptoms are part of the normal steps of how trauma survivors process the recent event. However, if these symptoms persist for more than one month (and begin to functionally and socially impair – and significantly upset – the survivor), then the diagnosis is changed to Post-Traumatic Stress Disorder."[16]

## What happens when we are involved in a traumatic event?

The following information, which is referring to any traumatic event, not particularly a birthing scenario, can be really helpful when trying to understand what has happened to you.

In times of stress: "Humans have a set of adaptive, life-saving responses… During the 'fight or flight' response when faced with terror, less critical body functions (e.g. the parts of the brain where memory, emotion and thinking are processed) get 'turned off' while the body prioritises immediate physical safety. As a result, the traumatic experiences are not integrated. Unprocessed feelings associated with the terror and memories of the trauma can appear unexpectedly and unpredictably, causing complex problems".[17]

## What would be considered a 'traumatic event' in birth?

In her groundbreaking research in 2004, Professor Cheryl Beck, from the University of Connecticut, described birth trauma as an event occurring during the labour and birth that "involves actual or threatened serious injury or death to the mother or her infant".[18] She wrote, "The concept of birth trauma involves traumatic experiences that may occur during any phase of childbearing".[19] The experiences considered to be a 'birth trauma' in her study included a wide range of events such as emergency caesarean, stillbirth, inadequate medical care, fear of epidural, premature birth, separation from infant in a Neonatal Intensive Care Unit, prolonged painful labour, rapid delivery or a degrading experience.[20]

---

16 Rosenthal, M. *PTSD Symptoms*. Retrieved from *http://healmyptsd.com/education/symptoms-of-ptsd*, accessed April 2014.

17 National Alliance on Mental Illness. (2013). *Posttraumatic Stress Disorder Factsheet*. Retrieved from *www.nami.org/factsheets/ptsd_factsheet.pdf*, accessed January 2014.

18 Beck, C. (2004a). Birth trauma: in the eye of the beholder. *Nursing Research*, *53*(1), 28–35.

19 ibid.

20 ibid.

Professor Beck has since refined this definition, in an interview in 2014, saying that after her first two studies on birth trauma and its resulting PTSD, she has learned that, "Traumatic childbirth can also occur even if a woman does not perceive that she or her infant is at risk of serious injury or death. Women can perceive their birth as traumatic if they perceive that they were stripped of their dignity during the birthing process... Some women shared that they felt like a piece of meat on an assembly line. Women did not feel cared for by the obstetrical team. To me, this lack of caring stripped women of a protective layer during their labor and delivery and left them prime to perceive their birth as traumatic."[21]

## What if it wasn't actually a 'life-threatening event'?

Sometimes the 'threat' component of PTSD may be perceived, rather than 'actual', and this issue of perception is really important to understand. The US Department of Veteran Affairs state in their *Policy guidance on the Assessment and Treatment of Post-Traumatic Stress Disorder (PTSD)* that "the perception of threat (distinct from the level of actual threat) is an independent predictor of PTSD symptoms".[22] Other research across different types of traumatic events reports that people who had a perception that their life was in danger during the traumatic event "reported higher levels of PTSD symptoms or higher rates of current PTSD".[23] While these findings related to a range of traumatic events, they are echoed in research particularly relating to childbirth, where results suggest that "women's subjective birth experiences are the most important factor in the development of post-traumatic stress symptoms".[24]

This means that even if you or your baby were never in danger, if you *perceived* the situation as threatening due to what you were feeling/hearing/interpreting, then this perception – your subjective view of the experience – is *what matters* in terms of your experience and its effect.

---

21  Beck, C. in Karaa, W. (2014). *Book Review: Traumatic Childbirth and an Interview*

22  Department of the Army Headquarters, United States Army Medical Command. (2012). *Policy Guidance on the Assessment and Treatment of Post-Traumatic Stress Disorder (PTSD)*. Retrieved from *http://cdn.govexec.com/media/gbc/docs/pdfs_edit/042312bb1.pdf*, accessed November 2014.

23  Ozer, E.J., Best, S.R., Lipsey, T.L., & Weiss, D.S. (2003). Predictors of post-traumatic stress disorder and symptoms in adults: a meta-analysis. *Psychological Bulletin, 129*, 52–73.

24  Garthus-Niegel, S., Soest, T., Vollrath, M., & Eberhard-Gran, M. (2013). The impact of subjective birth experiences on post-traumatic stress symptoms: a longitudinal study. *Archives of Women's Mental Health, 16*(1), 1- 10.

## What are trauma symptoms according to research?

Some of the symptoms of post-traumatic stress for any traumatic event, not specifically birth, are included below. These behavioural symptoms, from the DSM-5 (*Diagnostic and statistical manual of mental disorders, 5th Edition*), can be clustered into the following areas: re-experiencing, avoidance, negative cognitions and mood, and arousal.[25]

**Re-experiencing:** recurrent, involuntary and intrusive distressing memories of the event; recurrent, distressing dreams, flashbacks, intense or prolonged distress after exposure to stimuli that symbolise or resemble an aspect of the traumatic event.

**Avoidance:** Avoiding thoughts or feelings associated with the traumatic event, or external reminders (e.g. people, places, conversations, activities, objects, or situations).

**Negative thoughts and mood:** Persistent and exaggerated negative beliefs or expectations about oneself or the world (e.g. "I am bad", "The world is completely dangerous"); persistently seeing self or others as the cause of the traumatic event or its consequences; persistent negative emotions (e.g. fear, horror, anger, guilt or shame) and persistent inability to experience positive emotions.

**Arousal:** Irritable behaviour and verbal or physical aggression; reckless or self-destructive behaviour, hypervigilance, exaggerated startle response, problems in concentration and sleep disturbance.[26]

Brain imaging studies show that the psychological problems of hypoarousal (numbness and avoidance) and hyperarousal (the heightened 'startle response') are controlled biologically.[27] These states of hypoarousal and hyperarousal "demonstrate the difficulty people living with PTSD have in regulating their emotional and physical responses".[28]

- We have met many women who report these symptoms, manifesting in ways such as:
- flashbacks to a certain part of the birth that was intrusive and distressing
- feeling the same panic and fear when in situations that remind them of the birth, for example in the dentist's chair

25    American Psychiatric Association, 2013, *Posttraumatic Stress Disorder*
      *www.psychiatry.org/File Library/Practice/DSM/DSM-5/DSM-5-PTSD.pdf* accessed July 2015

26    American Psychiatric Association. (2013). *Diagnostic and statistical manual of mental disorders* (5th ed.).
      Washington, DC: Author. pp.271-272

27    National Alliance on Mental Illness. (2013). *Posttraumatic Stress Disorder Factsheet*.
      Retrieved from *www.nami.org/factsheets/ptsd_factsheet.pdf*, accessed January 2014.

28    ibid.

- avoiding driving past the hospital where the birth occurred
- feeling emotionally numb towards their child and/or partner
- hypervigilance in the care of their baby, for example checking on the baby a great many times during the night.

## What factors contribute to the woman experiencing these trauma symptoms?

Factors that can contribute to the development of trauma symptoms, according to Professors Jenny Gamble and Debra Creedy, are:

- "poor medical care, such as a poorly performed procedure causing unnecessary pain or care inconsistent with the best available evidence;
- poor communication by care providers;
- physically traumatic or emergency birth, such as emergency caesarean section;
- physical damage to the baby; or
- admission to the special care nursery or intensive care unit."[29]

Australian research has shown that a strong predictor of acute trauma symptoms was the level of obstetric intervention, in particular emergency caesareans, forceps delivery and the extent of postpartum analgesia, and that when there was a high level of obstetric intervention plus the woman perceived she had poor maternity care, the likelihood of trauma symptoms increased. That is, women who experienced both a high level of obstetric intervention and dissatisfaction with their care during the birth were more likely to develop trauma symptoms than women who experienced just one of these.[30]

This makes sense when you consider that a woman who perceives she is receiving inadequate care is likely to feel helpless and out-of-control, as the vulnerability of birth usually means she cannot leave the situation. If you combine these feelings with an intervention such as an emergency caesarean, or having analgesia for an extended period postpartum, which both require a woman to be completely 'at the mercy' of staff for her basic care needs, as well as keeping her alive during surgery, this could understandably create a situation where she feels unsure if she or her baby will emerge safely, and perhaps she is unable to communicate this.

---

29     Gamble, J., & Creedy, D. (2013). *Mothers need better care to reduce post-traumatic stress after childbirth.* Retrieved from *https://theconversation.com/mothers-need-better-care-to-reduce-post-traumatic-stress-after-childbirth-12272*, accessed January 2014.

30     Creedy, D. K., Shochet, I. M., & Horsfall, J. (2000). Childbirth and the development of acute trauma symptoms: Incidence and contributing factors. *Birth, 27*, 104–111.

## Does the birth need to be 'outwardly' traumatic to qualify as a traumatic birth?

A birth absolutely does not have to be outwardly traumatic to qualify as a traumatic birth. This point is extremely important to remember when you are struggling to explain why you are feeling so bad about your birth, especially when those around you don't understand. Remember our definition for a *bad birth?* We shared that a bad birth can appear completely 'normal' to an outsider, and offered a new definition of a bad birth, which involved feelings of powerlessness, confusion, fear and isolation.

This definition has been echoed in the findings of some studies around birth trauma that suggest that the trauma can arise from events that might be unseen by most people present at the time – events such as a degrading experience, or the psychological distress of fear of an epidural, or the woman perceiving the lack of a caring approach.[31]

What we have found at Birthtalk (echoed in the findings of Professor Beck) is that even if everything seems completely okay to an outsider during the birth, if a woman perceives that she or her baby is threatened with damage, even with a procedure that is routine to medical staff, she can experience that as a traumatic event. We have found this to be true regardless of her level of pain relief at the time, or the fact that she and her baby leave the hospital alive and physically healthy.

You can read more about this in our section, *Common 'hidden factors' that can make a birth traumatic* (p99).

## How many women are having traumatic births?

According to research, about a third of women report that their birth was traumatic for them, and in the early weeks after birth they experience at least three symptoms of trauma.[32] According to Professor Jenny Gamble and Professor Debra Creedy, the reported symptoms of the women "relate to re-experiencing birthing, emotional numbing or avoidance and hyperarousal about the birth".[33]

---

31   Beck, C. (2004a). Birth trauma: in the eye of the beholder. op. cit.

32   Creedy, D. K., Shochet, I. M., & Horsfall, J. (2000). Childbirth and the development of acute trauma symptoms: Incidence and contributing factors. op. cit.

33   Gamble, J., & Creedy, D. (2013). *Mothers need better care to reduce post-traumatic stress after childbirth.* op. cit.

Penny Simpkin, founding member of Prevention and Treatment of Traumatic Childbirth (PAATCH) in the USA, writes that the number of women reporting a traumatic birth is between 25 and 34 per cent.[34] According to Ms. Simpkin, a traumatic birth is one where the individual… "believes the mother's or her baby's life was in danger, or that a serious threat to the mother's or her baby's physical or emotional integrity existed."[35]

Simpkin says, "Most women who have had a traumatic birth do not develop PTSD. Studies report rates of PTSD after childbirth, as varying between 1.5 per cent and 9.0 per cent of all births. The differences among study findings are partly explained by differences in study designs, assessment tools, study populations, usual maternity care practices and caregiver attitudes. Those who have traumatic births but are not diagnosed with PTSD have fewer symptoms of the disorder or a duration of symptoms of less than a month. These women are referred to variously as having Post-Traumatic Stress Symptoms (PTSS), Post-Traumatic Stress Effects, (PTSE), or Partial Post-Traumatic Stress Disorder (PPTSD). All these terms refer to a less severe manifestation of birth trauma, meaning they had some symptoms of PTSD, but not enough to qualify for the diagnosis."[36]

Acute stress disorder, say Professors Gamble and Creedy, is developed by between two per cent and six per cent of women and involves more dissociative symptoms, that is, feeling disconnected from thoughts, feelings or memories.[37] (At the time of Gamble and Creedy's article, acute stress disorder could be diagnosed between two days and one month after a traumatic event, unlike PTSD which requires symptoms to be present for at least a month.[38] However, the new DSM-5 requires acute stress disorder symptoms to be present for "at least 3 days and up to a month"[39] after exposure to trauma)

However, we agree with Creedy and colleagues, who comment that "the tendency to use "posttraumatic stress disorder" or "non-posttraumatic stress disorder" groupings [in research studies] does not acknowledge the high level of distress suffered by some birthing women."[40]

---

34    Simkin, P. Traumatic Births and PTSD: Definition and Statistics. Retrieved from *http://pattch.org/resource-guide/traumatic-births-and-ptsd-definition-and-statistics/*, accessed January 2014.

35    ibid.

36    ibid.

37    Gamble, J., & Creedy, D. (2013). *Mothers need better care to reduce post-traumatic stress after childbirth.* op. cit.

38    ibid.

39    American Psychiatric Association. (2013). *Diagnostic and statistical manual of mental disorders* (5th ed.). op.cit. p. 281

40    Creedy, D. K., Shochet, I. M., & Horsfall, J. (2000). Childbirth and the development of acute trauma symptoms: Incidence and contributing factors. op. cit.

As we have explained in our chapter *Do I need a diagnosis?* (p81), it may not be necessary to receive a diagnosis in the manifestations of birth trauma to begin the path to healing. These manifestations are a description of symptoms that are common after a traumatic experience of birth. We have mentioned them here just to demonstrate that a marked emotional impact to a birth experience is definitely possible and is documented and acknowledged in research and clinical practice

## Does birth trauma only happen to certain women?

Professors Gamble and Creedy note that while "previous traumatic childbirth, sexual abuse, intimate partner violence and other traumas also play a role… many women without known predisposing factors experience birthing as traumatic".[41]

Anecdotally, we have supported women impacted by a traumatic birth from varied socioeconomic, cultural and educational backgrounds, with or without previous trauma experience, of varying ages, accessing varying models of care, and with different personality types.

## How can the effects of PTSD from birth manifest for women?

PTSD following childbirth can manifest in different ways. As Sheila Kitzinger, a leading authority on childbirth and author of *Birth Crisis* describes it, "Women usually feel numb at first, simply relieved that it is all over. Later the floodgates open, and gratitude that they and their babies are alive is mixed with a sense that they have been violated … Scenes from the labour and birth are played over and over again in their minds like a video on a loop that cannot be switched off. They suffer nightmares and flashbacks to the trauma. …. They have little confidence in their bodies, and breastfeeding is turned into a struggle. These women suffer from post-traumatic stress which may last months or even years, it may adversely affect their relationship with a child and with their partner".[42]

We asked a group of women who had each received a diagnosis of PTSD to share their symptoms with us:

---

41    Gamble, J., & Creedy, D. (2013). *Mothers need better care to reduce post-traumatic stress after childbirth.* op. cit.

42    Kitzinger, S. *Becoming a mother.* Retrieved from *www.sheilakitzinger.com/articlesbysheila/badbirthhaunts.htm*, accessed January 2014.

*I felt detached from the real world, like I was watching myself in a disaster movie. I would catastrophise every scenario and was waiting for disaster to strike. All my anxieties were focused on my little girl and I just could not find any positives.* **Nikki**

*[I experienced] intrusive thoughts, flashbacks, guilt about the birth. Everything, all the time, is about the birth – all day, every day, every minute – it's always there. I'm obsessing over it.* **Libby**

*When my son was four-months-old it started taking me two hours a night to get to sleep because I kept going over my hospital experiences. If my son woke during the night it would take another hour to get to sleep again. I had flashbacks about my hospital stay. I couldn't remember much of his birth. I couldn't remember the first time I held him. I still can't walk into the hospital he was born in without huge anxiety attacks. I have trouble even driving past it. I can't go up in the elevators there; I can't go onto birthing suite or the maternity ward without huge anxiety.* **Nic**

*I had the happiest, smiliest baby in the world but all I wanted to do was cry. I felt like I had PMS every single day. I wanted to yell at my other half for absolutely no reason. I relived my labour and post-birth experience over and over, always finding ways that I had failed as a mum.* **Evie**

*I actually had no idea I had PTSD at first. I struggled for thirteen months before receiving a diagnosis. For me, the signs were anxiety, nightmares and panic attacks over silly little things that took me back to my birth. I was/am extremely anxious about all sorts of things. I see danger for my son and I in everything. I had nightmares – I'd relive the whole experience at least once a night and had no control over it. I couldn't retell my birth story or listen to other people's stories, especially if they were good stories. I felt angry and upset; it would always induce hysterical, uncontrollable crying. I can't watch birth on any television program or film – possibly still my worst trigger. I couldn't even drive past the hospital without getting very panicky and feeling sick. I certainly couldn't go there. Even a visit to the dentist is traumatic and sets off all sorts of emotions. In the early days of my PTSD (before I knew I had it) I cried a lot and felt very depressed. Due to my birth experience, my son and I didn't bond well at all and I am so anxious over everything with him. I can barely let him out of my sight.* **Hannah**

*I would burst into tears several times a day, for no reason. I felt violated. I would watch my baby sleep, keeping an eye on her, fearing her death (as I had nearly lost my life). I am over-cautious, dramatising situations in my mind where my daughter could get hurt. I distanced myself from my friends. I have flashbacks to the incident – anything would trigger flashbacks. I would try to go through the birth again in my mind to piece everything together and make sense of it.* **Kim**

## Is something wrong with me if I experience PTSD symptoms?

We agree with the Birth Trauma Association when they say, "It is important to remember that PTSD is a normal response to a traumatic experience. The re-experiencing of the event with flashbacks accompanied by genuine anxiety and fear are beyond the sufferer's control. They are the mind's way of trying to make sense of an extremely scary experience and are not a sign [of an] individual'[s] 'weakness' or inability to cope."[43]

That is, you are experiencing a normal response to an abnormal situation, because it is not normal for birth to be an event where the life of yourself or your child is threatened, whether that threat is real or perceived, despite what you might hear from those around you.

As Dr Judith Herman says in her book *Trauma and Recovery*, "Traumatic events are extraordinary, not because they occur rarely, but rather because they overwhelm the ordinary human adaptations to life"[44].

According to the Royal College of Psychiatrists, "About 1 in 3 people will find that their symptoms just carry on and that they can't come to terms with what has happened. It is as though the process has got stuck. The symptoms of post-traumatic stress, although normal in themselves, become a problem – or Post-Traumatic Stress Disorder – when they go on for too long".[45]

Kendra Cherry, author of *Everything Psychology*,[46] identifies a psychological disorder as "a pattern of behavioral or psychological symptoms that impact multiple life areas and/or create distress for the person experiencing these

---

43    Birth Trauma Association, UK. *What is Birth Trauma?*
      Retrieved from *www.birthtraumaassociation.org.uk/what_is_trauma.htm*, accessed January 2014.

44    Herman, J. (1997). *Trauma and Recovery: The aftermath of violence – from domestic abuse to political terror.* New
      York, NY: Basic Books. p33.

45    © 2013 The Royal College of Psychiatrists. Post Traumatic Stress Disorder leaflet produced by the Royal College
      of Psychiatrists Public Education Committee., Series Editor: Dr Philip Timms, Expert: Dr Gordon Turnbull
      *www.rcpsych.ac.uk/healthadvice/problemsdisorders/posttraumaticstressdisorder.aspx*, accessed January 2014.

46    Cherry, K. (2010). *The Everything Psychology Book 2nd Edition.* Adams Media.

symptoms".[47] So aspects of your life can become disordered, but this is not because your response is abnormal. It is because you experienced a birth that was not normal, and this experience has, understandably, had an impact.

This can be important information to know in the months following a traumatic birth, not only for the woman, but also for her partner and family.

Lynn Madsen, in her book *Rebounding From Childbirth*, suggests that a diagnosis of PTSD can be useful as a recovery tool, explaining that "when doubts occur that what happened to her was traumatic, recalling the characteristics of PTSD is helpful. If a woman has nightmares about the birth, or terrifying thoughts come into her mind unbidden, this tool will help her know that she is not crazy, but she is recovering from trauma".[48]

## Why can't I just get over it?

Research has shown that women do not spontaneously recover from post-traumatic stress (after childbirth).[49] This can be challenging for those around her to understand, but knowing more about the issue can help.

Some describe having PTSD as being 'stuck'. Dr Julian Ford, Professor of Psychiatry at the University of Connecticut's School of Medicine, says ,"PTSD begins as an adaptive reaction to life-threatening or horrifying stressors. PTSD's symptoms … are classic stress reactions. They are absolutely normal when our survival is threatened, because they are the result of calls from our brain's alarm to put everything else aside and mobilize our body to deal with the threats or dangers facing us".[50]

Dr Ford explains that "having the alarm center on constant high alert is why trauma often seems to never end for many people suffering from PTSD, even though they objectively know that it is over. After weeks, months, or even years of living in a state of alarm, the stress reactions no longer protect us, but instead actually have the unintended effect of making the noxious memories of past traumas more present and vivid".[51]

---

47    Cherry, K. (2010) *What Is a Psychological Disorder? Definition, Diagnosis and Prevalence*. Retrieved from *http://psychology.about.com/od/psychotherapy/tp/psychological-disorders.htm*, accessed January 2014.

48    Madsen, L. (1994). *Rebounding From Childbirth: Toward Emotional Recovery*. Westport, Connecticut: Bergin and Garvey. p.25.

49    Söderquist, J., Wijma, B., & Wijma, K. (2006). The longitudinal course of post-traumatic stress after childbirth. *Journal of Psychosomatic Obstetrics Gynaecology*, 27(2), 113–119.

50    Ford, J. (2013). *3 Lessons PTSD Teaches About Stress Management*. Retrieved from *www.psychologytoday.com/blog/hijacked-your-brain/201305/3-lessons-ptsd-treatment-teaches-about-stress-management*, accessed January 2014.

51    ibid.

Another way of describing this 'getting stuck' is that "the brain keeps retriggering itself all over again into the hyper-alert state".[52]

Another area of confusion can be in understanding about the emotions accompanying trauma. Many women we meet feel a sense of loss after a traumatic birth, and may describe their feelings about their birth as involving sadness and grief. After a traumatic birth, however, it's not usually just sadness and grief that women are dealing with.

Grief is "the normal, natural and inevitable response to loss".[53] Although it can be painful, according to the Australian Centre for Grief and Bereavement, "most people (85–90%) find that, with the support of their family and friends, and their own resources, they gradually find ways to learn to live with their loss".[54] (The challenge for women who have had 'bad' births – with or without trauma – is that often they feel there has been a loss without being able to identify it fully. We explore this more in our chapter *I feel sad* (p245).)

According to psychotherapist Tom Cloyd, "Trauma always has in it loss, and that invariably leads to grief".[55] This is where it might get confusing for a partner or others (or even yourself) to understand why you can't just move on... because they might expect your emotions – that have perhaps been labelled as grief – to be resolved in a certain amount of time. However, when the birth that has resulted in these feelings of loss has also involved traumatic events resulting in symptoms of PTSD, then simply using your own resources and waiting for things to gradually improve may not work.

Just hoping that 'time will heal' or expecting someone to 'just get over it' do not seem to be helpful answers for dealing with PTSD.

## What should I do if I think I have PTSD?

We would suggest a combination of approaches, depending on how severe your symptoms are, and how supported you feel at this time. Of course, if you are feeling desperate, or that you might be a danger to yourself or your children, please seek immediate help. There are some helplines for various countries listed in *Appendix A*.

---

52    Howard, S., & Crandall, M.W. (2007). *Post Traumatic Stress Disorder What Happens in the Brain?* Washington Academy of Sciences. Retrieved from *www.washacadsci.org/Journal/Journalarticles/V.93-3-Post Traumatic Stress Disorder. Sethanne Howard and Mark Crandalll.pdf*, accessed August 2015

53    Australian Centre for Grief and Bereavement. (2014) *Information sheet: About Grief.* Retrieved from *www.grief.org.au/resources/information_sheets/grief*, accessed January 2014.

54    ibid.

55    Cloyd, T. (2014). *Grief, PTSD and Your Brain.* Retrieved from *www.healthyplace.com/blogs/traumaptsdblog/2014/01/16/grief-ptsd-and-your-brain/*, accessed November 2014.

## Using this book

Reflection, gaining new information and emotional support have been suggested to be effective in reducing distress after a traumatic childbirth.[56] This information is from the work of Dr Sarah Allen, whose research also suggests that talking about the event is effective as well.[57]

If you feel safe, we suggest continuing to explore the information, ideas and tools in this book at your own pace and as the need arises. It may be helpful to do this in conjunction with an appropriate counsellor, or a support group of women working through similar issues. Ideally, this support group would be led by a health professional who not only specialises in birth, but also understands its impact, such as Birthtalk in Brisbane.

## Talking to the right person

According to Professor Beck, "Support and trauma counseling are essential for diminishing the impact of traumatic childbirth".[58] You may want to learn more about PTSD and approach a health professional specialising in this area. It is essential that you find the 'right' person for you.

Sheila Kitzinger believes that what women who have been impacted by their birth really need is to "be able to talk with someone who understands, a person who does not try to explain or justify the treatment they received, or to criticise them and the way they feel about what happened to them, and who knows how to listen reflectively".[59]

We also recommend connecting with health workers who understand both PTSD and birth, who are empathetic and embracing of wherever you are on your healing journey, and are open to a variety of modalities of healing, depending on what may be needed at each stage of the journey.

## Therapies and modalities

There are different therapies and modalities available that women have found helpful in dealing with the symptoms of PTSD after birth. These therapies and modalities include Eye Movement Desensitisation and Reprocessing (EMDR), Cognitive Behavioural Therapy (CBT), Emotional Freedom Technique (EFT),

---

56    Allen, S. (1998). A Qualitative Analysis of the Process, Mediating Variables and Impact of Traumatic Childbirth. op. cit.

57    ibid.

58    Beck, C. (2004b). *Post-traumatic stress due to childbirth: the aftermath*. op. cit.

59    Kitzinger, S. *Post Traumatic Stress Disorder*. Retrieved from *www.sheilakitzinger.com/articlesbysheila/badbirthhaunts.htm*, accessed January 2014.

acupuncture, hypnosis and more. While it is not the purpose of this book to address each of these therapies and modalities, we want to acknowledge that some women have found great relief in a range of different therapies.

Professors Gamble and Creedy have, over the past ten years, been testing a counselling intervention for women dealing with traumatic birth experiences called Promoting Resilience in Mothers' Emotions (PRIME).[60] PRIME aims to "support women to express their feelings and enable them to identify and work through distressing elements of childbirth".[61] There is a focus on "developing individual situational supports for the present and near future, affirming that negative feelings and events can be managed, and developing a simple plan for achieving this".[62] Professors Gamble and Creedy report that this combination of strategies "diminishes emotional distress, promotes constructive coping mechanisms and allows recovery to start".[63]

Dr Julian Ford believes that effective psychotherapies for preventing or treating PTSD "help us to regain the ability to stop, step back, and think clearly when our brains' alarms are triggered by normal stressors, so that we're not always reacting to manageable life challenges as if our survival is still being threatened".[64]

He recommends a form of mindfulness, that he describes as drawing on the brain's capacity to shift from reaction to focusing. It is a "shift from a purely alarm-driven reaction to the mindful choices that are possible when the thinking center in the brain, the prefrontal cortex, is activated and frees us from being hijacked by the instinctual automatic survival demands of the brain's alarm".[65] Dr Ford recommends becoming aware of moments where a choice can be made between reacting and focusing and suggests "simply being mindful of what is happening at that moment that is important to us" as a tool towards making that shift.[66]

---

60    You can read more about PRIME in: Fenwick, J., Gamble, J., Creedy, D., & Barclay, L. (2011). Women's experiences of the PRIME midwifery counselling intervention: Promoting Resilience in Mothers Emotions. *Women and Birth, 1*, 24.

61    Gamble, J., & Creedy, D. (2013). *Mothers need better care to reduce post-traumatic stress after childbirth.* op. cit.

62    ibid.

63    ibid.

64    Ford, J. (2013). *In the blink of an eye: shifting from reactivity to focusing after trauma.* Retrieved from *www.psychologytoday.com/blog/hijacked-your-brain/201309/in-the-blink-eye,* accessed January 2014.

65    ibid.

66    ibid.

## Social support

Social support is also really important in healing from a traumatic birth (see *Common 'hidden factors' that can make a birth traumatic* (p99) for more information) and, unfortunately, this support is often difficult to access when friends and family don't understand. Finding a support group for women who have experienced traumatic births may be a step in the right direction. Judy Crompton, a midwife also trained as a trauma therapist says, "Access to a group who are able to advise, educate and de-pathologise the intense emotions which the women may be feeling is of primary importance".[67] This is what we do at Birthtalk, combining the support of peers, with the expertise of a birth specialist. We believe the presence of such a specialist is vital. If there are not any support groups like this local to you, some online groups can offer good support. Of course, providing family and friends with appropriate sections of this book to read can help too!

## Choosing the best for you

Our own recommendation is that you look very carefully when assessing whether a therapist (or a certain therapy or support group) is the right one for you. If you are feeling unsafe, uncomfortable, or that something just isn't 'right', or if you feel you are receiving hidden messages along the lines of 'you should be grateful' or 'you should be over this by now', then it is completely okay to reconsider whether this therapy/therapist/group is what you need right now. You deserve the utmost care and nurturing at this time, and it is worth shopping around to find the health professional and support services that can meet your needs. You can contact us to see if we have suggested contacts in your area.

You are so important and how you feel is incredibly important; we want you to know that you are not alone and that many women have been right where you are standing now.

---

67    Crompton, J. *Post-traumatic Stress Disorder and Childbirth.*
      Retrieved from *www.tabs.org.nz/pdfdocs/jrcrompton tabs.pdf*, accessed August 2014.

## Important points to know

- PTSD following childbirth is a recognised phenomenon.

- PTSD symptoms are a *normal* reaction to an *abnormal* situation. People tend to heal from grief gradually, but trauma can remain 'stuck', which is why a woman might not be able to 'just get over it'.

- PTSD is not the same as PND, although depression can present in women with PTSD. Women can experience both PTSD and PND at the same time. See *Have I got Post-Traumatic Stress Disorder or Postnatal Depression* (p104) for more information. You may find you do not fit the criteria for any recognised postnatal diagnoses. What is of importance for all women who didn't have a great birth is to be able to identify, acknowledge and understand any feelings of disappointment, grief or trauma. And to process the impact of these feelings with as much support and information as needed to be able to 'make sense, make peace and move on'. We encourage you to continue this healing journey, knowing there are many benefits to you and your family.

*Note: Since we began writing this book, there have been changes made in the Diagnostic and Statistical Manual of Mental Disorders (DSM) regarding the definition of a traumatic event. In the DSM-IV, one of the diagnostic criteria was that a person's response to the event needed to include intense fear, helplessness or horror. However, in the DSM-5 released in May 2013, this criterion has been removed. According to the American Psychiatric Association (APA), the publisher of the DSM-5, "Language stipulating an individual's response to the event – intense fear, helplessness or horror, according to DSM-IV – has been deleted because that criterion proved to have no utility in predicting the onset of PTSD".[68] All the studies we have cited here were undertaken prior to this change.*

68      Grohol, J. (2013). *DSM-5 Changes: PTSD, Trauma & Stress-Related Disorders.* Retrieved from *http://pro.psychcentral.com/dsm-5-changes-ptsd-trauma-stress-related-disorders/004406.html*, accessed January 2014.

# COMMON 'HIDDEN FACTORS' THAT CAN MAKE A BIRTH TRAUMATIC

How women are experiencing birth is being collated and recorded in various studies internationally. Some studies discuss the 'hidden factors' that can make a birth traumatic, which may resonate with your own experience. It can be so important to know this, especially if you are struggling to have your experience validated by those around you.

What we have found at Birthtalk, (echoed in the findings of Professor Beck and others) is that even if everything seems completely okay to an outsider during the birth, if a woman perceives that she or her baby is threatened with damage, or feels horror, fear or helplessness towards a procedure that is routine to medical staff, she can experience that as a traumatic event. We have found this to be true regardless of her level of pain relief at the time, or the fact that she and her baby leave the hospital alive and physically healthy.

The results of one recent study "indicate that the most important factor in the development of post-traumatic stress symptoms following childbirth is women's subjective birth experiences".[69] That is, it is the woman's interpretation of events that matters most in regards to how she will be impacted afterwards by her birth.

Below, we list some additional comments by academics in this field and list references to research that further support our observations from working with women over the years, following the theme of 'hidden factors' that can contribute to a birth being viewed as traumatic.

---

69    Garthus-Niegel, S., Soest, T., Vollrath, M., & Eberhard-Gran, M. (2013). The impact of subjective birth experiences on post-traumatic stress symptoms: a longitudinal study. *Archives of Women's Mental Health*, *16*(1), 1–10

## Not acknowledged, included or respected

- In an interview with Jenny Gamble, Professor of Midwifery at Griffith University and Professor Debra Creedy, from the Centre for Health Practice Innovation at Griffith University, they commented that stories of traumatic childbirth frequently include accounts of "being excluded from decision making, lack of informed consent, or patronising, impersonal, disrespectful and abusive interpersonal communications".[70]

- Professor Beck noted that "during a traumatic birth, women often felt invisible".[71] She describes a situation as simple as clinicians speaking to each other "as if the woman were not present"[72] as a factor that contributed to a birth being perceived as a traumatic experience.

## Feeling abandoned and unsupported

- Situations such as the women's perceived lack of a caring approach by health carers, feeling stripped of their dignity, feeling abandoned, a lack of interest in them as unique individuals, and lack of support and reassurance all contributed to the birth trauma of the women in Professor Beck's research.[73]

## Feeling powerless, out of control, confused or as though the 'right thing' didn't happen

- Women's perceptions of control in birth have been investigated in research, with conclusions drawn such as "feeling in control during the birth and knowing what to expect were important protective factors against the development of PTSD"[74] and that it was more likely for women with symptoms of PTSD to, among other things, perceive their partners and staff as less supportive, have lower levels of perceived control, and feel less listened to by staff.[75]

- Associate Professor Gillian White from Massey University in New Zealand notes, "It is not always the sensational or dramatic events that trigger childbirth trauma. For example, not all women who experience a major surgical or obstetric intervention such as caesarean section or forceps delivery

---

70    Gamble, J., & Creedy, D. (2013). *Mothers need better care to reduce post-traumatic stress after childbirth.* Retrieved from *https://theconversation.com/mothers-need-better-care-to-reduce-post-traumatic-stress-after-childbirth-12272*, accessed January 2014.

71    Beck, C. (2004a). Birth trauma: in the eye of the beholder. *Nursing Research, 53*(1), 28–35.

72    ibid.

73    ibid.

74    As discussed in Bailham, D., & Joseph, S. (2003). Post-traumatic stress following childbirth: a review of the emerging literature and directions for research and practice. *Psychology, Health, and Medicine, 8*(2), 159–168. Discussing Lyons, S. (1998). A prospective study of post traumatic stress disorder symptoms one month following childbirth. *Journal of Reproductive and Infant Psychology, 16*, 91–105.

75    Czarnocka, J., & Slade, P. (2000). Prevalence and predictors of post-traumatic stress symptoms following childbirth. *British Journal of Clinical Psychology, 39*, 35–51.

develop post-traumatic stress because, to them, the intervention is not traumatic, their experience was of freedom from pain, a good and trusting relationship with their maternity care provider, input into the decision and the belief that the right thing happened. On the other hand, some women who have a normal birth do experience a traumatic follow-up because they felt out of control, had a poor relationship with their maternity care provider, experienced pain they could not handle or reacted to pain in a manner that frightened them, and became powerless. They do not believe the right thing happened".[76]

### Others ignoring the trauma of the birth if the baby is okay (i.e. a healthy baby is all that matters)

- An indicator of a traumatic birth in Professor Beck's study, *Birth Trauma – in the eye of the beholder*, was when the mothers perceived that their "traumatic deliveries were glossed over and pushed into the background" [77] as attention was focused on the healthy newborn. "If the baby was born alive with good Apgar scores*, that was what mattered to the labor and delivery staff and even to the mother's family and friends. The safe arrival of a live, healthy infant symbolized the achievement of clinical efficiency and of professional and fiscal goals".[78] At Birthtalk, we meet many mothers who have experienced this phenomenon in comments from others along the theme of 'you should be grateful'.

We believe it is important to highlight these points, as our culture has a misguided definition of a traumatic birth as 'one in which there was overt physical injury or obvious threat of death'. Of course a birth with these overt factors would likely be experienced as traumatic; however, this definition does not take into account the less obvious, yet still traumatic, events that can skew a woman's experience of her baby's birth.

Because of the possibility of a woman being traumatised by these 'unseen events', it is essential for those supporting birthing women to 'check in', to see to see how she is feeling on a regular basis during the birth, and especially if there is an observable change in her experience. We have found this is most easily facilitated by the adoption of a team approach, encouraging open communication, where the woman is acknowledged as being central to the experience, however it may unfold.

---

*Apgar score: a measure of the physical condition of a newborn infant.

---

76 White, G. *Childbirth and the Development of Post-traumatic Stress Disorder (PTSD).* Retrieved from *www.tabs.org.nz/pdfdocs/childbirthdevptsd.pdf,* accessed January 2014.

77 Beck, C. (2004a). Birth trauma: in the eye of the beholder. op.cit.

78 ibid.

## In the aftermath

A hidden factor that can affect the development of PTSD postnatally is the level of social support a woman has available to her. Miranda Olff, Professor in Psychotraumatology at the University of Amsterdam, says, "A lack of social support and recognition by the environment is one of the most consistent risk factors for PTSD. Moreover, if the disorder *does* occur, the patient will recover faster through proper social bonding".[79]

Dr Krzysztof Kaniasty puts it rather more bluntly in an article titled "Social Support and Traumatic Stress", stating that "interactions with people who are insensitive, uninterested, or dismissive impede recovery from all traumas".[80]

This does not mean it is your partner's or your family's 'fault' that you aren't feeling any better. Their reasons for perhaps appearing to lack sensitivity, or failing to show interest in the impact your birth has had on you, is most often a result of our culture and our community's understanding of birth. That is, it is likely to be ignorance that is fuelling a seemingly insensitive response. We have found that when those close to you are properly informed about traumatic birth in a way that does not incite defensiveness; they can often begin to respond differently and show true compassion and support. That's one reason why we have written this book! So, we have included Dr Kaniasty's comment to highlight that after a traumatic birth women are often struggling with isolation due to insensitive comments or attitudes, which can make it even harder for them to recover.

Professor Olff also notes that, in relation to social bonding, there appears to be gender differences. She writes, "A lack of social support turns out to be more strongly related to the development of PTSD in women than in men".[81] This might be important information to know, if you are feeling socially isolated and in need of support and are trying to explain this to a man in your life, especially if he has had a different experience dealing with trauma at some time himself.

---

79    Olff, M. (2012). Bonding after trauma: on the role of social support and the oxytocin system in traumatic stress. *European Journal of Psychotraumatology, 3*. Online publication. doi: 10.3402/ejpt.v3i0.18597.

80    Kaniasty,K. (2005). Social Support and Traumatic Stress. PTSD *Research Quarterly, 16*(2), 1–3. Retrieved from *www.ptsd.va.gov/professional/newsletters/research-quarterly/V16N2.pdf*, accessed August 2015.

81    Olff, M. (2012). Bonding after trauma: on the role of social support and the oxytocin system in traumatic stress. op. cit.

## Women are being heard

We have presented this information about the hidden factors that can make a birth traumatic because, sometimes, just knowing that other women have been impacted by similar things to you and that it has been documented and acknowledged as significant, can be part of your healing journey as well. Some professionals are aware of this situation, and do care about your experience and are working daily to make changes within our health system to reduce the likelihood of women having traumatic births. Knowing this may increase your feelings of being supported, of being heard and of being understood.

# HAVE I GOT POST-TRAUMATIC STRESS DISORDER OR POSTNATAL DEPRESSION?

*Before my baby was even a year old, I knew things were not right. I practically begged the local health clinic nurse at the pharmacy to give me the checklist for Postnatal Depression (PND), as that was the only possible thing I could think of that might explain why I felt so bad. But as I looked down the checklist, I felt my heart sink: this didn't describe me. It didn't outline the anxiety, the feeling like I'd been in a car crash, the confusion, the desperate love I felt for my child that I somehow couldn't turn into a joyous celebration. I had never heard of Post-Traumatic Stress Disorder (PTSD) after birth. And if I had heard of it, I wouldn't have thought that I had it. My birth wasn't traumatic, was it? My baby was fine, I recovered from the surgery, and we left hospital together. What was my problem? I rang a special baby sleeping centre in our city. You could stay overnight there with your baby and learn settling skills. I was clawing for support, and wondered if maybe I just needed to learn how to look after my baby. But they wouldn't admit me unless I could get a doctor to agree that I had PND. And I knew I didn't have it. Back to square one.* **Melissa**

*I was diagnosed with PND after the birth of my second child as I had a re-occurrence of an anxiety and depression that I experienced previously with the birth of my first child. I recognised the feelings and went for help sooner as I needed to support myself to get better. This diagnosis did not feel like it fitted me. I think the anxiety component of how I was feeling was way out of perspective in relation to the PND diagnosis. Many, many times I did feel that I was reacting to the trauma of the birth/s and the sense of being unable to birth without fear and anxiety and crushing, debilitating fear that anything could harm my babies. This led to a spiral towards the PND diagnosis; however, I think the doctor just didn't get it. My doctor was keen to provide medication for depression, but I fought for a mental health plan and organised to see a psychologist and we worked on restoring my mental health through kindness, explaining how the mind and the body work and encouraging me to take it easy on myself.* **Julia**

## What is Postnatal Depression?

PND or PPD (Postpartum Depression) is a type of clinical depression that can affect women after childbirth. According to Perinatal Anxiety and Depression Australia (PANDA) (formerly Post and Antenatal Depression Association), "symptoms can emerge at any time during the first year after birth, but most cases have their onset within the first four months".[82]

Some symptoms of PND that women have described include:

* sleep disturbance unrelated to baby's sleep
* changes in appetite
* crying – feeling sad and crying without apparent reason or feeling like you want to cry but can't
* feelings of being unable to cope, daily chores or caring for baby or self-care can seem insurmountable
* irritability
* fear of being alone – either going out a lot or needing someone at home with them at all times
* Memory difficulties and loss of concentration
* Feeling guilty and inadequate
* Loss of confidence and self-esteem[83]

## Is Post-Traumatic Stress Disorder the same as Postnatal Depression?

Some of the symptoms of PTSD and PND are the same, so the two can overlap, but PTSD and PND are distinct from each other, and need to be treated individually.[84]

Sheila Kitzinger, renowned author and social anthropologist specialising in pregnancy and childbirth says, "PTSD is distinct from post-natal depression. PTSD is essentially a state of panic – and while it can include depression, that is not its primary state".[85]

---

82    Post and Antenatal Depression Association Inc. *Fact Sheet: Women and Postnatal Depression.* Retrieved from *www.panda.org.au/images/stories/PDFs/Panda_FS14_WomenPostNatalDepression_FAcopy.pdf,* accessed July 2015.

83    ibid.

84    Birth Trauma Association, UK. *What is Birth Trauma?* Retrieved from *www.birthtraumaassociation.org.uk/what_is_trauma.htm,* accessed January 2014.

85    Kitzinger, Sheila in Hilpern, K. (2003, June 5). The Unspeakable Trauma of Childbirth. *Sydney Morning Herald, www.smh.com.au/articles/2003/06/05/1054700311400.html,* accessed January 2014.

Knowledge of how PTSD and PND differ from each other is essential for health professionals, and important for us all as unfortunately, because of a lack of awareness of the ways a traumatic birth can impact on women, some health professionals are wrongly diagnosing, and subsequently prescribing medication that may not be appropriate for the situation.

> *My midwives diagnosed me with PPD after the birth of my first child. The diagnosis never felt right, because I was often very happy and not depressed and would suddenly crash or be triggered by things like my daughter screaming. I had been depressed before and this felt totally different.*
>
> *A friend had a similar traumatic caesarean section and directed me to a site with forums and as I read through the PTSD symptoms, I realised that fitted better. It was harder to get treatment for PTSD after childbirth as it was not really recognised. Everyone simply wanted to give me drugs which actually didn't help. They thought I was faking when I functioned well sometimes and got 'flooded' at others.* **Josie**

Sheila Kitzinger shares that, "Many women who are haunted by what has to be done to them in childbirth are treated by GPs with anti-depressant drugs"[86] and she believes that "anti-depressant drugs do not help, and can even make it worse".[87]

Often, screening is only routine for PND, which can create a situation where competent care-givers, operating according to the health system's guidelines, may either misdiagnose women (since their questionnaires are aimed at screening for PND)[88] or fail to diagnose them at all.

> *The GP gave me the diagnosis of PND after doing the Edinburgh Score survey/test. She referred me to a psychologist who changed my diagnosis to PTSD during the second visit with her. She said that I didn't have PND, that I had PTSD due to the traumatic nature of the birth I had experienced with my daughter. The primary reason for identifying the birth as traumatic was due to my constant flashbacks of seeing my baby lifeless at birth (she was born stunned due to going into distress and being delivered via vacuum extraction).* **Caroline**

86    Kitzinger, Sheila in Hilpern, K. (2003, June 5). The Unspeakable Trauma of Childbirth. *Sydney Morning Herald*, *www.smh.com.au/articles/2003/06/05/1054700311400.html*, accessed January 2014.

87    Kitzinger, S. *Post Traumatic Stress Disorder*. Retrieved from *www.sheilakitzinger.com/articlesbysheila/badbirthhaunts.htm*, accessed January 2014.

88    Solace for Mothers. *What is Birth Trauma*. Retrieved from *www.solaceformothers.org/what_birth_trauma.html*, accessed January 2014.

*Solace for Mothers*, a US-based online trauma support network, comments that there is a high likelihood that "some women currently diagnosed with PPD may actually be exhibiting a traumatic response to their childbearing experience".[89] Meanwhile, research has suggested that with the use of common screening measures, it is possible that twenty-five per cent of women who are not showing depressive symptoms but are fully symptomatic with PTSD would not be detected.[90]

> *I was diagnosed with PND at about four months postpartum.*
> *The diagnosis of PND never felt right; in fact, I told my doctor,*
> *and later the psychiatrist that I saw, that the problem was that*
> *I was 'grieving' the birth that I didn't have – the loss of the*
> *safe, physiological birth, feeling supported and empowered as*
> *I entered motherhood. I grieved the loss of the experience I had*
> *envisioned for myself and my daughter: of pushing her out, of*
> *holding her skin-to-skin, of delayed cord clamping for her. I felt*
> *that my first act as a mother was to put both of us at risk; as a*
> *mother, I was supposed to keep her safe, and my sense of safety*
> *for both of us had been violated. Later, I grieved that I was not*
> *able to care for her independently. I was angry and resentful that*
> *I was in so much pain, and that I was so deeply angry as a result*
> *of what happened to us. I was not diagnosed with PTSD, but*
> *was hypervigilant and plagued by intrusive thoughts (it was like*
> *watching the movie of the birth unfold in detail, repeatedly, trying*
> *to figure out 'what went wrong'.)*
>
> *I still believe that that initial diagnosis of PND was wrong;*
> *although I was clinically depressed, it was not (in my opinion)*
> *due to hormones, or coping (or lack thereof), or unrealistic*
> *expectations. I expected to be listened to and treated with respect;*
> *that is not unreasonable. I had no history of mental health issues.*
> *I had a difficult birth, where I was worn down by the medical*
> *system that was supposed to care for us, into having interventions*
> *I didn't want and may not have needed, and I grieved the loss*
> *of autonomy, bodily integrity and respect that I experienced.*
> *I grieved for the trauma that this was physically as I recovered,*
> *and that this was considered 'uncomplicated' by the medical*
> *system, when I could not care for my child independently in the*
> *first weeks as a result.*

89    Solace for Mothers. *What is Birth Trauma.* Retrieved from *www.solaceformothers.org/what_birth_trauma.html,* accessed January 2014.

90    Czarnocka, J., & Slade, P. (2000). Prevalence and predictors of post-traumatic stress symptoms following childbirth. *British Journal of Clinical Psychology, 39,* 35–51.

*I found the diagnosis missed the mark; it didn't speak to the underlying issues of birth trauma, and that I had a reason for feeling the way I did, and that I was not being selfish or over-reacting. I have sought out alternative ways of healing that were validating and restorative; I was only able to access these supports because I could afford to.* **Evelyn**

## But what if I do feel depressed?

It can get confusing, as PND "does not always derive from birth trauma"[91] and PTSD "commonly occurs with other psychological conditions".[92] The Birth Trauma Association (UK) explains that "depression can go hand-in-hand with postnatal PTSD, so not everyone is misdiagnosed".[93] According to one longitudinal study, sixty-five per cent of women who were identified with post-traumatic stress symptoms also had depression eleven months after their baby was born.[94]

*I had a diagnosis of PND, but I didn't feel right! I had suffered depression before, but wasn't entirely sure how (if at all) PND differed from the type of depression I had experienced previously. I was glad to get a diagnosis and get some closure, but it did feel incomplete. I had flashbacks constantly and consistently for 14 months. It was like a movie that played in the left-hand side of my head and I had to live my life while watching my birth experience over and over again. That was the biggest red flag for me. I also avoided everything related to pregnancy and birth, but hoarded odd keepsakes from my pregnancy, things like receipts and notes scrawled on scrap paper.*

*I received an additional diagnosis of PTSD a few months after my son turned one. The diagnosis of PND was still applicable in my case. I was glad that my PND was diagnosed quickly, and I think my GP intuitively knew that I couldn't handle rehashing anything at that stage and so she monitored my wellbeing, and I am really grateful for that. However, I do wish I had known sooner that I had PTSD too. I want to make it clear that I don't blame my*

91    White, G. *Childbirth and the Development of Post-traumatic Stress Disorder (PTSD).* Retrieved from *www.tabs.org.nz/pdfdocs/childbirthdevptsd.pdf*, accessed January 2014.

92    Gamble, J., & Creedy, D. (2013). *Mothers need better care to reduce post-traumatic stress after childbirth.* Retrieved from *https://theconversation.com/mothers-need-better-care-to-reduce-post-traumatic-stress-after-childbirth-12272*, accessed January 2014.

93    Birth Trauma Association, UK. *What is Birth Trauma?* op.cit.

94    Söderquist, J., Wijma, B., & Wijma, K. (2006). The longitudinal course of post-traumatic stress after childbirth. *Journal of Psychosomatic Obstetric Gynaecology, 27*(2), 113–119.

*GP for this. I feel blessed to have had her unconditional support throughout my journey. She knew a lot more than anyone else I confided in and treated me holistically. My son's birth and his first six months were the darkest, most debilitating days of my life, with the next 12 months coming a close second. It should have been a time when all the cherished memories of my son were formed, but it was the polar opposite. I was a zombie. I had no ability to look after myself or immerse myself in my beautiful baby; my only ability was to simply ensure he survived. I will never get any of that time back. It's gone forever and I have a very limited recollection of his first 18 months.* **Mai**

This association between PTSD and depression makes sense for a woman who has experienced a 'bad' birth, followed by experiencing symptoms of PTSD. Having ongoing symptoms of flashbacks, hypervigilance or emotional numbing, especially without appropriate support, would likely lead most people to be drowning in confusion, guilt and anxiety, which could understandably lead to depressive symptoms.

It is important to know that any anti-depressants you have been prescribed may well be an appropriate course of action in your particular situation. However, if you are concerned about this issue in any way, or have queries regarding any medication you have been prescribed, we encourage you to speak to a health professional for further advice.

## Working towards wellness

*It has been helpful to have a formal diagnosis of both PND and PTSD. It puts a name to the beast and helps me to give myself a break by acknowledging that it's not just all in my head. That being said, once my psychologist acknowledged that I had these conditions, we focused on debriefing, healing and implementing strategies to break the cycle of their power, rather than focusing on the conditions themselves. I really needed that approach! It was only in retrospect that I realised that's what she had done and I will be forever grateful to her.* **Mai**

In working towards wellness, Perinatal Anxiety and Depression Australia (PANDA) (formerly Post and Antenatal Depression Association) recommends, beyond diagnosis, factors such as counselling, support from those around you and self-care including good nutrition, adequate rest, exercise, and relaxation.[95]

---

95    Post and Antenatal Depression Association Inc. (2014). *Recovery from PND.*
       Retrieved from *www.panda.org.au/practical-information/recovery-from-pnd*, accessed June 2014.

We know some of these can be challenging to accomplish when caring for a small baby, and especially in the midst of dealing with the impact of a less-than-great birth, so we encourage you to enlist any support you can with this aspect of your healing.

Interestingly, we have found that by addressing a traumatic pregnancy, birth or postnatal experience directly (by using the ideas in this book), many women have reported positive changes in emotional wellbeing. Even if a woman might not describe her birth or maternity experiences as particularly 'traumatic', and perhaps may simply recognise they were 'disempowering', we have found that the exploration of this experience can give her insights that can support a move towards stronger mental health.

## For more information on PND:

In Australia: Perinatal Anxiety and Depression Australia (PANDA) (formerly Post and Antenatal Depression Association) *www.panda.org.au*

International: Postpartum Support International: *www.postpartum.net*

# Sharing your story – finally being heard

After women have their babies, they may tell others about their birth. They might tell snippets of the story to friends or family who ask. They may give a brief rundown to the lady down the street. Or they might blurt out the whole saga in way more detail than they intended at a dinner party. There are also mothers who have not let even one bit of their birth story out for fear they will dissolve into tears, or perhaps because they just don't know how to talk about it. Any of these scenarios can leave a new mother feeling dissatisfied, embarrassed or unheard. This is largely due to the response they receive – or that they are worried about receiving – from those around them. It is also partly due to not knowing why storytelling is important, or how to do it, or with whom.

In our section *How do I share my story so people get it?* (p155) we discuss ways to reframe the story of your birth so people get more of an idea of the impact it has had, without feeling like they need to fix you or tell you to move on. But before you reframe your story, you need to know what your story is.

## The first time

For many women we have met, our 'Healing from Birth' meetings are their first opportunity to tell their entire story.

> *I remember going to my first 'Healing From Birth' meeting [at Birthtalk]. I just let my story roll out uncensored, without holding back. It was like I had permission to say anything, so I did. It was amazing.* **Kerri**

What is the difference between telling your birth story at coffee with friends, and telling it somewhere like Birthtalk? Of course, when a woman attends a Birthtalk 'Healing From Birth' meeting, she knows she is in a custom-built forum for healing from a challenging birth. Most women know they can tell their story there, and many want to get it out, to find out how to heal from it. Coffee with friends, however, is a far more social gathering, usually not particularly set up with a birth debrief in mind. So broaching the topic in any depth in that environment can be awkward or uncomfortable, depending on the friends' experiences and understandings. There is much value in a purpose-built gathering where sharing birth stories is the intent, particularly as part of a healing process.

Why can it be so affirming and satisfying to share your story in a group that is set up for that purpose? Kerri (whose quote is above) shares more about why she describes the experience of telling her story at Birthtalk as 'amazing',

> ... because it was the first time someone acknowledged what a hard journey my first birth was and how well I had done. It was amazing to hear someone praise me for how well I had done when I always thought I had failed. It really started to turn my thinking around from self-blame to breaking down why it felt like such a bad experience. **Kerri**

Kerri has explained beautifully what many women have expressed to us – that the first time they told their story at Birthtalk was the first time they received acknowledgement and validation for what they had been through. These are some of the first steps in the healing journey.

## Awareness, acknowledgement and validation

The first step in the healing journey after a traumatic birth is that of awareness. You become aware that your birth has affected you and that you don't want to continue to feel such intensity surrounding the birth. You become aware that you want things to change, even if you don't know how to create that change. This awareness can lead to seeking out help, and then further steps towards healing can follow.

The next vital steps beyond the initial awareness are those of receiving acknowledgement and validation for what you went through in your birth (and antenatally and postnatally too).

Kerri mentions that Birthtalk was the first place she found acknowledgment and validation for her experience. It is important to ask – why is finding this acknowledgement and validation so hard? It all comes down to the listeners.

Their capacity to offer acknowledgement and validation will depend on their insightfulness, compassion and empathy. It also will depend on their understanding of birth.

For someone to be able to acknowledge that a journey like Kerri's could be hard, and offer support and insights that can lead to healing, they would need to have a certain set of information beforehand:

- They would need to understand that birth matters and has an impact.
- They would need to know that how a woman felt during her child's birth is key to understanding how she experienced that birth.
- They would need to know that it is important to know how she experienced birth, because that would enable them to gain insight into potential ways she could be impacted by it.
- And they would need to know that the impact of a negative birth could ripple through a woman's entire life, and colour every experience she encountered afterwards.

Unfortunately, in our culture most people don't know any of this, including some health professionals.

Simply put, the telling of the birth story is of most benefit as a healing tool when the people listening to the story know how much birth matters, and have an understanding of trauma and birth. Ideally, these people's responses will offer acknowledgment and validation, and a new phase of healing can begin.


## Letting it all out

The key to Kerri's positive experience is her feeling that she could "let her story roll out uncensored".

At Birthtalk, we believe that a woman's story is her own, and it does not serve her well if the listener is judgemental towards what the woman felt, or saw or expresses about her experience. Even if there may be discrepancies in the woman's story, that is not to be addressed within the first telling of the story. A traumatic birth can feel all jumbled up, and often it is only in the recounting of the story from beginning to end that a woman may herself realise that there are gaps in her knowledge of what happened, or that something couldn't have occurred in the way she thought it did. This is part of the gift of the narrative experience, and those facts and discrepancies can be cleared up later. There will also be time later for clearing up any misunderstandings about birth that might help the healing. What matters firstly is (a) that she gets to speak and (b) that she is heard.

## A different telling of the story

We find that when women come to our 'Healing From Birth' meetings, they tend to share their story differently to how they have shared it in other more social gatherings, or even with a health professional such as a GP or counsellor. As we have mentioned, this may partly be because they recognise the Birthtalk forum as a safe space to let it all out and perhaps to go into more detail or share aspects they have never aired publicly before. There might be some things they wanted to shelter other people from when telling their story elsewhere. However, there is also another reason they might find themselves sharing their story differently.

The mainstay of our philosophy involves the understanding that 'what happened' is only part of the story. In our section *Birthtalk Breakdown – a new tool* (p47), we discuss the importance of knowing how a woman felt at each step of her birth, in order to understand more fully how she experienced the birth. So, a key feature of our meetings is having a Birthtalk mother – who has already undertaken the healing journey – share aspects of her story first. Deb, as facilitator of the meeting, will invite this woman to share her story, and the woman talks about her birth using language that demonstrates the value of the emotional experience of birth, such as, "Then I felt…", "I was so…", "It made me feel so…", "It just brought up so much…".

As the woman shares, other women usually resonate with her experience, and might nod as she talks about certain feelings, or lean forward listening intently, or perhaps sit quietly with tears streaming down their faces. Hearing a story shared in this way can be extremely powerful. It can release the other women to recognise that their own feelings that accompanied 'what happened' are worthy and valid for sharing too. Their own sharing may then involve a 'releasing of the floodgates' where their innermost emotions from the birth can become aired, and finally heard. It can also bring on a realisation that other women have been through what they themselves have experienced, because the focus is on the feelings, which is the commonality between the women present, regardless of their story.

## The next steps

Once the woman has articulated her story unencumbered, and received genuine acknowledgement and validation for her experience, she can begin moving to the next stages of healing: understanding and processing. Throughout this next part of her journey, she may share her story again and again. However, we have found that the narrative now evolves, and her account reflects the shifts as she heals and grows.

We often witness women returning to Birthtalk over a number of months, and listen to their story evolve during this time. They can see, themselves, how differently they tell the story of their birth once they have received acknowledgment and validation, as well as developed a new understanding and begun to process their experience, using the philosophy, tools and ideas compiled in this book.

This is not an indication of them now 'telling it right', either. The way they told their story the very first time we met them was perfect for what they needed right then. We want to make it clear that how the woman tells her story is not an assessment of how 'good' she is at healing. It is simply an expression of her relationship with her birth at that particular time, which is always a very personal relationship.

## To whom do I tell my story?

Understanding the value in sharing your story as part of your healing is one thing – finding the right person to listen can be quite another. As we mentioned earlier, in order to be able to offer the acknowledgement and validation needed, the listener needs, ideally, to know how much birth matters and to have an understanding of traumatic birth. Which might explain why it can feel less-than-satisfying to share stories with our partner, mother or friend – even if they are empathetic and loving in their responses.

Our first suggestion is to make sure you protect yourself and your story. Consider only sharing it with people you are fairly confident have enough of an understanding of the possible impact of a traumatic birth to be able to hold your story and reflect back appropriately. This might take the form of a support group designed for this purpose, such as Birthtalk's 'Healing From Birth' sessions. Although Birthtalk is currently only available in a few areas in Australia, there might be other groups that could offer you appropriate support.

## Groups for debriefing and support

You might find a 'birth debrief' group, or an International Caesarean Awareness Network (ICAN) chapter local to you, or something similar. Even if you have not had a caesarean, we still recommend contacting your local caesarean support network as they might be easier to find on the internet than other support groups and they will hopefully be able to direct you to health professionals such as independent midwives or doulas who provide a birth debrief regardless of how your child was born. Another avenue may be your local birth reform group, such as Maternity Choices (formerly Maternity Coalition) in Australia, or AIMS in the UK. Members of these organisations generally have an understanding that birth matters, which is why they are pushing for reform in how our maternal health systems operate. They may be able to suggest local groups, or individual doulas or independent midwives who can offer support. See *Appendix A* for caesarean awareness groups, birth reform groups and individuals whom we suggest contacting if you are looking for a group, or guidance towards a suitable health professional for a debrief.

## Online communities

Another choice may be finding an online community where you can share your story and receive an appropriate response. This is the path Melissa took when there were few local support networks in her hometown at the time. Telling your story to a group of strangers in different countries bound together by similar experiences, who have intimate personal understanding of what you went through, can be liberating and releasing. A degree of anonymity is advised for online safety, and this anonymity may even enable you to share more than you would otherwise, which can be helpful in the healing process, if the environment is safe.

The challenge can be finding an online community where birth trauma is understood, and where your story will be honoured. Sharing your story on a general parenting forum or even a purpose-built birth trauma forum may not be advisable. It completely depends on the other members of the forum and the level of moderation used, as well as who is moderating. We recommend 'sitting in' on these forums or chat lists or Facebook groups for a while, reading the comments and responses women receive to their sharing. If there are any comments along the line of "You should be grateful" or "At least the baby is healthy", then that forum is likely not going to be able to offer genuine and informed acknowledgement and validation.

Ideally, the members of a suitable forum will offer a safe space to share your story, in as much or as little detail as you prefer. They will provide acknowledgement and validation of your experience, without trying to change your story, or fix you, or tell you what they think you did wrong. They will share their own experiences and point you towards accurate evidence-based information for further reading, without leaving you feeling that you need to take their advice or follow their beliefs.

There are some spaces like this online; it will just take some investigating and some patience as you get a feel for the group and whether it is right for you. You may want to combine some online sharing with meeting with an individual health professional in person, which could give you the insight and support from a group of similarly affected women, as well as the input from someone who understands birth. Melissa luckily had this available to her in her discussions with Deb (who was a midwife) as well as with counselling sessions. There are good reasons why this combination may work well to move your healing forward.

## Peers plus professional support

The stories and encouragement of women who have been similarly affected by their births (peer support) is powerful and important, and can create some major turning points in a woman's healing journey. Other women's stories can provide inspiration, reduce isolation, and renew determination to keep on the healing path. Yet without the input of an informed birth professional, the healing may stagnate at certain points where information and knowledge about evidence-based practices in birth could have moved the healing in a new direction. Having someone who is an expert in normal birth gently provide information that clarifies or even sometimes counteracts what the woman thought, or had been told, can be extremely potent for healing. Even if that information is difficult to hear, it can enable the woman to gain facts about birth, or about her birth, that give her true understanding and invaluable insights for planning future births. This can also open a pathway for further grieving and healing.

Peer support alone often cannot counteract our culture's myths and misconceptions about birth, as women may not have enough information to know exactly what is myth and what is evidence-based fact, and they may inadvertently perpetuate myths that keep themselves and other women bound by their trauma.

Similarly, professional support alone may not be enough either as it is the voices of women similarly affected that enables a woman to know that she is not alone, is not crazy and is having a normal response to an abnormal experience. However, when peers and informed professionals come together with a goal to support women towards healing, the combination can be powerful.

This is what Birthtalk has always offered at our 'Healing From Birth' meetings. We have seen both types of support combine to spur women on to a level of healing that enables them to move forward into their life without the intensity, with a new peace, and with new tools and insights for any future births.

## A new stage

We really hope you can find that person, or people, who will enable you to share your story in a safe space. If you cannot, we encourage you to work through the exercise *Writing your birth story – a healing step* (p445), as this exercise can still be of benefit even if you do not yet know where you will share your story, or with whom. It will give you more clarity about your experience and its impact on you. Reading the personal experiences of the other women in this book can also give you more self-understanding and a wider view. You may even be able to begin to acknowledge and validate your own experience as you learn more about traumatic birth and how others have been impacted.

Women often tell us that before they attended Birthtalk they had told versions of their story over and over again to different people, with dissatisfying results. However, they noticed that after the first telling at Birthtalk, or perhaps after a few tellings, they no longer needed to share their story with people outside the Birthtalk circle. It was as if that need was met – they had finally been heard. Then they then could turn their energies to healing.

So, however you are able to share your story initially, whether in a group, with a counsellor, with a friend or online, this sharing will hopefully lead you into new stages of healing. The next sections of our book are designed to support you with these continuing steps in your healing journey.

# PART TWO: HOW DO YOU FEEL RIGHT NOW?

# POEM: TO MY SON

did I let you down
by not being able to give you
the birth experience I so wanted
for you?
And for me?

I feel I did

I feel wretched that there was not
something more I could do

I feel your arrival was
surrounded by
pain
confusion
fear
drug-induced stupor
deep sadness
intense feelings of failure
inability to care for myself
or you
and frustration at my weakness
mixed in with
awe
at your miniature perfection
your likeness to your daddy
the way the pain went when you were in my arms
the pain went
when you were in my arms
I clung to you
willing it to all be 'worth it'
I despaired as you struggled to feed
was it because you, too, were drugged?

the guilt is searing
what more could I have done?
what affirmation did I not say?
what deep secret of my past did I not uncover
that would have allowed me to birth you
the way I wanted?

I had planned for a
gentle birth
soft lights
soft music
and yes, pain
but healthy pain
not the gut-exploding
brain-searing torture that happened
I had planned to breastfeed you
straight after you were born
and a relaxed loving introduction to life
with you, me and your daddy
together in the big bed

instead
I was getting stitched up
under the brightest lights
while you met the world
without me
I wanted to be there
so you were always with me
too soon to be separated

daddy held you instead
close
with your bare skin
to his bare chest
I am glad that was the case
but I wanted to be there

did I let you down?

all my pain
disappeared
when they held you over the sheet
my little friend

I felt disengaged from what was going on
I wanted to hold you
whisper greetings
stroke your little cheek
hold you near my heart
where you will always live

but you were plonked on my chest
too close to really see you
you squawked bravely
I could see your little face
but I wanted to hold you close
and welcome you into a world of
joy
love
peace

why did it have to be
pain
confusion
fear?

why is it still?

a year has passed
the grief is stronger
the acknowledgement of what I missed
and what I was unable to give you
has brought new sadness
when will I be able to just live?
when will I be able to give you
love NOW

peace NOW
how can I settle this in my head
so I am not
the bad guy?

can I possibly let it go?

maybe I can start again
with a new year
a new city
a new understanding of my strengths

what can I give you NOW?

peace
quiet
love
joy
in my own life

they can only extend to you
when I feel them myself

I can let what happened go
there will always be pain
surrounding my memories of your arrival
but that pain
has made me strong
and given me what I needed most

you

*by Melissa Bruijn©2000*

# HOW TO USE THIS PART OF THE BOOK

Now that you have read the first part of this book, hopefully you have widened your understanding of what has happened for you, and why you are feeling so bad.

So – what now?

Just knowing the information in the earlier part of this book might not be enough to heal, but it is a great foundation for the process. We believe that women mostly instinctively know what they need to do next, when they have appropriate knowledge that sets them up for moving into healing. This part of the book is not required to be read in a chronological order – just dive in to whichever chapter resonates for you when you ask yourself this question: "How do I feel right now?"

Each chapter explains and explores a particular emotion or issue, and some suggested tips for healing are offered at the end of each section. Often these tips will guide the reader to particular sections in *Part Three: Tools for your healing journey* (p403), where you will find specific exercises and ideas to further your healing. So you may find yourself flipping back and forwards between Part Two and Part Three, as you gain further understanding about your experiences or certain situations, and then gather more tools to support you in processing and moving on.

Your journey may be about to begin winding down a few different pathways as you ask yourself, "How do I feel right now?"

## What will your path to healing look like?

We don't know yet how your path will unfold. You can likely hear the grief and confusion in Melissa's poem above. This poem was written very early on in her healing journey, before she even really knew what was happening, way before she had heard of the words 'birth trauma'. Even if she had heard those words, she would never have thought of them as being remotely connected to her birth. She just knew she felt bad. You can read more of her experience in various sections throughout the book, as she took the very journey you are about to embark on.

However, your birth was your own, and your pain is your own, so your path will likely be different. As you move forward, you may find that many of the women's quotes in this book will resonate with aspects of your own path to healing, although their journeys are also their own.

So, as your path is not yet traversed, we can't tell you how it will look. However, if at each fork in the road, you can ask yourself, '*How do I feel right now?*' and answer honestly, then you will know more about which direction to take next.

Go easy on yourself, and know that you are strong and courageous in undertaking this journey and that we are here with you. And we stand beside you as you ask the question; "How do I feel right now?"

To read Melissa's reflections of her birth and healing now, thirteen years since her son's birth, go to *Melissa's own story of birth trauma and healing* (p23). You can also read what her son has to say in *How do I tell my child about the day they were born?* (p426).

# I feel isolated or alone

## WHY DOESN'T ANYONE GET IT?

*Even my mum couldn't understand why I couldn't get over the birth, even though she was with me in the birth and agreed the doctor was an awful man, and it upset her at the time how he was treating her daughter.* **Sophie**

*My mum has said on many occasions that I am not missing much by not having had a vaginal birth. I have had lots of different people comment that at least my vagina is still intact! I have had a lot of invalidating statements from people over the years.* **Sienna**

*I joined a new parents group when my baby was eight weeks old. I told the child health nurse that I couldn't stop thinking about my son's birth, at the first meeting in front of the group. Some of the mothers who had a vaginal birth went on to tell me I hadn't missed out on anything and that vaginal birth was horrible anyway. Those who experienced a good birth kept quiet, but I did not realise that at the time. Those who had a good caesarean told me their experience was fine. I felt very invalidated and honestly thought I must be the only one in the world who felt their caesarean birth was horrible.* **Kerri**

*My friends and family said, "You usually get on with things – come on, you have a healthy baby and you got your natural birth so why are you still worrying about this? It is always chaotic at the end". The end of my birth is the part that was traumatic for me.* **Sally**

*I hated catching up with friends. Life just seemed to go on for them. They were excited over my baby but I felt so much anguish and loss. They couldn't understand why I didn't just let it all go and get on with life.* **Angie**

*I have a few friends who have had caesareans and none of them regretted it. In fact, they all congratulated me on finally doing it the easy way! They gave no hint of any emotional fall out whatsoever, and when I tried to talk about it, they all just assumed I was referring to the physical discomfort and that was the end of that.* **Lara**

## What you need to know

Why don't people understand that a birth can impact on a woman? The best way to explain it is to use an analogy, so bear with us as we compare birth to a mid-air Qantas flight emergency. The following is an excerpt from an article on our blog:

> Remember a year or so ago when that Qantas jet had a gaping hole in it and performed an emergency landing? The TV news footage showed the passengers arriving in Melbourne on another jet, and embracing their loved ones. Most were crying, some were shaking and all were visibly affected by the experience.
>
> Passengers told of the few minutes when they wondered if they would die, as the plane plummeted 19, 000 feet, their voices choked with emotion as they recalled their extreme fear, panic and anxiety. I imagined these people going home with their families who welcomed had them at the airport with outstretched arms. They would likely be cosseted and fussed over, offered comforting food and drink, and their moments of terror openly listened to with shock and interest and appropriate, "Oh My Gods" from listeners as they talked about their experience.
>
> But would anyone just say to them, "At least you didn't die" and try to shush them up if they tried to talk about it? Would anyone tell them, "Well, I understand that plane trip didn't go quite how

you'd planned, but all's well that ends well, hey?" Of course not. And would family understand if these people were a bit shaky for a while afterwards, and needed to feel safe? I'd say they would.

Now imagine the same scene after a woman has a traumatic birth. Is there anyone waiting for her with outstretched arms? Generally not. After a traumatic birth, women are not usually cosseted and fussed over or comforted beyond a perfunctory 'there, there'.

As a community, we seem quite comfortable with telling a woman traumatised from her birth, "at least you have a healthy baby", and placating her with, "I understand that birth didn't go quite how you'd planned, but all's well that ends well, hey?" And then she has to learn how to look after a child, cope with sleep deprivation, usually without the hormones designed to support her with this due to the trauma of the birth, and tackle a mountain of laundry, cooking and home duties. Welcome to motherhood.

The truth about birth, traumatic or otherwise, is this: we do not just leave our birth at the hospital. Birth's impact has a ripple effect on a woman's whole life. If it was a positive experience, then that radiates outwards like warm sunshine on everything that happens postnatally. But if it was a negative experience, then it can feel like a domino effect – the woman keeps getting knocked down with every challenge. She is 'behind the eight ball' to start with, and that ripple effect means that the birth's impact can spread to all aspects of her life.

Yet this does not stop people telling a woman to just 'get over it'. Why?

Perhaps we need to look again at that dramatic plane flight. The big question is, why it is understood by virtually everyone that those passengers might need some time to process the event? The answer is: because we EXPECT air travel to be safe, easy, simple, and uneventful. And when it is NOT those things, we understand that it might have an impact.

However, with birth, most people EXPECT it to be painful, horrible, unbearable, out-of-control and unpleasant. That's what it's like in the movies, TV shows, and often in the stories passed down through generations. So when a woman expresses that her birth was difficult or traumatic, our culture's response is, "So? Isn't that just birth?"

And that's the biggest myth of all – that birth is bad. But that's just not true. The way most women experience birth in our culture IS bad and that's not their fault. Yet birth itself is not bad. Unfortunately, most people in our culture have either had bad births, seen bad births, or been birthed in a traumatic way themselves and had the story regaled to them for years.

Birth can be good. Which can be a hard thing for a woman traumatised by her birth to hear. Yet really, it explains one of the reasons that it hurts so much emotionally when a birth is traumatic, because it's not meant to be that way. Nature didn't intend it to be that way. But because most births in our culture are that way, it is very difficult for most people to 'come to the party' and admit that maybe your birth could have an impact on you. Because then they'd have to face the multitude of myths and misconceptions thrown their way by the media and family horror stories over the years. And that's too hard. A woman's distress post-birth can cause massive discomfort in others who need the myth to continue.

If we return to the plane flight analogy again, imagine the passengers' family and friends perhaps not acknowledging that the experience was tumultuous and fraught with potential disaster. Imagine if you had lived through that flight and a few days later the people around you are saying, "Are you still going on about that? Can you just move on? You're fine, you're healthy, so what's the problem?", and meanwhile you are struggling with flashbacks, anxiety and a need to debrief and talk about what happened, to try and make sense of it. But no one will acknowledge your situation. Sound isolating?

The truth about traumatic birth is that validation is difficult to find in our culture. The experience of trauma after birth can be intensely isolating if it goes unacknowledged. So it is up to us to re-educate ourselves and those around us so they are able to support women in the upheaval and aftermath of birth trauma.

If we do not just leave our birth at the hospital, if we take it with us into our postnatal life, then it matters when it's not right and it's not good and it doesn't feel safe.[96]

---

96    Birthtalk.org. (2010). *Childbirth: as traumatic as a midair Qantas flight emergency?* Retrieved from *http://birthtraumatruths.wordpress.com/2010/05/09/childbirth*, accessed September 2014.

## To put this in other words:

The main reason people don't understand is because of our culture's thinking, which is actively promoted everywhere – the media, movies, books and conversations among friends. Our culture says, "As long as the mother is healthy and the baby is healthy, that's all that matters". Our culture says, "Birth sucks – and that's just the way it is". Our culture says, "Birth is just a way of getting a baby out". But our culture is *wrong*. And most of the population *doesn't know the truth*.

## So, what's the truth?

The truth is that 'what matters' goes beyond a mother's and baby's physical health, as you probably already know. Birth doesn't have to be terrible, in fact, it can be wonderful. Having a bad birth is not 'just the way it is'. But in our culture, you need certain information and support to increase the chances of having a good birth. Birth is way more than just extracting a baby. We'll explore more about these truths below. This information is very difficult to find, so it's not your fault if you didn't know about it before now.

## How did it get to this?

It is important to look at how these myths that abound in our culture came about. We would like to ask you this question: when people are talking about 'birth', do you know what their definition of birth is, and do you know where they get their definition of birth from?

## How do you, yourself, define birth?

We find people's definition of birth is mostly influenced by two things:

1.  They define birth based on their own experience of birth within our culture, that is, as a birthing mother, or as a witness/support.
2.  They define birth using information given to them through word of mouth, watching television and movies, reading popular magazines, and listening to their own family stories passed down to them about birth.

They use these experiences and information to form an understanding and definition of what they perceive 'birth' to be. You might want to take a moment to think about how you formed your own early understanding of 'what birth is'.

Perhaps you remember:

- movies that had images of birth, even comedies, such as *Knocked Up* or *The Back-up Plan*
- educational videos you were shown in school
- whispered conversations by adults overheard when you were young
- birth stories in glossy pregnancy magazines.

These cultural depictions of birth lead most of us to a definition of 'what birth is'. But do you know if your definition is an accurate one?

These definitions of birth that we form over time can be very different to a true definition of 'birth as it is designed to be'. They can be very different to how birth can be if you have appropriate information, caregivers and support.

This leads us to why people don't 'get it' when you talk about the impact of your traumatic birth.

## What is 'normal' and what is 'usual'?

People assume that just because it is *usual* for a woman in our culture to feel frightened, out-of-control, unsupported and in excruciating pain during birth, that this means it is normal. But it's not normal. It's just usual. Most people don't understand. Not because they are unfeeling or uncaring, but because of the many negative experiences of birth and the amount of inaccurate information about birth that exists in our culture.

As we said, it is very difficult to get accurate information about birth. Most people go for a lifetime without discovering it.

## What do you mean traumatic birth isn't normal? So is birth designed by nature to be anything more than just getting a baby out?

Some will argue that it is 'normal' to experience trauma in birth. They will say that nature does not care about a mother's happiness and she just wants the species to survive. This is our answer from another blog post we have written titled, 'Birth Trauma – Does Nature Give a Damn?'

> Yes, all that matters for evolution is that enough survive to continue the species. And it is for that reason that nature DOES support us in a happy transition to parenthood. You say that, "… nature doesn't give a damn", but if mothers are not

happy and attached to their offspring, the species will not survive. Why? Well, for mammals at least, happy, attached mothers produce milk. Happy, attached mothers have 'let down' of their milk, and happy attached babies latch onto their mother's breast easily. Not to mention that unhappy mothers who are not bonded to their babies struggle to care for them. An example of this would be sheep that reject their lambs.

> "Sometimes ewes reject lambs because the lamb doesn't act normally in the minutes or hours after its birth… Sometimes they reject lambs that have been warmed in water because they lose their unique odor. Sometimes they reject lambs because the ewe herself is too sick to care for a baby." [97] ***Joan Jarvis Ellison**, shepherdess and writer*

Similar situations occur for humans. A human baby in a high-intervention birth acts differently in the time immediately post-birth to babies from an intervention-free birth where the baby is given skin-to-skin contact with the mother. This can affect their ability to latch on for breastfeeding, and perhaps potentially does not unlock the instinctual maternal care patterns of the mother. Women often find bonding and breastfeeding difficult when their babies have been bathed prior to receiving them as unbeknown to them, the smells and feelings of the gooey newborn ignite hormones within the mother that enhance her breast milk production, milk let-down and maternal instincts. These hormones include prolactin and oxytocin.

It is important to know that excess adrenaline, which can be present due to fear or merely from feeling 'watched' during labour, interferes with the output of prolactin and oxytocin. So that means that a traumatised mother, with racing levels of adrenaline, can struggle to breastfeed and care for her young. That doesn't appear helpful, in the name of evolution, nature, or survival of the species.

So you can see that nature truly does SUPPORT mothers to be happy and to be non-traumatised, for the continuation of our species. Unfortunately some common hospital practices thwart these early attachment processes, leading to breastfeeding difficulties, bonding issues and miserable mothers. Now, of course,

---

97    Ellison, J.J. (2009). *Bottle Babies*. Retrieved from *http://sheepnotes.blogspot.com.au/2009/03/bottle-babies.html*, accessed November 2014.

we are not sheep and we can overcome these hurdles to instinctual attachment and feeding. But why would this be beneficial from an evolutionary point of view?[98]

## So, what *really is* normal?

The truth is: birth is much more than just getting a baby out. If we look at 'normal' birth as being 'birth as nature intended to ensure the survival of our species', then we see many more positive consequences resulting purely from the birth itself. Dr Sarah Buckley describes these positive consequences by explaining the hormonal orchestration taking place in a normal, that is, as nature intended, birth.

> *Oxytocin, the hormone of love, builds up during labour reaching peak levels at the moment of birth and creating loving, altruistic feelings between mother and baby. Endorphins, hormones of pleasure and transcendence, also peak at birth, as well as the fight-or-flight hormones adrenaline and noradrenaline (epinephrine and norepinephrine). These fight-or-flight hormones protect the baby from lack of oxygen in the final stages of birth and ensure that mother and baby are both wide-eyed and excited at first contact. Prolactin, the mothering hormone, helps us to surrender to our babies, giving us the most tender of maternal feelings as our reward.*
>
> *But these passionate hormones are not just feel-good add-ons. They actually orchestrate the physical processes of birth (and sexual activity) and enhance efficiency, safety and ease for both mother and baby. This hormonal cocktail also rewards birthing mothers with the experience of ecstasy and fulfillment, making us want to give birth again and again. All mammals share virtually the same hormonal crescendo at birth, and this is a necessary pre-requisite for mothering in most species, switching on instinctive maternal behaviour.[99]*

Birth gives us gifts to support the survival of our offspring. Its design gives us opportunities to practice patience, strength, surrender, flexibility, determination, focus and centering on the moment – all fine skills for parenting a newborn.

---

98    Birthtalk.org. (2012). *Birth Trauma – does nature give a damn?* Retrieved from *http://birthtraumatruths.wordpress.com/2012/05/14/birth-trauma-does-nature-give-a-damn/*, accessed September 2014.

99    Excerpt from Healing Birth. (2009) Healing the Earth. *Gentle Birth, Gentle Mothering: A Doctor's Guide to Natural Childbirth and Gentle Early Parenting Choices* (Sarah J Buckley, Celestial Arts, Berkeley CA, 2009) Previous version at *http://sarahbuckley.com/healing-birth-healing-the-earth*

These skills can be practiced and explored when a woman feels safe, supported, nurtured, and listened-to during her pregnancy, postnatal period and especially in her birthing. Unfortunately, often we are not able to do this as we are too busy being scared, struggling to advocate for ourselves while at our most vulnerable. We are often just trying to get through it, or feeling like we're just trying to survive the experience which, when you think about it, is probably how many of our mothers experienced childbirth. We'll look at their experiences further in this section.

## Just to be clear

Before we go any further, we just want to summarise:

- Feeling scared and out-of-control in birth is usual in our culture, but that does not make it normal.
- Most people don't know that birth can be different, and that we are not supposed to birth with fear and trauma. They see our 'usual' births as commonplace and misinterpret it as being 'normal'. This means that they are unable to understand the impact of your experience, because they see it as a normal life process for women to go through and therefore assume that we should have a 'normal' response of moving into motherhood.
- Many of us are carrying definitions of birth that are based on hearsay, non-factual movies and television shows, and misinformed magazine articles. No one questions these definitions, because in our culture, these definitions are supported by the majority of people's experiences. But that still doesn't make them accurate.

## Further barriers to other people 'getting it'

### A painful past

Many of our mothers would have had miserable births through no fault of their own. Women were often left to labour alone, forced to lie on a hard bench (with no partner attending in the 1960s and 1970s), denied food, treated like naughty children, forbidden from vocalising their pain and suffered numerous indignities that were considered routine at the time such as enemas, pubic shaving and having to birth in stirrups.

If everyone was having births like that, then that must be birth, right?

But what if our mothers learned today that their births weren't normal? That their experience of birth was usual, yes, but not normal?

It can be very hard for someone to question what they have been forced to accept for a long time. It may be a hugely painful admission that maybe their births didn't need to be that way. This can make it hard for them to be okay with you being angry and upset about your own birth.

This is not to say that other people will never understand.

Many women (and men) that we know have travelled the path to understanding and healing, and they've brought family members down the road with them. It is mainly a matter of others being open to questioning what they 'know' about birth. They might not 'get it' yet; however, if you are doing your own work and creating your healing journey, then you will be in a much stronger position to be able to support them if they begin their own tentative exploration of the issues. And this book can help.

### But my birth was fine

If your mother or friend had an 'easy' birth or a well-supported birth, she may also not be able to 'get it', especially if she is not aware that the good support she had, or the 'textbook' nature of her labour (possibly resulting in having few decisions to make and no interventions), were possibly what allowed her birth to be a positive experience. She may genuinely have no experience or understanding of what you are going through, especially if she then transitioned smoothly into motherhood.

> *I found myself negatively comparing myself with my mother who appeared as a 'superwoman' figure in her attitude to birth and I was very upset when she commented about the length of my labour. I felt that she considered it was almost inconsequential whereas, to me, it had been overwhelmingly frightening and unbearable.* **Anna**

Responses from these women may hurt as they simply do not have any awareness from their own personal experience of the possibility of birth having a negative impact, and our culture gives them little information that enables them to think more widely. We offer ways to increase others' understanding in our section *How do I share my story so people get it?* (p155).

## Questioning the practice of health professionals

Another reason the people around you may not be able to 'get it' might be that they find it difficult to hear anything they perceive as being negative about health professionals. Since we were very small, most of us have been told, "Do what the doctor tells you. Be a good patient. Doctor knows best." The truth is that any health professional, especially within the health system, is acting with factors that influence them. Yes, they try to make most of their decisions with the woman's best interests in mind. But some of their decisions are made as a result of what is best for the healthcare institution they are operating within. These decisions, often made according to 'hospital policy', are also based on issues such as staffing, liability, funding and 'accepted' (most common) practice, which is different from evidence-based practice.

Many of us don't know that it is okay to ask questions of our health carers, and that asking questions can actually enhance the experience and safety of our care. Our culture definitely does not encourage this.

So by saying we feel bad about our births, some people see that as saying that we don't think the health professionals did a good job. These people might ask, then, how can *you*, a lay person, say that the decision making should have been different? After all, 'doctor knows best'. It can be a huge challenge to many people to entertain the idea that a birth could have gone differently with different care.

If you read the section *Why wouldn't my body work in labour?* (p230), you can see how easily the care we receive can affect the hormones that help us labour. Also read *When health professionals don't get it* (p148) to see why their care may have been less-than-optimal for a positive emotional experience for you. This may help you in discussions with those around you.

## Challenging the accepted ideas

If people hear you question how you were treated, then you are challenging the idea that the health carers are always right. People may make comments such as, "If they weren't being empathetic to you, it's because they were busy saving your baby's life – and you should just feel grateful".

However, there is *never* a reason for you to not receive an explanation about what is happening. You should expect that you will be given options on which to make a decision. Interventions should only proceed with your informed consent. You should *never* be treated like a piece of meat. Even in an extreme emergency, there is usually time to acknowledge your emotional wellbeing. This can be very hard for the general public to hear. And it is very hard when this general public includes your nearest and dearest, especially your partner and your mum.

## Tools for healing and reconnecting

We encourage you to find other people who are able to support you as well, perhaps outside your family. Keep in mind that it is not your responsibility to educate all of those around you, beyond offering the initial access to information and the occasional well-placed comment! Your journey is towards empowerment, and if you are feeling you are relying on them to 'get it', then that not only puts pressure on them, but also takes your own power away. Focusing on your healing and releasing them to their own path gives everyone space.

Below are some tools to support you in supporting others to 'get it'. Remember that they still may need time for processing all they learn, even if they are willing to support you.

- If you haven't already, now may be the time to do a *Birthtalk Breakdown* (p47) and see what feelings were going on for you during the birth. You might begin to explore whether those feelings you experienced are a necessary part of birthing, as most of our culture would accept. This might lead to some new understandings that give you insight into why others can't understand your pain.

- You may find that the more you do this work and travel this path, the more you notice how those people who don't 'get it' talk about birth. You don't need to say anything or try to change their minds, just notice the cultural assumptions about birth, and you will see how much of it is coloured by fear, family myth and misinformation.

- Read *Dealing with your family's birth legacy* (p491) to explore your mother's (or mother-in-law's) definition of 'birth', and what has been passed down through the family. These insights may help explain why certain family members don't 'get it', and move you towards reconnection and a reassessment of what birth legacy you will leave your own children.

- You might ask your mum (or others close to you) to read the chapter titled *The foundations of your healing journey* (p37). Reading this chapter may be all it takes for them to be able to understand. To support someone you care about to gain some understanding, you could say something like, "There are aspects of my birth that I am struggling with. I have been really confused about why I feel that way, but I am beginning to see what's going on. I was wondering how you'd feel about reading this section of this book I'm reading, just so you know what's happening as I am doing everything I can to move on from this, and I would love to have support from other people who understand".

- If your mum, or others close to you, are able to read appropriate sections of the book, and as a result provide positive and encouraging feedback, you may find it appropriate to eventually share your *Birthtalk Breakdown* with them. They may gain more insight about what you have gone through by seeing it written down on paper, especially once they know that those feelings can have huge consequences, as explained in *The foundations of your healing journey*. We recommend you go carefully with your family and friends, as this information can take a while for others to process and assimilate. You may find it best to share your *Birthtalk Breakdown* with someone separate to the family, who is less involved personally and has more understanding of traumatic birth.

# WHY DON'T MY FRIENDS FEEL BAD ABOUT THEIR BIRTHS?

*I was incredibly jealous of other woman that I already knew or just met who had vaginal births. Every time a friend or family member gave birth I would get upset, either because I was jealous things went so well or easily, or because their caesarean was easier for them, so there must be something wrong with me.* **Kerri**

*When friends had their baby I would feel a really uneasy feeling when they didn't seem to feel the distress that I'd felt over the final stages of my birth. I kept wanting everyone to say how traumatic the final part of their birth was, and when they didn't I was so jealous that I didn't feel like they did.* **Sally**

*I also burst into tears at Playgroup last Monday. Two of the girls have had their second babies and were talking about their birth experiences and how great they were, and everyone was joining in about how great it was when they saw their baby, and joking about how loud they yelled, etc. It was just too much for me.* **Jane**

## What you need to know

It can be so confusing hearing other women, especially good friends, speaking about their births in completely different ways to how you want to speak about your own. Hearing them either speak in glowing terms, or with indifference, or acknowledging the experience wasn't that great, but seeming to be unaffected by it, can raise overwhelming feelings. You might feel jealousy, or isolated and alone, or worry that something is 'wrong' with you because everyone around you seems to be so 'okay' with their births. But you are not the only one feeling that way. And it is good to understand why other women's responses to birth can be so vastly different from your own.

## Maybe you're not getting the whole story

Listen to other women's stories at mothers' group or dinner parties. Are they talking about 'how they felt'? Or are they just telling you 'what happened'?

Remember the *Birthtalk Breakdown* (p47), the tool you can use to give yourself more information about how you experienced your birth? Did you discover new things about your own birth, once you filled in the 'How I felt' column in the Birthtalk Breakdown? This applies to other women too: until you know 'how they felt' in their births, knowing 'what happened' won't give you enough information. We often need to break through our culture's conditioning to be able to connect with others in the area of birth, or to understand how their births really were for them.

Remember that a *bad birth* is a birth where the woman felt powerless, confused, fearful, isolated or abandoned, unacknowledged or unheard regardless of what was actually going on in the birth. Sometimes, just asking a woman 'how she felt' in the birth can shed an enormous spotlight on what was really going on.

## You can't figure out why your friend 'coped' better in a similar birthing situation to you

You might be in a situation where another woman you know had a similar birth to you (say, for example, you both had a caesarean, or an induction or a drug-free birth). If she expresses positive feelings about her birth, while you feel completely knocked down by yours, it can be challenging to know how to deal with it. It can also be easy to judge yourself harshly. But there's more you need to know. It's not likely because she 'coped' and you didn't. It is likely that she had different support, or different things happen that she hasn't told you about, which meant she had different feelings. How was she treated by the staff? Did she have someone she knew and trusted with her the whole time? Was everything 'textbook', meaning that she never had to decision make during labour? Did she have someone to debrief with afterwards?

Knowing the answers to these questions will give you more insight into how she experienced her birth, and perhaps shed light on why you both had such different responses to your births. It might become clear that you were actually dealing with completely different situations even though, on the surface, they seem similar.

### Melissa from Birthtalk shares a situation she experienced:

> I was at a BBQ when my firstborn was still young, and I had not yet fully unraveled the circumstances surrounding his birth. My feelings were still raw, and I still felt very vulnerable when 'birth' became the topic in social gatherings. A group of us was sitting in a circle, chatting, and one woman at the BBQ, whose baby was a bit younger than mine, was telling us how it was 'just because she was so determined' to have a natural birth, and that's why it worked out so well. I felt my heart sink. 'Wasn't

*I determined too? Didn't I work for thirty hours to have a natural birth? Was I just not as determined? Was I a failure?' The familiar arrow stuck in my chest, and my thoughts whirled again.*

*Then Deb (from Birthtalk, who was also at the BBQ), who had heard all of this and knew the woman's birth story, came and spoke quietly to me. She told me that this woman was in a birth centre with a different model of care to the one I attended. Unlike at my birth centre, she had one-to-one care from the same midwife, with whom she had a good relationship throughout her pregnancy, labour and birth. This would have meant that when she came into the birth centre during labour, she would have felt welcomed, safe, supported and confident. This would have allowed her all the best hormonal support to help her body do its job. In my own birth, I did not know the midwife who attended the majority of my labour, and we did not hit it off, which negatively impacted my labour progress.*

*Plus, unlike me, the woman at the BBQ had a textbook labour, so she didn't have to do any decision making or step outside the system because everything was 'within the bell curve'. So it had nothing to do with my birthing ability and everything to do with the other woman feeling safe and not having the same difficult situation to deal with. My healing took another step forward and I began formulating how I would plan differently for next time.* **Melissa**

Having these extra insights into other women's experiences can allow you to create connections with women you thought previously you had nothing in common with birth-wise.

## You can't hear the woman who had the fast birth 'complain'

Take for example, a woman who had a four-hour vaginal birth with no drugs, who might mention that it was a challenging experience. Some women who have had very lengthy labours, and especially if those labours ended in caesarean, might look at her with barely concealed envy. They may find it hard to listen when she talks about what a miserable experience it was.

Some women who have fast births are told things from other women that can hurt – like being called a 'lucky cow' because the labour was short. This can add to their own feelings of invalidation and isolation.

Remember Naomi, who had the lightening-fast birth in the section *What is a traumatic or bad birth anyway?* (p42). Imagine connecting with her because you know to ask her about how she felt? Imagine if you said, "Gee, that must have been pretty intense." Remember her response and how her birth impacted her? She said, "It all was happening so fast. No one told me things were okay. I couldn't hear anyone and I didn't know if I was okay or not. I was terrified. My husband had not rung my other support person so I felt alone and isolated and helpless to change things. I felt, "Everything hurts; this is wrong, it's all wrong!" No one listened when I screamed at the pain of my hip being damaged. I was completely vulnerable, exposed and powerless. My baby was doing okay by the time we left hospital, but I was so NOT fine. I had an anxiety attack when we went to leave the hospital. There was another baby leaving that day who looked so perfect and in one piece, and not yellow. We ended up in counselling for an hour or two before going home as I couldn't stop crying. I was still in shock. I was feeling very broken and like my baby had been ripped out of me. I felt I had really bashed my baby up because of my failure. I felt I had damaged my child by somehow being responsible for his speedy and horrible entry. I had trouble sleeping, I had nightmares and flashbacks, I felt like my marriage was over and I completely lost my confidence for months afterwards. And I had ongoing symptoms from the damage to my hip."

You may find you felt the same as Naomi which allows for a new level of connection. Or it might be that there were vast differences between the way you felt and the way she felt. Now you can see why misunderstanding could happen and it allows you to be understanding and supportive of each other. What a great way to gather support and work together, rather than perpetuate the constant competitiveness we see among new mothers.

## Some words of caution

When you are wanting to talk more about birth with the women around you, it is worth considering that some women do not want to 'go there'; they don't want to talk about any negative feelings about the birth. They may have been told too many times that they have nothing to complain about, so have learned to just keep it inside. Or they may think, "That's just birth. Why complain?" (It's not just birth. See *What is a traumatic or bad birth anyway?* (p42)) Or, they may not have negative feelings. Only they can tell.

Another reason for caution: let's say that you do find out more about a friend's birth, and you feel that she feels okay about it more because of the support she had available or because of the caregivers she had, or because she was in a situation where no decision making was involved. However, it might not be appropriate to initially share that information with her. If she does not have the insight you now have, she might feel that you are trying to take away from the determination or strength she had.

So you may need to wait until you are further along in your healing journey. It will take a degree of tact and carefully placed words to find a way to share that her determination and strength were enabled to shine because of the other things she had in place, things that were not available to you. This might be a wonderful chance for her to be able to empathise with your situation, or to perhaps reassess her own birth and think more carefully about the things that enabled her to emerge positive. It may give you new opportunities to connect. Or you may decide to keep that information to yourself as part of your own journey.

## Tools for understanding and healing

If you haven't already, now may be the time to do a *Birthtalk Breakdown* (p47) and see what feelings were going on for you during the birth. Consider that even if your friend had the exact same things as you on the 'What happened' side of her Birthtalk Breakdown, she can still have completely different things occurring on the 'How I felt' side. If she felt differently and had a positive outcome emotionally, this is not because she is a better person or more able to cope; it is because she had different resources available to her, different support, different care, different information or a different situation to deal with.

The situation of another woman having different support, care or information can feel completely unfair. It actually is unfair, which may mean that you need to grieve. This can involve completing the *Shifting from anger exercise* (p433), where you focus on what you are sad or angry or upset about in each instance. In this case, you may write a 'Shifting from anger' letter to the woman who received better treatment and had a better experience. This letter should never be sent, of course. It is simply an exercise to process strong emotions safely. See *Shifting from anger exercise* for more details, for example:

> Dear Chloe, I am so annoyed that you feel so great about your birth. I am so angry that you got all the good stuff, when I was the one who really wanted that natural birth. I am annoyed that you didn't have to fight as hard as I did postnatally to just feel okay.

I am so sad that my baby was robbed because I was so completely out of it. I am so sad that I didn't get what you had. I am aching because my heart is hurting. I am devastated that I now have to go through this healing process.

I am afraid that I won't be able to get the good things that you got. I am afraid that it will keep hurting every time I see you.

I regret being so snippety with you. I am sorry I have held it against you when it wasn't your fault that I was so poorly looked after.

I understand that you don't know why I am so mad. I appreciate that you have showed me that birth can be different to what I experienced.

I know that you want only the best for me. I know that you don't know what I am learning about bad births either, so it is difficult for you to understand.

As Debby said to Melissa after the aforementioned BBQ, it would be normal and okay to feel happy for your friend. But sad for yourself.

For some more tips on processing grief, go to the chapter called *I feel sad* (p245).

# WHEN HEALTH PROFESSIONALS DON'T GET IT

*Almost two years later, a midwife I met said, "Oh that's just birth" when I tried to explain what I'd felt after my daughter's birth.* **Sally**

*On day three in hospital I got the baby blues but I knew it was more than a rush of hormones, and I could not stop sobbing. I felt like a volcano ready to explode with emotion, not just teary. I was told, "Try not to think about it" by the midwife. I felt very unsupported by the staff and my husband was just trying to be there for me, but probably was very confused. It was not just hormones. It was a buildup of raw emotion that needed to be vented.* **Kerri**

*I ended up seeing a psychologist for a few months, but in the end I felt that she was expecting me to 'get over it'. As you can imagine, that's the last thing I was able to do. How can we possibly be expected to get over what we went through???* **Kathryn**

*I went to a GP for depression at the start of the journey and he just didn't get it; he kept talking about how I had a healthy child and I didn't die in childbirth etc. He had no idea why what I have been through could possibly still be following me around four years later. I spent most of that session explaining to him how birth trauma was disenfranchised.* **Leonie**

*Neither the psychologist nor the social worker seemed to get why my birth would be causing me angst. However, a friend who'd had a traumatic birth and had been to Birthtalk was able to explain to me that I had had my support interrupted in the crucial part of my birth and that would explain why I was feeling so sad about the birth even though it was a 'successful' VBAC.* **Sally**

*I was a failure, not good enough, fragile, demoralised, so sad and utterly disappointed. I dreaded it every time my husband had to go home to sleep while I was in hospital. I have never felt so alone in my whole life even though I was surrounded by hospital staff.* **Kerri**

One of the reasons it is so difficult to find support after a traumatic birth is that even the 'experts' often don't understand. If a so-called expert is dismissing your situation, it can be very hard to gain support from partners and other family.

There are some beautiful health carers out there who do get it. There are also others who believe in woman-centred care and the importance of a woman being heard and acknowledged, even if they do not fully understand the implications of a traumatic birth and how to support the healing process. They spend hours supporting and encouraging women and families to recover from the birthing period, and to move into family life.

There are also, unfortunately, a lot of health professionals in many segments of the health industry who have very little information about the value of birth or how a birth can affect a woman.

Knowing why this is the case can be an important step in the healing process.

## Why many health professionals don't understand

One reason that many health professionals don't understand the value of birth or how a birth can affect a woman is because they live within our culture. So our section called *Why doesn't anyone get it?* (p129) will partly answer the question about the reason health carers don't get it. They may be highly educated, very informed and even experienced with birth, yet that in no way means they understand the issues surrounding traumatic birth and all its repercussions.

Like all of us, health professionals have their own internal definition of what birth is. As well as holding all the common cultural beliefs about birth, they also have their own experiences with birth as they know it, plus birth as they were taught it and they assume that this gives them insights into how birth is, which is not always accurate.

Michael C Klein, emeritus professor of family practice and paediatrics at the University of British Columbia, writes, "So many providers think they know, but what they believe is not evidence-based"[100]. He cites one Canadian national study[101] and comments that this study "demonstrated many providers, especially obstetricians, have several non-evidence-based views".[102] As an example, twenty percent of obstetricians in that study believed that "cesarean surgery was as safe or safer for mothers and babies as vaginal birth".[103]

---

100　Klein, M.C. (2011). Many Women and Providers Are Unprepared for an Evidence-Based, Educated Conversation About Birth. *J Perinat Educ, 20*(4), 185-187. doi: 10.1891/1058-1243.20.4.185.

101　Klein, M.C., Kaczorowski, J., Hall, W.A., Fraser, W., Liston, R.M., Eftekhary, S., ... Chamberlaine, A. (2009). The attitudes of Canadian maternity care practitioners towards labour and birth: many differences but important similarities. *J Obstet Gynaecol Canada, 31*(9), 827-40.

102　Klein, M.C. (2011). Many Women and Providers Are Unprepared for an Evidence-Based, Educated Conversation About Birth. op.cit.

103　Klein, M.C. (2011) Many Women and Providers Are Unprepared for an Evidence-Based, Educated Conversation About Birth. op. cit. (discussing Klein et al 2009)

Our health carers are influenced by the information and support they have been exposed to during their training and the births they see during placements. They are also influenced by the institutional and legal requirements of their working environment. All of these factors can influence a health carer's philosophy and, in turn, the type of care they offer. These factors also influence their response if you express concerns about how your birth has impacted on you.

Possibly, a lack of insight may come about because of health professionals' exposure to procedures on a daily basis. They might not consider that something that is routine to them might potentially be traumatic to someone else. While they are likely to be aware that patients do not have the same level of understanding into what is going on as they do, they may not consider how this can impact negatively on a patient's emotional wellbeing. Health professionals can become so focused on doing the technical aspects of their job that they lose sight of the possible emotional and physical impacts of certain procedures. This is rarely because they are cold-hearted or mean-spirited – it might simply be that they are unaware that it matters to women.

## Isn't birth just a way to get a baby out?

Many health professionals don't get it because they don't understand the value of birthing beyond bringing forth a new life. These health professionals can see birth almost as an 'obstacle' to getting the baby, rather than as an important and necessary step towards motherhood. This view is reflected in the results of a study comparing the views of obstetricians aged forty years or younger, to those older than forty.[104] The researchers found that the obstetricians in the younger group were less positive than the older generation about the importance of maternal choice and the importance of women having a role in their own birth, and were more likely to believe that women were not missing an important experience by having a caesarean section,[105] viewing caesarean surgery as "just another way to have a baby".[106]

If birth is viewed in this way, then its relevance in a woman's life will be vastly underestimated. That is, if health carers see birth as merely a way to get the baby out, then they will be unlikely to see birth as being significant and important

---

104   Klein, M.C., Liston, R., Fraser, W.D., Baradaran, N., Hearps, S.J., Tomkinson, J., Maternity Care Research Group. (2011). Attitudes of the new generation of Canadian Obstetricians: how do they differ from their predecessors? *Birth, 28*(2), 129–39.

105   ibid.

106   Klein, M.C. (2011). Many Women and Providers Are Unprepared for an Evidence-Based, Educated Conversation About Birth. op. cit.

for the mother emotionally, beyond meeting her child. It also means they won't recognise the implications of a negative experience because, to them, giving the woman a positive experience was not a priority anyway.

Health carers with these views are not being purposefully unkind; they have often just been taught this approach and may rarely hear from women postnatally beyond the first few weeks. Therefore, they usually have not come across an opposing point of view.

## Feelings and hormones during birth can affect women afterwards

Many health carers have little knowledge of the effects that a woman's emotional state and her hormonal interplay during birth have on the emotional and physical outcomes of her birth. See *Why wouldn't my body work in labour?* (p230) for more on this. They might guess that if a woman feels good during birth, then she might carry that with her. However, there is generally little knowledge of the ongoing effects and challenges that a negative experience gives women and their families postnatally. And there is little understanding of how to support a woman who might be suffering in this way.

## You mean you take your birth with you when you leave the hospital?

Not many health professionals have an opportunity to develop an ongoing relationship with the woman throughout her transition into parenthood and beyond. So they are unable to witness the impact, positive or negative, of how a woman experienced her pregnancy, birth or postnatal period and its ripple effect on her transition into parenthood.

Rarely would they hear from women years down the track about the impact of their maternity experience on their life. So they don't have the opportunity to increase their awareness.

## Feeling the need to defend their practice

The ongoing impact of a maternity experience on a woman's life is a huge responsibility for health professionals to carry, which could be viewed as an honour, but could also be viewed as a burden if they develop an awareness of past mistakes. Health professionals already carry a huge responsibility for women's care during and after birth, and so it could be challenging for them to hear the negative impacts they may have contributed to. This message is likely to be dismissed unless it is delivered in a way that they are able to receive or understand it.

## A new awareness

Some health professionals are able to step back from their practice and hear new information. We received this email last year from a local obstetrician,

Firstly, I would like to thank you for the wonderful service you provide in Brisbane and online. Secondly, a confession, I only heard about your services last night. A very close friend and her husband were so supported and validated after attending your support group. Why is it so important to me, other than the help you provided to them? Because I'm part of the system that has caused the need for your services! The long-term impact of not only what we do, but how we do it has been really highlighted. I would really appreciate the opportunity to improve my understanding and future practice.

This obstetrician has gone on to meet with us and hear more about how birth experiences are affecting women, and what health carers can do to support women. This has been an uplifting experience for us and gives us hope that there are others who may come forward and reassess their practice.

## What to do when a health professional doesn't get it

Many women attending Birthtalk have had disappointing consultations with health professionals, and there are a number ways of handling this, depending on the individual situation and where you are emotionally at the time.

Firstly, make sure you get it yourself! Spend time working through this book, processing your own experience, and developing your own understanding about birth and traumatic birth. This way, you will be clear when talking about it to others.

## Counsellor or psychologist

- If you are working with a counsellor you trust, whom you believe could work with you if they understood more about traumatic birth, then try giving them a copy of this book to peruse. Melissa had this happen in her own healing process, where she already had a good relationship with a counsellor and then had the realisation that a lot of her issues were due to unprocessed emotions from her traumatic birth. She explained her needs to this counsellor, and gave her information about the effects of traumatic birth, and the counsellor willingly (and beautifully) supported her in aspects of her healing journey once she understood.

- Or if you are hearing, "You should be over that by now" or, "But aren't you grateful for…" or, "I think you should just focus on your baby" or other dismissive comments, then it may be that this is not the counsellor or psychologist for you. It may be time to look further afield for someone who can validate your experience.

## Doctor or midwife in the postnatal period after a traumatic birth

If you are asking a doctor or midwife for support, or expressing your situation and hearing negative or dismissive responses, then you have a few options:

You can attempt to explain things to them from a *Birthtalk Breakdown* (p47) point of view, focusing on 'How I Felt'. For example, "I am really happy to have my baby, but I am finding that the birth is having an impact on me emotionally, due to how things unfolded. I was wondering if you could talk me through a few things relating to the birth." Or, "I am struggling to make sense of some things that happened during the birth, and I feel that being clear on some of these things might be helpful to me in working through this. Are you able to help me?"

- Gather support from your partner or support people and ask them to be present at a consultation with your doctor or midwife. You may need to get them to read part of this book first!

- If you feel the doctor or midwife is not open to exploring things with you in a kind way, or if you are feeling too vulnerable, you can end the consultation and then take steps to locate a different practitioner.

## Doctor or midwife when in consultation for the next birth after a traumatic birth

- You can explain your needs in terms of the *Birthtalk Breakdown*, and share what is important to you emotionally. For example, "During my last birth, I didn't understand what was happening to me. This really affected me as I felt helpless and scared, and I took those feelings home with me, which made things really hard. This time it's really important to me to know what's going on. I want to make sure that all procedures are explained to me before we decide whether to go ahead with them. Is there some way you can help me with that?"

- You can also gather support from your well-informed (!) partner or support people and ask them to come to a consultation with you. They might need to read parts of this book first!

- If you are finding a lack of understanding from a doctor or midwife in this situation, you have every right to shop around to find the right health professional for you for your next pregnancy. Read the sections in the chapter *Birthing again* (p507) for more ideas.

It is important to know that not all health professionals will understand or will want to understand. Yet many, given the opportunity, may be willing to absorb new information and find ways to support you that they had not thought of before. You are actually giving them the chance to enhance their practice, and paving the way for other women who have had traumatic births to receive better support.

# HOW DO I SHARE MY STORY SO PEOPLE GET IT?

*Before coming to Birthtalk, I found it hard to express my situation. This made me feel stupid as, on the surface, people saw everything as okay, with a healthy child and uncomplicated labour.* **Sophie**

*I would tell people what happened about my birth – and it is quite long and detailed – and having got through the story they would be no clearer as to why I felt so troubled about it. Wasn't all birth full-on?* **Sally**

*A friend who'd had a traumatic birth and had been to Birthtalk was able to explain to me that I had had my support interrupted in the crucial part of my birth and that would explain why I was feeling so sad about the birth, even though it was a 'successful' VBAC.* **Sally**

## What you need to know

It may never be particularly easy to tell your story in a way that people understand because you are fighting against a lifetime of conditioning about birth. However, you can certainly reframe your birth story so people get more of an idea of the impact it has had, without feeling like they need to fix you or tell you to move on, which would be an improvement on the way many people respond.

To do this, you might need to brush up on your own understanding about traumatic birth, as well as your understanding of your own experience. Until you are clear, you might not be able to express your situation in a way that makes it easier for people to relate to what you are saying. So you might find it helpful to go to *The foundations of your healing journey* (p37) to understand traumatic birth better, and do a *Birthtalk Breakdown* (p47) to find out more about your own birth, if you have not already. Then think about how you can better express your story – the key is to focus on the '*How I felt*' column of the Birthtalk Breakdown, as that gives people insights about your actual experience, rather than what they assume your experience was.

Sophie, who we met in *One night at a Birthtalk meeting* (p13), used to practise telling her version of her birth story so she could get it out without breaking down. Part of the reason she was concerned about breaking down was because all her emotions were blocked up; she had not found any way to release, express and explore her emotions, so they were all sitting there, simmering under the surface. This is why we recommend processing your birth a bit before you consider how to reframe your story. Sophie attended Birthtalk for a few sessions and visibly changed as the months progressed, and she began to heal. We asked her to complete a questionnaire to help in the writing of this book. Her answers are peppered throughout the chapters. One question asked her to describe her birth. What a difference we saw from her first Birthtalk session, where she could barely speak; what a difference from the prepared version of her story she had previously shared with others.

| What happened | How I felt |
| --- | --- |
| It was a one hour birth, no pain relief, no stitches, all fine. (This is how Sophie had practised describing her birth prior to coming to Birthtalk because going into more detail made her feel upset.) | My labour was fine until I went to hospital, then I felt scared and nervous. I felt vulnerable once the obstetrician arrived as there was no communication and he didn't explain what he was doing. My mum was with me for support and the obstetrician told my mum to leave. This made me feel alone. The obstetrician proceeded to yell at me while doing an internal because I didn't relax to his liking to break my waters. Maybe if he told me what he was doing, and hadn't told my mum to leave, things would have been calmer. I ended up in tears. The doctor laughed, saying, "See you in a few hours," before walking out. I had my daughter in one hour. There was no encouragement from the nurse or the obstetrician. He yelled at me to push. I told him I didn't have a contraction. His response was, "I *don't care!*" Then he rolled his eyes. I couldn't focus on what I was doing, as he made me feel useless. |

Before getting to the point where she could describe her birth to other people in the way that she has in the *How I Felt* column above, Sophie worked hard to release and express the grief and anger that arose when she first explored this area of her birth. This was a vital part of being able to share her story, as it meant she was not 'dumping' others with her unprocessed emotions, which is uncomfortable for both parties, and does not facilitate understanding and compassion.

So, by doing the hard work to process her birth, Sophie was actually enabling others to be able to support her better, as she was clearer in her expression of what happened to her, and was in a position of being able to be vulnerable without worrying about 'breaking down'. This can lead to being in an interesting position of actually no longer desperately *needing* people to get it, as your needs are being met, and you are being heard elsewhere.

Sally shares how her 'telling of her story' changed after months of processing:

> *In the week before my final 'Healing From Birth' meeting at Birthtalk, before I birthed my next baby, I had an evening out with three of my close friends from my mother's group. It was a lovely night and we chatted for hours. They had known I'd suffered after my daughter's birth but I don't think they really understood why either. During the night I spoke of how I'd been doing lots of healing and was able to explain in a few sentences (without reliving the whole birth process with them) what I had been through. I was able to explain quite simply that, when I was so very vulnerable as I was birthing my baby, I was moved from where I felt safe and supported, and this meant I felt lots of trauma after the birth. I explained that because I didn't feel safe and supported at this important time, I was not able to pick up my baby and welcome her into the world and I felt grief because I had missed these precious moments as she came into the world. I was also able to explain it clearly to my mum and my sisters too, and things seemed clearer for them, which was good for them too, I think.* **Sally**

So we would encourage you to keep processing, keep exploring, and keep pulling apart your experience because, in doing so, you can actually garner more support for yourself as your ability to explain what *really* happened increases. You might be surprised where support comes from, and who can relate to your experience. It may inspire some people to open up more to you about their own experiences (we've seen this happen to mothers of women who have had traumatic births themselves) and create new relationships.

See *Why doesn't anyone get it?* (p129) to develop your understanding of why people may struggle to appreciate the impact of your birth on your life. Also see *Everyone keeps telling me I should be grateful* (p203) for some dialogue tips when discussing your birth with others.

# I'M STUCK IN PANIC ATTACKS OR FLASHBACKS

*I'd have panic attacks over silly little things that took me back to my birth.* **Hannah**

*I started to have panic attacks the week after she came home. I have only in the last year discovered that that is what those 'turns' are.* **Leonie**

*By the time my baby was four months old, I had my first panic attack, although I didn't know that's what it was.* **Tina**

*I have flashbacks to the incident, anything would trigger flashbacks.* **Kim**

*I had flashbacks constantly and consistently for 14 months. It was like a movie that played in the left hand side of my head and I had to live my life while watching my birth experience over and over again.* **Mai**

*I had flashbacks about my hospital stay. I couldn't remember much of his birth. I still can't walk into the hospital he was born in without huge anxiety attacks.* **Nic**

According to Sheila Kitzinger, renowned author and social anthropologist specialising in pregnancy and childbirth, "PTSD is essentially a state of panic".[107] If you are feeling hostage to your mind and struggling day-to-day with panic attacks or flashbacks, you are not alone. While we explain more about this in our section *Can you get PTSD after childbirth?* (p83), we want to highlight these issues separately here, in case you are feeling completely stuck and not sure what to do, or which part of the book is best for you right now.

## This is normal

Most importantly, you need to know that anxiety, flashbacks and panic attacks are normal. As we have said in *Can you get PTSD after childbirth?* (p83), we agree with the Birth Trauma Association when they say, "It is important to remember that PTSD is a normal response to a traumatic experience. The re-experiencing of the event with flashbacks accompanied by genuine anxiety

---

107    Kitzinger, Sheila in Hilpern, K. (2003, June 5). The Unspeakable Trauma of Childbirth. *Sydney Morning Herald*, *www.smh.com.au/articles/2003/06/05/1054700311400.html*, accessed January 2014.

and fear are beyond the sufferer's control. They are the mind's way of trying to make sense of an extremely scary experience and are not a sign [of an] individual'[s] 'weakness' or inability to cope".[108]

That is, you are experiencing a normal response to an abnormal situation, because it is not normal for birth to be an event where the life of yourself or your child is threatened, whether that threat is real or perceived.

## Giving you a sign

The most helpful thing, we believe, is to deal with panic attacks or flashbacks within the context of a traumatic birth, and to see them as a normal response. That is, they are not a sign that something is wrong with you. But they can be a sign that you need more support to be able to function enough so you can continue to address your birth, process the experience and take further steps along the healing journey.

We encourage you to treat yourself gently, and to reach out to a good friend, your partner* or an understanding health professional, for support if you are struggling. Hopefully you will also find additional support within the pages of this book, via the stories and information we share.

*This support may come from your partner, but they might need more information and understanding to be able to help. It could be helpful for them to read some sections of this book (such as *Can you get PTSD after childbirth?* (p83) and *Common 'hidden factors' that can make a birth traumatic* (p99)). Before you ask for their help, you might consider reading the chapter *Issues with your partner* (p291) to give you some ideas about how to approach them, and perhaps to lower any intensity between you both first.

108     Birth Trauma Association, UK. *What is Birth Trauma?*
        Retrieved from *www.birthtraumaassociation.org.uk/what_is_trauma.htm*, accessed January 2014.

## Some tools that may help

Dr Matthew Tull, from the University of Mississippi Medical Center, recommends using 'grounding techniques' to deal with flashbacks and dissociation, and compares these techniques with a form of mindfulness. He suggests these techniques as a way of 'grounding' a person in the present moment. He says, "To ground, you want to use the five senses (sound, touch, smell, taste and sight). To connect with the here and now, you want to do something that will bring all your attention to the present moment."[109] Techniques such as turning on loud and jarring music, gripping a piece of ice, sniffing strong peppermint, or biting a lemon are recommended, and Dr Tull also suggests simply taking an inventory of your immediate environment and connecting with the present moment by counting furniture, identifying the colours you see and listing sounds you hear.[110]

## Finding professional support

You might find it helpful to connect with an appropriate health professional to support you in putting these and other tools in place. We recommend connecting with empathetic health workers who understand both PTSD and birth, who are embracing of wherever you are on your healing journey and who are open to a variety of modalities of healing, depending on what may be needed at each stage of the journey. You are important, and your healing journey is important, so we encourage you to find the right support for you.

For further understanding of PTSD and birth trauma, see our section, *Can you get PTSD after childbirth?* (p83).

---

109   Tull, M. *Coping With Flashbacks*. Retrieved from *http://ptsd.about.com/od/selfhelp/a/flashcoping.htm*, accessed August 2014.

110   ibid.

# I feel angry

## DEALING WITH ANGER

*The anger I felt in the first couple of years after the birth actually frightened me. It would come up out of the blue (it seemed) and I would rage uncontrollably. I'd throw things, screech, yell and just explode, generally towards my husband. I had no idea why. This all began to change when I started processing my birth, and my anger suddenly had a reason, a focus and was a necessary part of my healing.* **Jane**

*Anger is a signal, and one worth listening to.*[111] **Dr Harriet Lerner**

Anger can be a very challenging emotion to deal with and it can be difficult to know how to release it safely, especially when you are parenting young children. Sometimes we try to push it down and ignore it, but angry feelings have a tendency then to arise in an uncontrolled outburst – not really a pleasant scenario for anyone.

### The message within the anger

Women have commonly felt uncomfortable or fearful of their anger. As Dr Harriet Lerner notes in her book, *The Dance of Anger*, women's anger and its expression have traditionally been seen as taboo.[112] However, anger usually contains a message that can act as a signpost for where to focus our attention in

---

111    Lerner, H. (1985). *The Dance of Anger,* New York, USA: Harper and Row Publishers, p.1.
112    ibid. p.2.

the healing journey. The message from the anger, says Dr Lerner, might be "that we are being hurt, or that our rights are being violated, that our needs or wants are not being adequately met or simply that something is not right".[113]

We have supported many women who have been holding in great waves of anger when they first attend our meetings, and who have struggled to know how to express this anger healthily. Others, however, when we first meet them are simply distressed and hurting. For some of these women, their anger comes once they begin to receive validation and acknowledgement and learn more about the factors that have come together to leave them so impacted by their birth.

We agree with Dr Lerner's belief that "anger… exists for a reason and always deserves our respect and attention."[114] Women who are feeling angry as a result of their birth experience may need support to discover where to direct it, and then to find an appropriate outlet and a means to move through this intense emotion, knowing it has a purpose. Listening to the anger and channelling the energy behind it into productive steps forward can be important in the healing journey.

Once you have acknowledged your anger, the next step becomes identifying its source, which can be challenging in itself after a traumatic birth. Then, the tricky part can be discovering methods of expressing anger that will not result in you feeling powerless,[115] and that are not damaging for those around you.

And that is the purpose of the following sections.

---

113    Lerner, H. (1985). *The Dance of Anger*, New York, USA: Harper and Row Publishers, p.1.
114    ibid, p4
115    ibid.

# I'M SO ANGRY WITH MY HEALTH CARERS

*I had a great amount of anger toward the hospital and the birth suite midwife for denying me the support of my husband at a point in my life when I needed him the most.* **Kerri**

*I was continuing to moan loudly and the midwife came right up close to me and said, "You are making too much noise. You are going to have a very sore throat tomorrow. There is no need to make this much noise," which made me very angry. How dare this midwife, who didn't know how I'd laboured and who didn't know me at all, tell me what to do! I began to be very aggressive to everyone.* **Sally**

*I was angry at the hospital for being treated as part of the general conveyer belt of care. I was angry at the doctor and private health systems for treating caesareans as the norm. [My birth] negatively affected my confidence in my body, as a woman, and this in turn affected my relationship and my sense of self. I felt I had failed to do what women's bodies were designed to do.* **Rita**

## What you need to know

This anger is completely understandable and often justifiable. What can make it very hard is that most health carers are unaware of the ongoing impact that birth can have, especially traumatic birth. Most don't know how many women take their birth experience with them when they leave the hospital grounds, and that often this experience is negative. Many do not know that a negative birth can derail a woman's entire universe for months and years afterwards. They are also often unaware of just how much their actions can impact on these experiences. So health carers may not be able to offer validation to a woman who so desperately needs it because many health professionals just do not have an awareness of the issues.

## I'm so angry I want to...

There are a few areas of anger that often come up, and in the upcoming sections we will explore ways of dealing with them. None of the solutions involve violence, although we have had many women talk of their desire for physical vengeance on a health carer – and sometimes they're only partly joking.

Violence is obviously never okay.

The most important thing is to express and explore your anger appropriately. It needs to be out of your head and body. It needs to be heard and acknowledged and, rather than being met with a, "There, there, dear – do you feel better now you have punched those pillows?" type response, it needs a real understanding of how the birth could impact on a family and *why* the anger needs expressing and exploring.

## Why it's important to acknowledge and address your anger

The impact of a bad birth does not necessarily go away on its own over time. Most women we meet need to first process and understand their experience and their response to it, with the myriad of emotions that can arise, for healing to be able to take place. Exploring the anger is an important part of that. The good thing to know is that the anger can be expressed and released without any action being required from the health carer for there to be 'closure' for you. It is important to get to a stage where you don't need the health carer to provide a particular response to move on; otherwise you would remain dependent on them for your future happiness and contentment. It's important to get to a stage of healing where getting a response would be nice, but not necessary to your peace of mind and your everyday functioning. You may choose to take further action, and you can explore your options in *I'm thinking about making a complaint or taking legal action* (p181).

However, it may not be necessary for you to do that, to move on. Only you will know what is needed, and you might not know yet. We encourage you to give it time, as you work through this book and continue on your healing journey.

## Tools for healing when you are angry with your health carer

To explore anger towards a health carer in more detail, see *Anger at what happened – or what didn't happen but should have* (p166), where we look at situations involving health carers that women often get justifiably angry about. This section explores what you can do to ease the anger and move to a new, empowered space.

# ANGER AT WHAT HAPPENED – OR WHAT DIDN'T HAPPEN BUT SHOULD HAVE

Sometimes women are angry at things that contributed to their emotional distress during and after the birth. Or they are angry at things that *didn't* happen that could have drastically altered the situation or their experience of it. Sometimes, a woman might not become angry until she realises that there *is* another way; that birth is not supposed to be as traumatic as hers was. (See *What is a traumatic or bad birth anyway?* (p42)) Often, after the anger has been expressed, sadness arises.

But before that, there is a whole range of things that can occur that increase the likelihood of a woman feeling a negative impact after a birth. There is also a whole range of things that, *because they did not occur*, increase the likelihood of the woman feeling a negative impact after birth. These tend to be the situations that added to you feeling (before, during or after the birth):

- powerless
- confused
- fearful
- isolated or abandoned
- unacknowledged or unheard
- that your innate knowledge about your body and your baby were disregarded.

The situations that made you feel like this are not 'little things that don't really matter'. They are the events that contributed to your birth experience. They can affect your whole life, postnatally – for weeks, months and years afterwards, if they are not processed. So they matter.

We have collated some of the more common events that occurred with real women's births, just to give you an idea of what can invoke (completely justifiable) anger.

## Situations women are often angry about (and understandably so)

- Being given information by your health carers during labour that you find out later is incorrect or incomplete. Correct information could have changed the course of your labour if you had been given the complete information, such as information about induction or epidural or other interventions.
- Being told not to worry and that it would all be taken care of when you try to get some straight answers to your concerns.
- Being turned away from the hospital, especially without acknowledgement or further information, when you are certain that something is happening with your body or your baby and you don't feel you are being taken seriously.
- Negotiating with your obstetrician for the birth you want and then discovering in labour that their back-up partner will not support your requests.
- Having a verbal agreement from your health carer to support the type of birth you are wanting (e.g. a natural birth), only to have them withdraw that support for unfounded reasons at the very end of your pregnancy or even during labour.
- Being left alone to labour when you need support and care from the person in whom you have placed responsibility for your safety and your child's safety.
- Not having your emotional needs considered – no one is talking to you, just about you; or feeling like a piece of meat. This is commonly expressed by women who have had medical equipment attached (e.g. Cardiotocography, often referred to as 'continuous monitoring' (CTGs), epidurals, drips, etc.) when interventions are occurring; when care providers are prioritising a woman's partner's needs over hers; or when they are vulnerable, such as young mothers or mothers whose first language is not English.
- Not being fully informed when decision making is required during the birth. You might find out afterwards that certain vital information was withheld, making a significant difference in the physical or emotional outcome of your birth.
- Being ignored when you try to ask what is happening.
- Being told you were having your waters ruptured, at the time they were being ruptured, without having time to think about it.
- Being offered to be 'given a hand' in second stage labour, accepting support that, unbeknown to you, meant an instrumental delivery.
- Not being asked before an episiotomy is performed.

- Having an invasive procedure performed without your consent and despite your refusal.
- Being left alone after the birth, bleeding, and not knowing where your child is and if they are alright.
- Having someone bathe your baby before you have got to hold them. This is *not* a little thing. The smells of birth are vitally important for initiating breastfeeding, enhancing bonding and emotional closure post-birth. See *Why wouldn't my body work in labour?* (p230) Plus, it is your baby and this is ultimately a disempowering act for a new mother.
- Having someone take silly photos of your baby with staff members before you meet them and finding the photos later on your memory stick. Yes, this has happened to a Birthtalk mum.
- Not having basic requests met or respected. For example, wanting to choose your own position for labouring or birth, a request for silence during contractions, dimming of lights, wanting interventions to happen in between contractions, telephoning your partner to come to the hospital in a timely manner.
- Being separated from your baby longer than was necessary.
- Not being given sufficient or appropriate antenatal education. A lot of women doing Birthtalk's antenatal sessions, after a previous bad birth, get angry and sad when we tell them certain information. They feel incredulous that just that one small bit of information could have made the difference in their birth. They trusted their carers to give them the information they needed and this didn't happen. There are often despairing cries of, "Why didn't anyone tell me this before?"

## So I'm angry, now what?

The list of situations that happen before, during and after birth is just to give you an idea of some situations that Birthtalk mums have expressed anger over. You might be angry about something completely different. Regardless of the situation, the anger can urge you to do something – anything – to release it. Yet while it may seem logical to march into the hospital and haul your health professional over the coals and let them hear loud and clear *why you are angry* and *what they have done to you*, it is unlikely to help. This is frustrating, but unfortunately true.

Why won't it help? Because in this situation, health professionals could understandably become a bit defensive, and be focused on protecting themselves, so they're not able to hear your message. They may possibly write you off as being unstable, hysterical or 'unable to be reasoned with'.

## So, the first question is: what do you want to achieve?

Realistically, the initial goal needs to be focused on your own healing. You may feel you want to communicate with your health professional, to share how you have been impacted by your birth. Writing a letter is a good start; however, we advise against sending it straight away. In the section *Writing a letter of complaint* (p495) we explore how to write a letter that may have some impact, but we suggest working on the tools recommended below, and reading *I'm thinking about making a complaint or taking legal action* (p181) first.

There are two things that can put you in a position to better express your situation, and the fall out for you postnatally, to someone in the medical profession. The first is gaining clarity for yourself about your birth and what happened, and the second is lowering the intensity surrounding your birth to a level where your life is not being affected on a daily basis. By working on both of these things, you may find you can more effectively communicate your situation when you do write the letter.

Following are some tools to get that process of gaining clarity and lowering the intensity happening.

## Tools for dealing with anger

- The first thing to do is to get the anger out in a healthy, safe way. At first, it is common to feel exploding anger without knowing exactly what or who you are angry at. An easy target is your partner – whether they deserve it or not! To explore this issue, turn to *Issues with your partner* (p291).

- If you are not sure of why you are angry, that's okay. The more you explore your birth and use the information and tools in this book, the more you tease the birth apart, which makes it easier to pull out specific situations (or people) that you are truly angry with.

- If you have read *The foundations of your healing journey* (p37) you will understand now that birth doesn't have to be the way you experienced it, which can bring up anger in itself. If this is what is making you angry, then 'go there'. You may find it helpful to write it down, by starting with, "I am angry because…" and writing the first twelve things that come into your head. You can then choose one of the things you list, explore it further and see where it takes you. See our section *Self-discovery: what's really going on for me?* (p457) for more tips on the writing process.

- Another topic that may be good to try is, "If [this situation you are angry about] never happened, then…" This can give you more ideas regarding what you are angry about, and also lead to discovering areas that you are needing to grieve. For example, "If the midwife had taken the time to get to know me, then I might have felt safe with her, and the birth may have progressed further". Then, to explore the impact of that, you can take it further with something like, "If I felt safe with the midwife and the birth progressed further then…" You may find one of the answers stands out. For example, "… then I wouldn't feel like such a complete failure and hate motherhood so much". This can then lead into some grieving and sorrow at the situation. For ideas on dealing with grief see *I feel sad* (p245). If you find that anger is the primary emotion arising, see the points below.

- Now might be a good time to explore some healing art. This sounds more 'airy fairy' than it is! Healing art can be an exceptional tool in reaching the anger and exploring it. Melissa used this too a lot in her healing, and many of her early pictures used bright-red heavy strokes of anger. It really helped to get the feelings out of her body and onto the page where they could be really expressed. A lot of Birthtalk women, after getting over some initial uncertainty, have used this tool as a very clarifying form of understanding exactly where they are at. See our section *Using art as a healing tool* (p461).

- If you are angry with a specific person, perhaps someone involved with your care, the *Shifting from anger exercise* (p433) can be a fantastic tool. It can be a great way to explore what's going on, without involving the other person before you are emotionally strong enough to do so. This tool focuses on moving through a set of emotions beginning with anger, moving through sadness and regret to hope and love – keep in mind that you don't have to end up loving a person you are angry with! You may, however, come to a new understanding about just what specifically you are angry about, and how that has pent up your other emotions, and how much energy has been invested in this anger. It is a chance to move to a new place, where you can feel the anger without it taking you over completely.

- Sometimes, women find they are angry with their own child for the damages inflicted by the birth and the aftermath. We have dedicated a section specifically for this, and strongly encourage you to go there and explore it, as it is definitely possible to move through these feelings and create a new relationship with your child. See *I feel anger towards my child for 'causing' all this* (p172).

- Now may also be a good time to get your birth records and go over them, preferably with a midwife who can decipher the medical jargon, help collate the information and explain it to you in a way that you can understand and that relates to your situation. This can help you gain clarity over exactly what happened in the situation you are angry about. It may also bring to light new information about your birth that you had no idea about, which could affect your level of anger and how you deal with it. Go to our section *Retrieving your birth records* (p437) for information on how to get your records.

- Writing your birth story may also be helpful at this stage. Go to our section *Writing your birth story – a healing step* (p445).

# I FEEL ANGER TOWARDS MY CHILD FOR 'CAUSING' ALL THIS

*After my son's birth, I experienced a lot of anger. It was mostly directed at myself for not having the birth I had set myself up for. I felt ashamed of myself as I had agreed to having intervention that clearly harmed my son. In response to my own sadness and depression, I became angry at my baby for crying, taking it personally that I was unable to comfort him, wishing he would stop crying. I definitely had feelings of helplessness. Unable to comfort my crying son, I actually felt so desperate that I made a hole in the wall with a vacuum cleaner. I was also alone much of the time after the birth.* **Holly**

*He was baby number six. All the rest were awesome natural births. There is a big part of me that feels extremely resentful and I can't identify if it is resentment towards me or my gorgeous boy.* **Maria**

*I was ashamed about how I felt about my daughter and confused because I didn't feel as maternal as I had been all my life before. I loved my nieces much more than I did her.* **Thea**

*I do remember resenting my child as I wanted my pre-pregnancy life back. The panic attacks were a response to not coping, although this was not identified at the time. I was very conscious of adding the new role of 'mother' in my life. Having always had a career, I was uncomfortable about being one of those women who walk around shopping centres pushing a pram. It felt highly unnatural. I started to recognise that I was not bonding with my baby.* **Tina**

In this section, we explore the often unspoken situation where strong and scary emotions are felt towards your child.

If you are not feeling safe to be around your child in the immediate moment, take steps *right now* to defuse: go outside and breathe, take the phone with you and reach out to someone for support. If you have a friend who would understand, call her. If it feels like a crisis situation, or you don't know who to call, contact a national helpline. In Australia, Beyond Blue's phone number is 1300 224 636 and it has online facilities at *www.beyondblue.org.au* for immediate one-to-one support from a trained mental health professional.

If you feel able, pop your child in a pram or sling and go for a walk, even if it's raining. Just get an umbrella or pram cover and walk, get out of the house, go to the shops, anything to get out of your own head.

Feeling these strong emotions does not mean that you do not love your child. It usually means that your birth has impacted you more than you thought, and that it is time to process things so you can let go of the intensity of emotions you are experiencing. Take this book with you, and when you feel less anxious, keep reading.

It can be so confusing when feelings of resentment towards your baby bubble up after a traumatic birth. We find that this can be part of the response to a bad birth, where your emotions feel all muddled up, and you can't quite pinpoint who – or what – you are angry at. Couple that with comments from others that tell you that you 'should' be happy, and that 'all that matters is a healthy baby', and it can leave you feeling shut off, isolated and alone, not to mention confused.

Sometimes, women attend Birthtalk who share that they are feeling angry and resentful towards their child. Usually, they tell us of their resentful feelings and then they share that they know it is not their baby's fault, that their baby didn't ask to be born, yet they still feel this resentment anyway. We understand both things – the resentment *and* the confusion.

Parenting a young baby can be demanding and intense, regardless of how the birth went. It is extremely difficult when you have experienced a traumatic birth and are reeling from the fall out to be able to make sense of things. It can become very challenging to cope with day-to-day tasks. A bad birth can create a domino effect in your life; maybe relationships fail, your self-confidence plummets, your body is damaged or slow to recover, you experience panic attacks or nightmares, you can't sleep, you are hypervigilant in caring for your baby or your nerves might feel jangled – or any combination of the above, and more.

If you don't know about the possible effects of traumatic birth, or you don't recognise that your birth was traumatic, then you might look for something or someone to blame for all this fall-out. You or others may simply put it down to being 'just' birth, which is an incorrect, although understandable, assumption. It is not 'just' birth. A woman who has experienced a positive, empowering birth is unlikely to have to deal with the intensity of these challenges. For more on this go back to *The foundations of your healing journey* (p37) to see how a good birth impacts on the postnatal experience.

Sometimes, the finger can be pointed to the baby because before the baby's arrival you were fine. Even if you know that this does not make sense, even if this baby was wanted and longed-for, when everything goes so decidedly wrong it can be hard to know what else the cause might be, especially when people expect you to just 'get over it'. It couldn't possibly be the birth because 'people have babies all the time'.

We find that once women begin the healing journey and really explore the birth by taking the plunge and being brutally honest about their experience and the emotions surrounding it, and having the courage to face what happened, resentful feelings towards the child are often resolved.

After a traumatic birth it is common for feelings of anger and blame to arise. However, if you do not have an understanding of the issues surrounding traumatic birth, as most women don't, it is also common for those feelings to be misdirected. Most often, it is the woman's partner who bears the brunt of the anger. You can read about that in our chapter *Issues with your partner* (p291). Sometimes it is directed towards a particular health carer, which may or may not be justified. You can read about this in our section *I'm so angry with my health carers* (p163). Sometimes it is towards the woman herself. You can read about this in our section *Why did I agree to that epidural/episiotomy/caesarean etc.?* (p210). And, sometimes, it is directed towards the child.

We find it helpful for a woman to pull apart her emotions by getting really clear about what she is feeling resentful or angry about. This can give clarity about where she needs to focus in her healing journey, which can enable her to understand more about her birth, and remove the intensity of feelings towards her child.

## Trying to work through the confusion

Maria is mother to six children, all natural births except the last – a caesarean for breech. She wrote to us, asking if it was normal to 'not really understand how your baby got here after a caesarean'. She told us,

He was baby number six. All the rest were awesome natural births and he turned breech at thirty-eight weeks. There is a big part of me that feels extremely resentful and I can't identify if it's resentment towards me or my gorgeous boy. It's more me, I think. I was too scared to try for a natural birth because I felt like my body had already let me down once by 'letting' him turn. I didn't want to trust it again and have something go badly wrong.

We responded to Maria by sharing with her common impacts a caesarean birth can have from a hormonal point of view, where due to the lack of hormones, the usual bonding process can be interrupted, which could explain her feeling of being distanced from her baby and not really sure how he got here. See *I don't feel bonded to my child* (p218) for more on this.

We acknowledged Maria's resentment and shared with her that other women have felt similar. We shared that it was natural to feel muddled about it all because most women don't understand what is happening to them. We shared that we know from personal experience that this was not a good place to be in and made some suggestions for Maria to understand her emotions further, encouraging her to find a good counsellor to support her. This is part of the response we sent to Maria:

> *Perhaps try asking yourself specific questions and write down a host of answers that just bubble up, things like, "I am feeling resentful because…" or "I am angry because…". Our guess is that it could also be resentment due to no one telling you of the possible emotional fall out of a caesarean birth. And perhaps no one told you that there are ways to limit this fall out. And perhaps no one has listened as you have struggled to regain a relationship with your son and recover from the impact this has had? There is a fair bit to be resentful about there. And getting it out on paper can help to clarify just what you are feeling. Doing this can then lead to grief and sadness, yet this is part of the processing, so it can be really helpful.*

Maria wrote that she wished she'd been braver, so she and her last child, "… could have had the same experience together that I had with the rest of them". We responded that we could completely understand that. We also suggested that perhaps it was less about her being 'braver' and perhaps more about her needing to receive more support in exploring her options and addressing her concerns when decision making. We asked if she could imagine what might have been helpful for her to hear when decision making at the time.

## Feeling some relief

A short time later we received a long response from Maria that read, in part:

> *Thanks so much for your reply. It's given me some food for thought. As I sat there reading it I just cried, but in a good way, I think! I guess I have just shut it out but it was almost a relief to sit there and have a good bawl about it all. I feel this strange urge*

*to apologise to my baby, like I have done something wrong by him but desperately want to 'make it up' to him now. Feeling like that makes it clear to me that the resentment I talked about was pretty obviously directed at myself.*

*I recall everything being super-rushed because the nurse didn't want to get in trouble with theatre staff for being late, I was first up for the day and apparently if they start the first procedure late it puts the whole day out. I had another quick scan making sure he was still breech, and the whole time I was thinking how stupid could I have been to not feel him turn around the first time. I had such belief and trust in my body and my baby; we were supposed to be working towards this day together so what was this about? He hadn't moved, so off we go along a long corridor and by the time I get outside the theatre door, I am nothing short of hysterical and hyperventilating to try and keep myself under control. I knew, at least in my head, what was going to happen – the procedure itself had been explained – but at that moment all I could think of were the words 'maternal mortality rate'. This was my first time in a theatre – not ideal I guess. I felt like a real idiot. The women in birth stories I read had home-birthed breeches and the feelings they talked about were something I could identify with strongly, so why had I ended up here? Because I was too bloody scared to trust my body was the answer.*

*I recall thinking at one stage before it happened that the fact I'd already had such beautiful and amazing labours would negate this experience. I would just have to console myself with those and write it off. It didn't work like that though. It just made the crappy reality of the surgery even more cold and clinical.*

*Man, I walked away for a few minutes, now am back and read over all that. It's all a bit full on. In the middle of typing that I felt really, really angry. Now I just want to sit here and bawl again! I realise now that if I am totally honest, I don't want to just have to bury this and forget, and thanks to Birthtalk, I now feel like I don't have to try and make sense of the whole thing on my own, like this is a real and valid issue. Thanks again for your time!*

Maria was aware before contacting us that she felt resentment, although she was unsure whether it was towards her child or not. By understanding more about her situation she was able to begin to identify that her anger was actually directed at herself. She was also beginning the process of debriefing with people who understand (us!), which is an important step to clarity.

In her reply, Maria was beginning to do a *Birthtalk Breakdown* (p47), which we would have suggested as another step in her healing journey. This would likely enable her to have some compassion for herself and the situation she was in, and lead to her realise that her decisions were made with the information and level of support she had available to her at the time. It also was becoming clear where she was let down by her health carers, namely in the areas of information and support.

Importantly, this could allow her to move through her resentful feelings and refocus them to more accurate sources, and her resentment was no longer directed towards her child or herself.

## The importance of understanding and support

Other women have worked through these challenging and confusing feelings as well.

Tina, whose quote is at the start of this section, worked very hard to process the premature birth of her son, attending Birthtalk and undertaking an intense but profound healing journey. Tina shares more of her story towards healing and moving on in *My baby was premature* (p342). She shares one particular experience, which took place after she had unravelled aspects of her birth, explored her emotions and moved to a new place of healing:

> *The problem was I didn't know how to [bond with my baby].*
> *Birthtalk provided a few ideas. I sat down with my son one*
> *day. [Ed. See more about this process in Saying the words you*
> *couldn't say at the birth: a reconnection tool (p421). He was still in*
> *his cot from a sleep and I sat on the floor so I was down at his*
> *level. I discussed his birth and explained the circumstances and*
> *how much I loved him. I wasn't even sure he could hear me as*
> *his ears were playing up again. However, he looked me straight*
> *in the eye and gave me the hugest smile as if to say, "I love*
> *you too mummy". It was the best feeling and a connection*
> *definitely occurred. From that day forward our relationship has*
> *strengthened and, now, approaching five years of age, he is my*
> *little buddy!* **Tina**

Thea, who also is quoted at the beginning of this section reported that she, too, has made great inroads with bonding with her child after using many of Birthtalk's exercises and tools as part of understanding what happened to her during her child's birth.

Holly says her recount at the start of this section, "… feels far removed from who I am now". She tells more about her journey, "Although I did not ever harm my newborn son, or want to, I felt helpless, lost, alone and afraid. The fact that I had drugs during birth played a significant role in my guilty feelings, for not giving him the start I dreamed of. I felt angry for a while, but never felt like my son was to blame for me having drugs in the birth".

Holly was supported with her healing, "A friend brought over a doula who was able to help me debrief about my birthing experience. She helped me in ways my midwife didn't. I was able to process a lot of my anger and sadness". Holly's parenting journey also helped in her healing, "I had struggles in the early years that were reminders of my own childhood. My son has been a huge catalyst for healing much of my anger. This journey has brought me to really live compassionately and with unconditional love".

She wanted to share some advice for women who are experiencing anger towards themselves or their baby, "Please speak with trusted doulas or midwives. Get your fears and resentments out there. Don't hide, be heard. There is nothing more precious and important than a loving connection to yourself. From this place you can treat your baby with unimaginable love and respect and patience".

## Tools for healing and reconnecting

Our suggestion for a woman with strong feelings of resentment or anger towards her child is to try the ideas we offered to Maria:

Get clear on why you are feeling resentment and anger by writing a letter or two to your child that they will never receive.

- Get clear on what happened in your birth by doing a *Birthtalk Breakdown* (p47).
- Address any areas of grief or anger that arise by reading *I feel sad* (p245) and *I'm so angry with my health carers* (p163) and *Issues with your partner* (p291).
- Begin to explore how a bad birth can affect bonding and feelings of maternal instinct by reading *Why wouldn't my body work in labour?* (p230)
- Begin to forgive yourself by reading *Why did I agree to that epidural/ episiotomy/caesarean etc.?* (p210).
- Acknowledge how you are feeling, and find appropriate support if you feel you need help working through the strong emotions, or if you are struggling to care for your child. You both deserve to feel safe and nurtured. See *Appendix A* for support resources.

- Know that it is likely that your anger and resentment will subside as you process and heal, and honour this huge journey that you are on.
- See *I don't feel bonded to my child* (p218) for more ideas on how to reconnect with your child.

## Getting immediate support

### In Australia:

Beyond Blue
Phone: Call 24-hours a day, 7 days a week: 1300 22 4636
Online: *www.beyondblue.org.au/get-support/get-immediate-support*

Lifeline
Phone: 13 11 14
Online Crisis Chat: *www.lifeline.org.au/Get-Help/Online-Services/crisis-chat*

PANDA (Perinatal Anxiety and Depression Australia) helpline is available in Australia from 10am to 5pm (AEST) Monday to Friday. 1300 726 306 (Note : PANDA was formerly known as the Post and Antenatal Depression Association)

### In the UK:

From the Birth Trauma Association website *www.birthtraumaassociation.org.uk*

Samaritans: *www.samaritans.org*: UK: 08457 90 90 90 or ROI: 116 123 a 24-hour helpline; "If something's troubling you, then get in touch. Talk to us any time you like, in your own way, and off the record, about whatever's getting to you."

SANEline: *www.sane.org.uk* (0845 767 8000) "Our mental health support services are completely confidential. Whatever your problems or concerns, you will receive non-judgemental emotional support. Our professional staff and trained volunteers have specialist mental health knowledge; we can help you consider options for support that address your individual circumstances."

You can also call your GP surgery for advice. During out-of-hours, you should hear a recorded message giving advice as to who to call.

If you don't have a GP to call, NHS 111 is the NHS non-emergency number. It's fast, easy and free when you need medical help fast but it's not a 999 emergency.

The Birth Crisis Network is a help line in Britain, founded by Sheila Kitzinger, which women can ring if they want to talk about a traumatic birth. It provides more of a debriefing role, although hopefully they could support you in your immediate situation and direct you to further support if necessary. See *www.sheilakitzinger.com/birthcrisis.htm* for the most up-to-date contact information.

## In the US:

The National Suicide Prevention Line: 1-800-273-8255: a 24-hour helpline for people in emotional distress. It provides free and confidential emotional support to people in suicidal crisis or emotional distress 24-hours a day, 7 days a week. Your state's Crisis Prevention Helplines can be accessed by contacting the 24-hour helpline, which links to local crisis centres.

## Worldwide:

Befrienders Worldwide: *www.befrienders.org*: A network of 349 emotional support centres in 32 countries, spanning five continents. Befrienders Worldwide centres provide an open space for those in distress to talk and be heard. This support is via telephone helplines, SMS messaging, face-to-face, internet chat, outreach and local partnerships.

# I'M THINKING ABOUT MAKING A COMPLAINT OR TAKING LEGAL ACTION

The decision around whether to take action regarding the care you received in your birth is not an easy one. There are many considerations that must be taken into account before deciding. Firstly, you need to decide if you want to take a course of action at all, and then you need to decide which course of action is appropriate for your situation. We will explore three main types of action:

an informal letter of feedback to the practitioner and perhaps their institution or employer

* a formal lodgement of a notification of complaint to the appropriate agency
* seeking compensation by taking legal action.

It is also important to consider why you might decide not to take action – at least not yet.

## Why do you want to take action?

It is very important to be clear about your reasons for wanting to take action, and this clarity can be enhanced by asking two questions:

1.   What do you want to achieve?
2.   Is this outcome likely?

For example, you might hope that your letter or formal action makes changes in the workplace, or makes changes to an individual health professional's practice, or brings about a sense of peace for you, or makes you feel justice and that a price has been paid by the professional for the damage done, or you wish and hope that your letter or final action will redeem the pain caused within your family, or that a health professional knows how deeply and chronically their actions affected you, or you may want an apology, or you might want to protect other families, or you may want compensation or follow-up care provided, or you may just want to stop feeling so bad.

But are any of these outcomes likely? The answer to that question depends on a great many things. Results such as bringing about change within an institution or a health professional's practice, or heightening a carer's awareness of how their treatment impacted you are possible. Feeling that justice has been done or revenge was served is also possible. Receiving compensation for an injury may be possible. Receiving an apology is also possible. However, the likelihood of these is another issue, depending on variables that are individual to each situation and it is not guaranteed.

Importantly, these outcomes might not bring about the emotional peace of mind you are chasing. Even if you achieve these results, there is no guarantee it will lead to your improved emotional state or healing. That is, you might still feel bad. Which leads us to a third question to ask yourself before making any decisions: what will you do if you do not get the result you are aiming for?

What if, for example, you get told it's "all in your head", that "it didn't happen", that the practitioner acted within hospital guidelines, that there is no evidence of the issues you are highlighting, or that you don't have a case? These responses could be quite difficult to hear, especially if you are counting on this action to move your healing forward.

## A realistic initial goal

At Birthtalk, we believe it is important to get to a stage where you pretty much don't need any reply. This might sound like a cop-out, but let us explain. If you are reliant on a particular reply and a particular outcome to be able to move on, then they (the hospital or the health carer) have power over your healing; they have control over your happiness. If your birth involved feelings of being out-of-control, then you don't want these to rise up again.

For this reason, we recommend that your overall goal be initially focused on your own processing and healing. We recommend getting to an emotional position where, if you decide to take action, whatever result you achieve does not create further significant trauma. Taking the healing journey, using this book as a guide, can move you towards clarity about whether you will take action, what form that action will take and, importantly, being less reliant on a particular response.

## Going in angry?

In the section *I'm so angry with my health carers* (p163) we discuss that, while it may seem logical to haul your health professional over the coals, and let them hear, loud and clear, why you are angry and what they have done to you, it won't work. This is frustrating, but unfortunately true. Why won't it work? Because communicating aggressively may result in health professionals (understandably) becoming defensive, and focusing on protecting themselves.

As a result, they may not be able to hear your message, and could possibly write you off as being "unable to be reasoned with". So we recommend taking a deep breath, not sending any letters just yet and reading on.

## Lowering the intensity

Another reason why we recommend taking the healing journey first is that this process can reduce the intensity of the emotions surrounding the birth. Before you are in a position to express your situation and the fall out for you to someone in the health profession, you need to gain clarity for yourself. It is, ideal to lower the intensity to a level where you are not being emotionally stressed from it on a daily basis. This, in turn, can enable you to more effectively communicate your situation when, and if, you do take action.

Feeling less intense about your birth may seem unimaginable to you at the moment, but it is definitely possible. This book was written for just this reason, to support you in this process. Gaining clarity and lowering the intensity are often the results of undertaking the healing journey, so if you have not yet worked through the rest of the book, we encourage you to do so before writing any letters to health or legal professionals. You might want to start with *I'm so angry with my health carers* (p163) and *When health professionals don't get it* (p148).

At the same time, keep in mind that formal submissions of complaint can be restricted to within a certain timeframe after the birth or your awareness of a problem. See *Time limit for complaints*. This may mean that your healing journey is taken alongside exploring the best path of action to.

## Levels of complaint

The formality of a complaint can range from simply writing a letter to your health professional, to making a formal notification to the appropriate health agency, to taking legal action. The procedures for making a complaint varies from state to state, from country to country, and even from political climate to political climate. For example, procedures might change when a new government is elected). So, the options women currently have in Australia are outlined below to give you an idea of what you might expect.

## Current options in Australia:

1. *Sending a letter to the practitioner.* This might be the best course of action if your aim is simply to make the practitioner aware of the impact of their actions on your life since the birth, and perhaps to instigate some system changes within the hospital or within that professional's practice. It involves:

   - composing a letter outlining your experience during the pregnancy, birth and postnatal period and beyond
   - perhaps comparing your care to Australia's Health Rights Charter
   - outlining the impact of the experience on your life and your child's life postnatally
   - listing the response you would like from your practitioner.

   An example of such a letter and a link to the Australian Health Rights Charter, the US Consumer Bill of Rights, and the NHS Constitution of England, is in our section *Writing a letter of complaint* (p495).

2. *Completing a patient feedback form from your hospital,* and perhaps copying the hospital in on the letter to the health practitioner. All hospitals have a complaints contact, with titles such as Patient Representative, Patient Advocate, Patient Liaison Service, Consumer Liaison Officer, Compliments/Complaints, Quality Secretariat or similar, with contact details available via the hospital's website. Try using the search term 'Feedback' on their website.

3. *Making a complaint to your state's health complaints entity,* which is an independent investigative body. Each Australian state has a health complaints entity (HCE). The role of HCEs is "to resolve complaints or concerns, including through conciliation or mediation".[116] The HCEs "deal with concerns about health systems, health service providers (like hospitals or community health centres), fees and charges and compensation".[117] The current list of Australian HCEs is here: *www.ahpra.gov.au/Notifications/About-notifications/ Working-with-health-complaints-entities/Health-complaints-entities.aspx.*

   This path might be relevant if you have found that complaining to the hospital or the health practitioner did not result in a satisfying outcome, or if you do not feel comfortable with addressing the

---

116    Australian Health Practitioner Regulation Agency. *Working with health complaints entities.* Retrieved from *www.ahpra.gov.au/Notifications/About-notifications/Working-with-health-complaints-entities.aspx,* accessed March 2015.

117    ibid.

health practitioner directly or if you think it would be more beneficial to go through an independent body. You might take this path if you felt that your care, while perhaps following policy, was less than optimal, or that a hospital's policy needed to be challenged. Examples could be if they did not offer support for Vaginal Birth After Caesarean or if they routinely bathed your baby against your wishes. This option also may be considered if you felt that the hospital staff may be limited in their power to reprimand a visiting practitioner (like a private obstetrician), especially without a formal complaint lodged externally. You can check out some ideas for putting together a letter in *Writing a letter of complaint* (p495).

4. ***Making a formal notification to the Australian Health Practitioner Regulation Agency (AHPRA) (or relevant agency in your country).*** According to AHPRA, "'Notifications' are concerns or complaints about registered health practitioners"[118] and can be made about "a health practitioner's health, conduct or performance".[119] AHPRA and the National Boards' role is "to protect the public, including by managing notifications about health practitioners, and when necessary restricting their registration and their practice in some way."[120]

    AHPRA suggests that you might choose this option if you have a situation where, for example, your health professional "did not provide safe care because their standard of professional conduct was too low",[121] or where the health professional "does not have reasonable knowledge, skill or judgement or exercise enough care".[122]

    More information about AHPRA what notifications can be about is here; *http://www.ahpra.gov.au/Notifications/What-is-a-notification/What-can-notifications-be-about.aspx*

    A link to the form for completing a notification is here: *https://www.ahpra.gov.au/Notifications/Make-a-Notification.aspx*

5. ***Taking legal action*** by employing a solicitor who specialises in medical law. This step may be applicable or advisable if there is a physical injury to you or the baby, or another outcome for which there is a very overt and clear breach of practice, and evidence of negligence for which you are seeking

---

118   Australian Health Practitioner Regulation Agency. *About Notifications.* *http://www.ahpra.gov.au/Notifications/About-notifications.aspx* accessed August 2015

119   ibid.

120   Australian Health Practitioner Regulation Agency. *Working with health complaints entities.* op. cit.

121   Australian Health Practitioner Regulation Agency. *What can notifications be about?* *http://www.ahpra.gov.au/Notifications/What-is-a-notification/What-can-notifications-be-about.aspx* accessed August 2015

122   ibid.

compensation. It is outside the scope of this book to be able to advise you in this area, beyond what we have mentioned above. If this is the course of action you are investigating, we recommend meeting with a respected legal professional specialising in this area to explore your options.

## Time limits for complaints?

You also need to check out any potential limitations on the period of time you have in which to make a complaint. This may vary between different states and countries, so check with your own hospital or health services commissioner (or equivalent). As an example, in Queensland, according to the Queensland Health Ombudsman Act (2013), "At any time, the health ombudsman may decide to take no further action ... if the health ombudsman reasonably considers [that] the matter of the complaint arose, and the complainant was aware of the matter, at least 2 years before the complaint was made."[123] However, this does not apply if the ombudsman "reasonably considers a registered health practitioner may have behaved in a way that constitutes professional misconduct."[124] Another state's health department explained to us in a phone conversation that if it has taken a woman longer than a year to complain for a good reason, such as dealing with a baby or due to her experience of emotional trauma, it would be worth attempting to complain and asking for flexibility on the time limit.

A further consideration is the length of time your chart will be held on file by your health service provider. In the short term, it may easily be accessed within the maternity unit and then it will be archived in the hospital for a required retention period. This period also varies between countries and states, with the most common timeframe between five to ten years, taken from your most recent health service provision. If the file belongs to a minor (as your baby's file does) then it is generally required to be kept for a period of time after they reach adulthood. In most parts of Australia, this age is 25 years. It is important to note that your child's file may just have a summary of the labour and birth rather than the full details along with their outcomes, plus any ongoing care. For specific Australian state or territory general medical record retention requirements, refer to the link at the end of this section. Retrieval of files may incur a fee, which currently in Australia is around $30 in most public hospitals, but it varies for private hospitals.

123   Queensland Health Ombudsman Act 2013, *Act No. 36 of 2013* , Section 44, Subsection (1)(b)(iii)
      *https://www.legislation.qld.gov.au/LEGISLTN/ACTS/2013/13AC036.pdf* Accessed July 2015

124   Queensland Health Ombudsman Act 2013, *Act No. 36 of 2013*, Section 44, Subsection (2)(a)
      *https://www.legislation.qld.gov.au/LEGISLTN/ACTS/2013/13AC036.pdf* Accessed July 2015

For more information about retrieving your medical records, see *Retrieving your birth records* (p437).

Please note that legal actions are also subject to time limits, although there are exceptions. If you are considering bringing a legal action, please seek legal advice about the relevant time limits for your situation.

## What is the most I can hope to achieve?

As we said above, the first question is, "What do you want to achieve?" More insights can be gained, however, from asking, "What is the most that you can HOPE to achieve?" Knowing the answer to this may affect the course of action you choose. Below we will look at why taking action might not be beneficial.

## Issues surrounding liability

In the area of maternal health it can be challenging to establish liability. Often it can be problematic to establish your health professional's liability unless there is strong evidence:

that their actions led to easily identifiable or objectively measured negative outcomes, e.g. mortality (death) and morbidity (illness, injury or infection) or

1.  that their actions went against 'accepted practice'.
2.  In *Appendix A* we have a summary of potential situations you could claim for. This section was compiled with the assistance of Dr Rhonda Powell, School of Law, University of Canterbury.

## Evidence-based practice vs accepted practice

Most people assume that all health carers would have to use the latest evidence as the basis for making decisions and the formation of hospital policies and protocols, yet often this doesn't happen. There can be much dispute over what is considered good evidence. For more on this see the *'Note about evidence'* at the end of this section.

One of the limitations of an institution such as a hospital is that it often takes many years for the latest evidence to become 'accepted practice' and upheld by all staff. There are many implementation challenges for institutions, for example formulating updated policies and rolling out education to retrain staff, while considering the cost-effective, efficient running of the institution.

Accepted practice describes how a health professional's peers would handle a particular situation, regardless of whether that practice is actually evidence-based or not. In a legal situation, a health professional is often held more accountable if their actions are outside accepted practice (what their peers are doing), rather than if their actions are outside current evidence-based practice.

Some examples of areas where this gap exists between evidence-based practice and accepted practice include the use of routine CTG* on admission, routine cannulation on admission for low-risk women and withholding food from labouring women, to name a few.

So, if your case came before an expert panel of doctors or midwives who use a similar practice to the one you are complaining about, regardless of the latest evidence, then the accused health professional may still be considered as practising within accepted practice standards and probably will not be reprimanded, but possibly only directed to reflect on their practice. Unfortunately, this can be the reality of the situation within the review processes of the institution or the regulatory body for a particular health professional or within the legal system.

For this reason, you need to consider whether your situation is likely to be acknowledged as a breach of accepted practice or not.

## Was it worth it?

We interviewed some women who have taken various forms of action, where they share their experience and reflect on the process. Their encounters may give you more food for thought in your own decision making. Keep in mind that these women all received differing responses to the actions they took. This is due not only to the differing experiences they encountered and the circumstances surrounding each case, but, inevitably, to the nature of the person or system responding to each letter or action.

### Marta wrote an informal letter of complaint to her GP, her obstetrician and the hospital:

*I wrote a letter to both my GP and my ob/gyn and the hospital in which the birth took place. I did this after receiving my medical records through the Freedom of Information Act, to make sure I had all the facts right prior to writing the letters. My motivations for writing these letters was to hopefully find that they would help with the healing process by helping me be able to truly*

---

*Cardiotocography, often referred to as continuous monitoring.

*understand my journey and advise my care providers how upset and traumatic the birth actually was and [hopefully] they might actually care enough not to make any other mother-to-be feel like I felt.*

*In the case of the hospital in which I birthed, I received a letter in response, offering free counselling services, which I found very helpful and very appropriate. I was relieved that I was acknowledged that something did go wrong, and they wanted to help make things right again with me. I was extremely disappointed that my obstetrician didn't follow up after receiving my letter. I have not seen him since.*

*The process of receiving my medical notes from my birth, processing them and physically writing how I felt about what happened during my birth was very overwhelming and frustrating but definitely worthwhile. I would say the process of taking action has affected me and my family emotionally. My husband and I went through the medical notes and it brought up a lot of memories from the birth. My husband wasn't able to get home in time to be there for my daughter's birth, so he got very emotional and actually knows everything that happened now and how bad everything was. He was the one who recommended me writing the letters, and I'm so glad he did!*

*The pros of sending the letters are that I find it's helped me to actually get help for my PTSD surrounding my birth. And now my obstetrician and the hospital know how upsetting my birth was to me and how I've felt about it after that time. Also, by writing a letter, I wasn't interrupted or upset by anyone giving me excuses for why it happened the way it did, I got to get everything on paper! The only con to writing the letter would be having to read through everything for the first time after her birth. Having to re-live everything all over again somewhat.*

*The advice I would give to other women thinking about taking this step is: get your medical records and notes to understand and process your journey. Go through it with a health-care provider and if you have any questions, don't be afraid to take notes. Most hospitals have mediation and legal sections where you can sit down and talk about what happened and why. I strongly suggest using this team if you can to understand your notes better.*

*I found just writing the letter very healing for me and I wasn't
initially going to act on it. I had it sitting on the top of the fridge,
addressed and ready to go for about a month before I actually sent
it. But then, I realised that the obstetrician wouldn't know how
I really felt and what I actually went through as a patient, and
I decided he needed to know and I couldn't sit down and face him
at that point. A letter was the best way to do that! I am glad I did.
It has helped so much in my healing process.*

Note: We discuss the benefits of writing letters that you might not send, as Marta discusses, in
our section *The unsent letter* (p468) and we provide information about retrieving your birth
notes and using this in your healing journey in our section *Retrieving your birth records: how to
get them and what to do with them* (p437).

## Savannah shares her experience with making a formal complaint via her Health Complaints Entity

*I made a complaint to the HQCC (my local Health Complaints
Entity) about my doctor. I got a response, but it wasn't all
that satisfying. What I wanted was for him to own his actions
and apologise for the way he treated me, but what I got was a
third-person expression of sympathy for the fact that my labour
didn't turn out the way I wanted. I'm so, so angry about what
was done to me, and I still find it difficult to believe that in an
Australian hospital, in this day and age, a person can be bullied/
forced/coerced into accepting drugs and procedures when they
are clearly not agreed to. Since when did "no" become "yes"?
Surely that's against the law? In any other context, that would be
against the law. Why is it acceptable just because I'm in a hospital,
and he's a doctor? I can't tell you how many times I said I didn't
want Syntocinon, but they just kept pushing and pushing until
I couldn't fight it any more. To my mind, in no way does that
constitute informed consent. I feel so incredibly violated.*

*I can't think of a single thing that was good about complaining
to the HQCC. The investigator who handled my complaint was
biased in favour of the doctor. Towards the end of the process, she
told me over the phone that she'd spoken at length to him and
had a good result. He was going to send me a letter of apology.
When I asked her what he'd said, she started with (and I quote!),
"He was actually very sweet". That was pretty much the end
for me. Any hope that I might get some closure, that he would
actually step up and own his actions that night, were dashed.*

*And it was a very, very bitter pill to have to swallow. Waiting for the letter to appear in the mail was terrible, and reading the condescending words when it finally did arrive was even worse.*

*I didn't take it any further. To be honest, I was quite scared of the hospital after what they'd done to me and at the time, the thought of any further contact with them was just a bit terrifying to say the least. It just got to a point where I finally had to accept I was never going to get anything back from the system or anyone in it. I had a baby I had to take care of, and I realised that I was going to have to dig myself out of the hole and move on – difficult as that was – because no one was going to do it for me.*

## Helen and her husband took difficult steps that led to change, after their child's birth

*The birth of our first baby turned into some kind of nightmare. Basically, our midwife called in sick, and a 'ring in' midwife turned up. She didn't share in the natural birthing philosophy of the birth centre, and she wasn't gentle or supportive in her approach. We were forced into having interventions we didn't need or want. The trauma stayed with us for months afterwards, and we wondered how we would ever recover, let alone have another baby. We had trusted our birth centre, and they let us down!*

*Two weeks post-birth we had a debrief meeting with our team of midwives, and they were horrified to hear our story. They encouraged us to apply for my medical records, and they even helped me go through them to understand what had happened.*

*I was so disappointed and furious, and I felt sure that this couldn't happen to another woman. I wrote a powerful and heartfelt complaint letter to the director of the hospital. I raised every issue we encountered, and offered real solutions to each problem. I told them we expected changes to happen, and that we had taken legal advice.*

*The hospital offered us an immediate meeting to discuss the problems. I think they were worried we were going to sue them. We were terrified and stressed out about reliving the details all over again. But we knew we had to do it! We had some counselling sessions with a wonderful lady who specialises in birth trauma to help us mentally prepare for the meeting. We went in with a list of objectives that we wanted them to action.*

*Our requests were:*

1. *Immediately fire the midwife who had mistreated us.*

2. *Fix my perineum stitches quickly, for free.*

3. *Free counselling sessions to help us recover from the trauma.*

4. *A promise that all birth centre clients would be told that their midwife may not turn up, and they could get a 'ring in' who has no idea. (We had no idea this could happen, with three midwives on our team, we assumed one would come when we needed her.)*

5. *To skip the waiting list for an eye specialist appointment for our baby son.*

*In attendance at the meeting were the Director of Gynaecology and Obstetrics, the Director of Surgeons, the Director of the Complaints Service, the Director of the Birth Centre, and Director of Counselling Services. First they apologised, then they tried to minimise our story, like, 'maybe you are a little confused' or, 'it's easy to get the story mixed up'. Well that made me furious! My partner and I told them very clearly what had happened, with tears streaming down both of our faces. There was definitely no 'mix up' in our story. Eventually they asked what they could do to 'make it better'.*

*I handed each director a copy of our list of objectives, and told them this is what we wanted to happen. I think they were a little surprised that we came so prepared! They said they would look over it and get back to us. They called us in for a second and then a third meeting. After about one month, four out of our five requests were actioned. We organised the fifth one, the eye specialist, ourselves.*

*We felt somewhat empowered. While there is no way of undoing the trauma they caused us, we did make them listen. We felt they were genuinely sorry, and they did take the actions we requested. We believe our complaint was worth all of the effort. And we did make a small difference.*

*Now, every woman at that birth centre signs a form to say she understands that her midwives may not show up. While this doesn't fix the problem of not having enough staff, it does give women a chance to make a Plan B for themselves. I wish I had been given that information before our birth. I would have employed a doula to be my support person, instead of relying solely on my midwife.*

*We feel satisfied that they heard us. And after another meeting with the Director of the Birth Centre, and a long discussion with our wonderful doula, we chose to trust the same birth centre with our second birth. (It is the only birth centre in our city!) And they were wonderful, supportive and nurturing. Just like we had expected for our first birth.*

## Sasha took steps as part of her counselling for PTSD

*I made the brave steps of entering counselling, getting my hospital notes, debriefing with my private midwife, researching about the factors that existed around my birth, arranging a meeting with the hospital complaints person, writing my story down, sharing my story with the hospital complaints person, and facing the head nurses at the hospital in a personal meeting. This was a long process that took a number of months. I see it as the beginning of my journey to healing, one which continued with marital counselling and personal therapy from a psychologist, which is now entering its third year. At this time I would say I am in 'remission' from PTSD but still using some supports to stay well.*

*The reason I took these steps was that I was being supported by a counsellor to manage debilitating PTSD at the time I took action. Being in counselling was a major motivator – if I hadn't been in counselling I doubt I would have ever spoken up. As it was, my whole life was in crisis and I was barely able to function so things were at a point where I was either going to get myself help, or ultimately get helped by social services.*

*I decided as a result of that therapy that being heard by the hospital would be a positive, but even if they chose NOT to hear me, speaking up – allowing myself to have a CHANCE at being heard – was a step I WANTED to take. I had felt so voiceless, just the act of complaining in itself was a huge step for me, to 'own my own voice'.*

*The response from the hospital far exceeded my expectations. At first it was extremely hard to get any words out but the hospital's liaison person was very patient with me. She saw how difficult I was finding it to tell my story and suggested I try writing it and sending it to her before meeting again. I did that and it was a process that let me release a lot of hurt that was trapped inside me. Up until that point I had been unable to write, speak or even think about the WHOLE story because the emotions were just too overwhelming. Ironically, the hospital at the centre of my trauma was also the catalyst to resolving it!*

*After writing the story and meeting again I decided with the patient liaison that I wanted the story shared with the head of the hospital midwifery service and the senior nurse in charge of the ward where I was. That meeting was also an important one. I can't say that I got EXACTLY what I wanted. What I wanted, at the time, was for them to agree 100% with my perspective. That wasn't what I got, and in retrospect that wasn't a reasonable expectation. What I did get though, was two women who were mothers just like me, and who sat and listened to me cry and rage and thump my fist on the table (oh yes, I did!) without becoming defensive once. It was a good experience and I felt heard, which was the most important. I should add that the hospital is looking at upgrading their facilities in postnatal rooms as a result of my feedback.*

*This process is very hard. Whether to go through it or not has to be a personal decision. I would say if you are coping and don't feel like you want to go there, then don't. Being in control is important and it could be detrimental to dig up wounds if you are not ready to do so, and don't have good support.*

*My advice to others: your health provider may never agree, you may not be heard, but it doesn't really matter. The gift you can give yourself in speaking out is to realise you have a perfectly good, valid voice. Value it for its own sake even if others don't, and it will give you strength. Secondly, get support from someone who will be in your corner regardless of what the outcome of debriefing is. My counsellor (first) and now my psychologist have constantly reminded me of my own strength and worth as a person and that has allowed me the emotional freedom to complete my own healing.*

**Jade spoke about the journey she and her husband have been on, taking action on behalf of their daughter, who has cerebral palsy**

*We are taking legal action and went down the complaints avenue. We've been through the hospital's complaints process, which was a complete waste of time, and [we have] been to our state's Health Complaints Entity and AHPRA to complain about the midwife. AHPRA's investigation has been ongoing for more than three years! The last time I bugged them they said that our case was going national and it will mean that it will take even longer. We need to wait on AHPRA's findings to go to the Health Ombudsman or the press. We are not primarily suing for the birth trauma but for damages to our child, which had been caused by negligence (severe loss of oxygen). Secondarily, we are suing for compensation of loss of income and psychological damage due to PTSD.*

*We chose the hospital's complaints system because we wanted to improve the hospital's care, and act as some sort of a patient advocate to prevent what happened to us from happening again. We wanted full disclosure of the midwifery team to know why nobody reacted to our repeatedly voiced concerns that our daughter was showing signs of seizures and hypoxia (becoming lifeless and blue). The midwife at the time was writing notes at a desk nearby.*

*We are seeking legal compensation because our daughter is now disabled with cerebral palsy and will need therapy and treatment for the rest of her life. We are primarily seeking monetary compensation for these costs. Our secondary motivation is that we wanted to be a bigger 'pain in the ass' for the hospital in the hope of changing something this way (which we were told by everyone is a waste of time but we are pursuing it nevertheless). And then, AHPRA is the last avenue of complaint for us. We have complained about the midwife who did not react and behaved really badly as well all throughout labour and afterwards also. She was a complete bully.*

*The whole process has been very frustrating, lengthy and actually very bad for the healing as we are not able to move on because we keep being dragged into the trauma and pain. The hospital is not admitting to any wrongdoing and we have been invalidated, ridiculed and intimidated in the mediation process with the hospital, which is why we stopped it and are now pursuing things legally. We believe the only reason that the hospital has a mediation team is to deflect any potential lawsuits. They did nothing but brown nosing and deflecting.*

*[As a result of this process] my trust in medical professionals is shattered. I feel incapable of daring another pregnancy for fear of repeating the birth trauma. The invalidation ("This is all in your heads; we are not at fault") was devastating for the PTSD, as it threw me back again and I had to have higher doses of medication and subsequent therapy.*

*Pros and cons? There are not many 'pros' for me at this point in time – maybe further down the track once the legal case and AHPRA complaint is over. Well, there would be monetary compensation although I have been told that the compensation for pain and suffering is negligible and does not justify the expenses – currently at about $15,000 (apparently if you go for a pre-trial settlement and your child fortunately is doing reasonably well, your damages are very moderate\*). Even the PTSD claim is deemed not necessarily economically viable. We are doing it for the sake of justice taking place. Hopefully I'll get a sense of closure and of justice being served. I do have a sense of empowerment, knowing I have had the strength and courage to take on Goliath – even if we only tried.*

*I'm still hoping for admittance of guilt and responsibility for what happened (which we are again told is not going to happen) so I don't have to blame myself.*

*The cons? It costs loads of money to take legal action! Expert reports alone cost us about $20,000 to $30,000. The lawyers will only charge if we get a settlement so (to speak in monetary terms) we break even if the hospital is willing to pay us about $40,000 to $50,000.*

*It triggers you every time you have to focus on the case. You live your life and keep being dragged in. Last time it really triggered my PTSD by looking at the MRI images that had been taken shortly after birth. I can actually SEE into my child's head and see the bleeds… not nice to see.*

*Also, it all takes so much time! And can be very frustrating – you cannot move on for years, as long as the legal case is open. In our case it will be for some time to come still as the damage to the brain can still manifest itself in other neurological conditions such as epilepsy. We can only push forward with the settlement and trial once our daughter's condition has stabilised, which won't be until she is about six or seven years old, which means six or seven years of not being able to move on. The other side uses mean tactics, invalidation, and denial in order to get out of paying, which is also not good for your mental health.*

*The advice I would give to others considering this path is: think twice before taking legal action. I would not sue for birth trauma unless you have a rock-hard case, which is absolutely clear cut. It is very lengthy, emotionally draining and you are very likely not going to get the things out of it that you want. If lucky, you get some monetary compensation, which you pay very dearly for with quality of life. Everyone who had been through the process of legal action said the same thing to me – leave it be, if you can live with it somehow. Back in the days when we decided to sue the hospital, I could not live with the injustice. Now, after about four and a half years and a move across the planet, I pretty much can... but prefer to go through with it because I believe I owe it to my daughter to provide her with the funds she will need to cater for her special needs.*

### Katrina's baby has Erb's palsy due to the circumstances surrounding his birth in the UK. She shares her experience

*Three years on from the birth and we're still at the beginning of the legal process. It's something that is going to take many years to resolve. So far, the process has been difficult, challenging and frustrating! Despite the fact that hospitals almost always pay out claims like ours, the hospital has so far denied all allegations of medical negligence, apart from one aspect about inadequate note-taking. That one admission is purely so they can maintain the lie that I was given certain warnings that I in fact wasn't given.*

*There are aspects of the birth that we are unable to challenge because of the medical records. That is incredibly frustrating given that the notes are inconsistent with the memories of myself and my husband.*

*Going through the legal process helps the healing to a degree, because of the knowledge that at some stage those who were involved will have to think back about it and be accountable for what happened. Yet at the same time it is incredibly painful to have to re-live it all and have it dissected for the legal advisers to understand what happened and for the necessary legal processes, such as witness statements etc.*

*The reasons I embarked on the legal route were two-fold. I wanted to make those responsible for the injuries my son and I suffered accountable for their actions. But I also wanted to secure some money for my darling boy's pain and suffering throughout his countless therapies and surgeries – and for his future needs. He may need more surgery and he may need extra help at school. He might need adaptations to, for example a car, when he gets older. The money he hopefully gets will go some way to assisting him.*

*The advice I would give to mums thinking of embarking on the legal route would be to find solicitors who really understand the injuries that you or your child have suffered. Some injuries (like my son's) are not generally well understood even within the medical field, so it is crucial for the solicitors to understand the birthing process, how it can go wrong, and the relevant injuries (and subsequent treatments), for them to be able to adequately represent your child's interests. Also, I would advise mums to write down, as soon as possible, everything you can remember, whether you think it will be relevant or not. Traumatic memories do unfortunately remain but the precise details can fade over time and although it is incredibly difficult to write things down, it is very important to record everything while matters are still completely fresh in your mind. Even if you don't end up taking action yourself, if your child has suffered injuries it may be that, in time, they want to take legal action. After a long passage of time, the medical notes become all that is really relevant. The medical notes can be inaccurate! A contemporaneous account of what happened may be crucial.*

### Kate wrote a letter to her homebirth midwife after a homebirth that ended in a transfer and a caesarean

*My only form of action was the letter I wrote to my midwife and the back-up midwife. I had an informal talk with my ob/gyn at six-weeks postpartum about his role in it, but really there wasn't much to say as he was mostly kind. There was nothing to be done legally. My difficulties were mostly a result of their poor treatment of me. The caesarean would likely have been the outcome even if they had been competent.*

*I wrote the letter because I needed to tell them how they hurt me. I needed them to know that their behaviour was not acceptable. I honestly shared my feelings with them because I wanted to help them be better. I also wanted an apology; although when I wrote the letter I was pretty sure it wasn't going to be forthcoming. For me, part of sending this letter was taking back my voice that I had lost.*

*Their response was a joke. I've never heard back from the second midwife, since she left my hospital room. The main midwife only replied eight months after I sent the letter because I asked someone else to contact her for my medical records. My feeling was that she was worried that I was maligning her so she was attempting damage control. None of our correspondence felt genuine. Her timing of her contact with me, her decision to not respond to my letter, and her wording were all completely unprofessional.*

*The process was both worthwhile and frustrating. The midwife's response to me was frustrating but it also allowed me to let go of some emotions. I got to tell her how I felt, and how her actions affected me. I can't control what she does with that but I can control what I do with it. In the end, even her terrible response gave me closure to know that she really did feel such disregard for me, to know that I wasn't imagining all of it.*

*The PPD (postpartum depression) and PTSD were much harder on our family than the process of writing this letter. However, I will say that shortly after I sent them the letter I realised that they weren't going to respond. It hurt. I trusted these women with my life and the life of my child. I thought we were not just professional acquaintances but also friends, as many midwives and women become. I had been keeping my head above water, so to speak, with the PPD before the letter, but that realisation that they simply did not care drove me to suicidal depression. It was the last weight that was added to me and I could no longer maintain myself. I don't particularly blame them for my reaction – let's just be honest, I was pretty close anyway – but they did have an effect. My husband suffered greatly during my depression and he still struggles now, even though I have recovered.*

*The benefits of writing the letter are that you can have your voice heard. You get your chance to say what you need to say and with a letter no one can cut you off or interrupt. BUT the hard part is knowing that you can't control what they do with it – they may or may not read it and they may or may not respond. Knowing for sure that your care provider isn't going to give you the time of day unless it kills them can be very painful, especially if you previously had a good relationship. It's about the type of closure you want.*

*The advice I would give is to write a first draft. Know that this draft is not what you are sending. In fact, that first draft will likely look nothing like what you intend to send. Don't try to make it that. Use the first and second and third drafts, however many drafts you need, to work through some really heavy emotions. Then, when you can write the letter clearly, give it a shot. It's okay to tell them how their actions made you feel. That's valuable feedback for them, should they care to improve their practice or your relationship. Have trusted friends or family read it. Make sure it addresses what you want it to address. Know why you are sending that letter. Asking others to proof it and then talking about it helps make sure that the letter is clear and concise. [Women need to think about] if they are ready for what could be a nice response (the one we want to get when we start writing), no response, or a hateful response. Don't just think about it for 30 seconds, but really sit with how these things would affect you. My only encouragement would be to say that if you feel like it's important to do – it is. You are the only person who can make that choice for you and if this is what you want, then you have every right to pursue it.*

*Note: These women's stories are provided to illustrate a variety of experiences in taking action after a traumatic birth, and do not constitute legal advice. Please be aware that these women's stories represent their own experiences, at different times, in different parts of the world with a variety of legal systems. The information provided may not accurately represent the legal system in your own state and country at this time. We recommend consulting a respected legal professional to access accurate legal advice for your own situation.

## Which way forward?

If you've spent some time processing your birth and exploring the different sections of this book, then you are likely gaining some insights about what happened in your birth. You have likely also lowered your own intensity and are beginning to really understand what you are upset about and where you believe your carers may have let you down. And so it might be time to consider taking some action.

As we said earlier, it depends on what you want to achieve; however, with a new understanding of what is achievable, and some progress along the path to healing, you may be getting closer to finding an answer to this question.

## The most important thing

In the end, the most important thing is to preserve your emotional health and your ability to function as a mother and a partner and a woman. It is up to you to figure out if any of this is at stake in making your decisions, and to decide how you will cope as a family, especially if things become difficult in the process. We wish you the best as you take on this challenge of figuring out what is best for you and your family.

## Note about evidence

The 'gold standard' of evidence is a randomised controlled trial (RCT), where women are randomly assigned to a research group. However, RCTs are often impossible to do in many aspects of birth care. This is because there are so many subjective variables involved in the life experience of birth, and randomisation is often unethical because it requires one half of the group randomly being chosen to receive or miss out on a certain type of care. This evidence is often the only type considered when reviewing the care women receive, meaning that, in many areas of maternity care, there appears to be 'no good evidence', because there might not be RCTs in this particular area.

There are other sources of knowledge and observation, such as systematic reviews and retrospective studies. Systematic reviews are a summary of the results of several studies referring to the same specific question, for example the Cochrane Reviews, which are "systematic reviews of primary research... recognized internationally as the highest standard in evidence-based health care".[125] Retrospective studies are where researchers look back through hospital records to create statistics, for example, looking at how many women have an epidural and then go on to have a surgical birth. These reviews and studies are not considered as valuable as randomised controlled studies because not all variables can be excluded. So all we can say is that there appears to be a

---

125    Cochrane Community (beta). *Cochrane Reviews*. Retrieved from *www.community.cochrane.org/cochrane-reviews*, accessed March 2015.

very strong correlation between the two. However, when these reviews and studies repeatedly give us similar information, this broader context of evidence should consistently be strongly considered in determining and assessing care provision, but, unfortunately, it is often used selectively. Another challenge that arises is the common time-lapse before new evidence becomes accepted practice. As a result, care based on relatively recent evidence may not be known or acknowledged by many peers called to provide expert witness statements to determine acceptable practice.

## Links

Australian state and territory general medical record retention requirements *www.yourhealth.gov.au/internet/yourhealth/publishing.nsf/Content/ pcehrlegals-document-toc~pcehrlegals-document-app04#.UszSi_09Wai*

Australian Charter of Healthcare Rights *www.safetyandquality.gov.au/national-priorities/charter-of-healthcare-rights/.*

UK Rights in pregnancy and childbirth *www.birthrights.org.uk/advice/your-rights/*

US Rights in pregnancy and childbirth *http://humanrightsinchildbirth.com*, run by an American lawyer.

# I feel guilty

## EVERYONE KEEPS TELLING ME I SHOULD BE GRATEFUL

*My friends and family said, "You usually get on with things – come on, you have a healthy baby and you got your natural birth, so why are you still worrying about this?* **Sally**

*I went to a GP for depression at the start of the journey and he just didn't get it. He kept talking about how I had a healthy child and I didn't die in childbirth etc. He had no idea why what I have been through could possibly still be following me around four years later. I spent most of that session explaining to him how birth trauma was disenfranchised.* **Leonie**

*If I tried to talk to my hubby, he thought it was my problem and I had to sort it myself, as all he could see was a healthy mum and bub. This made me feel anger towards him.* **Sophie**

*I found it hard to find people who understood, as everyone just expects you to be happy because you have a healthy baby.* **Skye**

## What you need to know

Chances are, if you are reading this book, you are *not* fine. You may be alive and physically okay, but that doesn't mean you are 'fine'. People always say, "Healthy mother, healthy baby – that's all that matters."

But a healthy mother has to mean 'one who is healthy emotionally'.

When you think about it, why *should* you feel grateful for a traumatic experience? Of course you are grateful for your baby. And of course you are grateful that you and your baby are alive.

But it makes *no sense* to feel gratitude for experiencing a situation where you felt out-of-control, unable to ask questions, unsafe and frightened.

It is *right* that you would want to process that, and talk about it, and share how it has impacted upon you. Yet often no one can listen. Which brings us back to what our culture considers to be 'normal birth'. (See *Why doesn't anyone get it?* (p129))

Our culture is so conditioned to expecting that a woman birthing *will* feel out-of-control, unable to ask questions, unsafe and frightened that people are sometimes a bit affronted that you would question that by raising any disappointment, or trauma, resulting from your birth. There is a sense of, "Everyone has to go through it – why should you get any special treatment?" But this shows a *huge* misunderstanding and poor education about birth.

You are not asking for special treatment. You are asking for acknowledgement and validation and are trying to make sense of an enormous event that has had a significant impact on your life. As you rightly should.

People are sometimes trying to be supportive by trying to identify a positive from your situation. Yet somehow, that message gets lost in any comment that starts with, "At least…" or "You should…"

The reality is these comments make no sense. It is as if receiving a 'healthy baby' is supposed to 'clean the slate' for whatever trauma the woman had to deal with during the birth. But it doesn't work like that.

Let's say a friend of yours was in a car that lost its brakes and became out-of-control, veering across both lanes and barely missing a traffic pole, before slamming into a hedge. Your friend emerges physically unscathed, except for a few scratches and bruises and a huge attack of the shakes afterwards. Would you smile and just say, "I'm glad you're okay" and expect them to just pick up and carry on? Or would you enquire about how they are doing or feeling about it all? Would you allow them to them retell their story while empathising with something like, "I'm glad you weren't hurt. That sounds totally full-on. I can't believe it wasn't worse. You must have had the biggest fright". And would you offer help and support over the next few days if needed?

Or would you just say, "You should be grateful it wasn't worse!"

Most of us wouldn't say that – it just wouldn't be kind. We would acknowledge it as a scary, freaky experience that could possibly have an emotional impact. And being given a newborn at the end of it all would not lessen the shock and the need for processing that your friend may have.

So consider what happens when birth is scary, freaky and out-of-control. There is an expectation that being presented with a healthy child will remove the impact of those roller-coaster feelings and negate any need for processing. It goes without saying that a woman is grateful for the life and health of her child. Telling her, "At least…" or "You should…" can induce feelings of guilt and shame for daring to share that she had a bad experience.

The difference is people in our culture *know* that cars aren't supposed to lose their brakes and go out-of-control, and to have that happen is *not normal* and *could have an impact* emotionally. So they are better able to imagine what it may have been like and say something that is acknowledging and supportive.

However, because our culture *expects* birth to be out-of-control and scary and involve feelings of helplessness and fear, people *don't know* what to say if you talk about the impact of that, because then they would have to acknowledge that *it could be different.*

You are not being 'greedy' or 'needy' by wanting to feel safe and acknowledged and supported during birth.

That's how it's supposed to be.

Yet sometimes, especially for our mothers, this can be unfathomable. Women birthing in the previous generation often felt all those feelings of a bad birth (see *Dealing with your family's birth legacy* (p491)), because of the restrictions and the culture of birthing back then. And *no one talked about it*. Now here you are, daring to put forth that you are suffering emotionally after your experience. It could well be outside your mother's realm of understanding and experience. (See *Why doesn't anyone get it?* (p129))

So, what are you to do when people say those time-honoured but damaging platitudes of, "You should be grateful," and the like? See below for some ideas.

## Tools for dealing with the 'healthy mum, healthy baby' comment:

- It can help to make sure you are really clear on the issues, yourself. Start by reading *Why doesn't anyone get it?* (p129), then *My partner wants me to 'just get over it' and move on* (p303) and *Why don't my friends feel bad about their births?* (p142).

- Make sure you have read the chapter *The foundations of your healing journey* (p37). The sections in this chapter will give you some insights into good versus bad birth and make it easier for you to understand your own experience, which then makes it easier to express it to others.

- Once you are clear, you can make it clear to others. Sometimes to receive appropriate support we need to educate those around us. Giving them this book can be a great start, although it is not always possible. We outline some ways to stop them in their tracks, and get the focus on the real issue, which has *nothing* to do with you 'being ungrateful'.

- Keep in mind, you might find that it is *not* helpful for you to share too much about what's happening for you with certain people. Mainly because it would take such a leap in consciousness and understanding for them to get it, and would take so much of your energy. It is tricky, because, while you will need to educate people to receive the right support, it is not your responsibility to educate everyone. So with these people – perhaps casual acquaintances or friends whom you do not think are open to exploring the new ideas you are discovering – just make a general comment when they ask how you are. This is not to hide what's really going on, but more to protect your space, until you are stronger and can take on their fears and misinformation.

**Sample conversation one: on the phone with your mum, a few days or weeks post-birth.**

Your mum:     "How are you going?"

You:          "Well, the baby's doing really well, but I'm still pretty shaken up by the birth, actually."

Your mum:     "Are you still thinking about that? Surely it's time to move on now?"

You:          "Moving on won't really help, Mum, until I can make sense of the whole thing. It was so full-on."

Your mum:     "Yes, I know, but you're fine and the baby's fine. Isn't that all that matters?"

You:          "Mum, I know you're really grateful that we made it through safely, and I am too. I am so blessed to have this little person. But from everything I am learning now, I am beginning to understand that the way we feel *during* our birth can have an impact *afterwards* emotionally, and that's certainly happening for me. It was *not* a good experience, and that is *not* a reflection on how I feel about my baby. It's just an acknowledgement that it was not right. And as a result, I'm not right. There are heaps of women who feel the way I do, and who have moved through to a better place. But I'm not there yet."

Your mum:     (Not really getting it, but hearing that you need support): "Well… would it help if I came and looked after the baby?"

You:          "Actually, mum, it would help if you could come and look after me. I know what I need to do to improve the situation, but I really need some help. I've got some stuff you can read, if you want to know how best to help. That would really mean a lot to me."

Your mum:     "Okay, well, how about I come over tomorrow, and you can show me?"

You:          "Thanks mum, that'd be great."

This is just a start, but *so* much better than your mum making her opening comments, and then you feeling unheard and unsupported, and both hanging up annoyed with each other. It might take a bit of time; however, there is room there for new understanding, and perhaps a new side to your relationship. For more about the relationship with your mother, and how her own experiences of birth may affect her responses, see *Dealing with your family's birth legacy* (p491).

### Sample conversation two: you are in your front yard, and your next door neighbour leans over the fence

Neighbour: "Oh, I heard you'd had the baby! Congratulations! How was the birth?"

You: "Thank you! Yes, he's arrived! Well, the birth was pretty full-on, but we're doing okay."

Neighbour: "Yes, as long as you both are healthy, I always say."

You: "Well, I wouldn't say we are both healthy yet. It might take some time. But he is so beautiful."

Neighbour: "Oh yes! He's gorgeous!

You: "Thank you! Had you heard that we'd named him now?"

The conversation continues, focusing on the name, how proud the grandparents are, and who he takes after. You have managed to acknowledge you are not okay and that this does not affect your gratitude for your son, and that it will not always be that way and also to deflect the conversation away from the focus on you and the birth, which is fine to do, as really, it is none of the neighbour's business!

### Sample conversation three: another mum in the park

Other mum: "How old is your baby?"

You: "Three months. (Smile) How old is yours?"

Other mum: "He's four months. Where was your baby born?"

You: "At St Francis Hospital. What about yours?"

Other mum: "Mine too! How was your birth?"

You: "Pretty intense, actually. Not really great."

Other mum: "Really? Mine was great. I guess you're both alive, so that's really all that matters, hey?"

You: "I'm glad yours went so well. (Smile). And yes, we're both alive, and of course I'm grateful for that. But I didn't really receive the care I needed and it's really affected my husband and I."

Other mum: "Oh really? I had such good care. I loved the whole thing!"

You:          "I'm so glad. I guess we both had quite different situations, didn't we?"

Other mum:  "Yeah, we did. I'm really sorry yours was so bad. I hope you can just focus on your baby and move on."

You:          "Well, I'm in the healing process now, and that's the thing that's helping us move on. Actually, doing that lets me focus on my baby more too, so we are really on the right path now. They're so sweet at this age, aren't they? Is yours rolling over yet? (or) Where did you get that wrap? I love it! (or) How are you finding that brand of pram?"

The conversation continues and turns to other baby issues you have in common. You have managed to acknowledge that your birth has had an impact on you, without invalidating the other woman's experience, and giving her information that enables her to understand your situation without feeling defensive. You have fed her useful knowledge about how the healing process works, and then deflected the conversation to other baby issues that accentuate the things you have in common with each other, rather than your differences. This means you can still converse with her and feel like a 'normal' mum, without having to deny you are feeling strong emotions about the birth. Plus you may have just planted a seed for her to be able to support other women she comes into contact with – what a gift.

# WHY DID I AGREE TO THAT EPIDURAL/EPISIOTOMY/ CAESAREAN ETC.?

Are you beating yourself up for agreeing to a particular intervention or following a certain path recommended during your labour? We meet so many women at Birthtalk who express a similar grievance and who are usually so confused or upset with themselves.

You may have read that self-blame is common after a traumatic birth, which is true. Knowing that doesn't fix the way you feel.

We meet lots of women who are upset with themselves for not 'gutsing it', or for 'giving in'. We hear many women say it was 'all their fault'.

The truth is that there are so many external factors that can impact on a woman's decision making during pregnancy and labour that rarely, if ever, could it be considered her fault. But most of us don't know this. Most of us don't have anyone telling us this afterwards.

We want to make something very clear – when a woman says 'yes' to an epidural or other pain relief or to an intervention, such as an episiotomy or a caesarean, she is not a failure.

Why? Because she is usually just saying 'yes' to the offer of help or support during a situation where she may be feeling helpless and scared. And she is usually not told of the possible repercussions from accepting the offer. She is not saying 'yes' because she 'gave in to' or 'couldn't cope' with a normal birthing situation. It's usually nowhere near that simple. Let's look at one example.

Kirsty agreed to an epidural, and has been beating herself up ever since. During her pregnancy, she imagined the birth would be painful, but in a supportive environment where she knew what was happening. But if we look at what was going on when she agreed to the epidural, a different story emerges.

She was labouring for a long time, with only her husband for support. He was doing his best, but was exhausted too and had never been at a birth before, so wasn't sure what was 'normal'. The midwives checked on her regularly, but muttered about her progress rather than supporting 'where she was at'. Kirsty was strapped to a monitor, and the midwives spent more time looking at the machine than at her. Because she was strapped to the machine, Kirsty was unable to get into positions that relieved the pain and that could have helped the baby to move down. She felt trapped, and uncertain about her abilities, as well as frightened and confused. The pain was intense; she did not know how long this would go on for. When the staff suggested an epidural, she gave her permission, despite being dedicated to a drug-free birth.

Kirsty ended up with a caesarean for 'failure to progress' and has regretted agreeing to the epidural ever since. She sees the epidural as the beginning of the downhill slide to the caesarean, which she also found very traumatic.

When you look at what was really going on, she wasn't saying 'no' to normal labour pain that she had been previously coping with. She *was* saying 'no' to the extreme pain brought on by feeling fearful, unsafe and out-of-control, being unsupported by her midwives and being unable to benefit from finding the most comfortable position.

Kirsty didn't know that when we are scared, labour hurts more. When our adrenaline is pumping (because we are scared) labour often progresses less and hurts more because the various hormones designed for that part of labour are being inhibited by the excess of adrenaline. So when we are not well-supported emotionally, if we are feeling abandoned or isolated, then it can hurt more. Way more.

Kirsty wasn't saying 'no' to a drug-free birth just because she 'couldn't hack the pain'. She was saying 'no' to continuing to feel frightened, confused and out-of-control.

Kirsty was saying 'no' to continuing to labour unsupported, with no natural pain relief. Who wouldn't say 'no' to feeling vulnerable, isolated, abandoned, scared and in excruciating pain? It was not that she couldn't do what hundreds of other women do. Other women may not have been in the same emotional situation, or the same physical situation. Or their bodies may have responded differently. Kirsty said 'no' to things that any human being would say no to. And this situation is not her fault.

Did you know that feeling safe, supported and connected with the health carer can actually affect labour progress and pain levels? If not, then you are not alone. Neither do many people in our community and culture.

Another situation we will look at is agreeing to an episiotomy or caesarean, and feeling as though you wish you hadn't. Many women find that, in hindsight, they weren't given complete information.

> *If I'd known that 'giving me a bit of a hand' meant lying me down, putting me in stirrups, cutting an episiotomy and doing a vacuum extraction, I'd probably have said 'no' and would have preferred to just keep pushing if everything was ok. But I wasn't given the option.* **Eliza**

*I had been labouring for thirty hours and was exhausted and traumatised from an unsupported and difficult posterior labour. Things were progressing, and my baby was not showing signs of distress. I was told I 'could labour for three days and still wouldn't birth my baby naturally'. However, there is no way my health carers could possibly know that. I felt later that I had agreed to the caesarean without full information.* **Melissa**

Neither Eliza nor Melissa was at fault.

Our culture encourages us to trust our medical professionals implicitly, without asking questions. However, doing so does not enable us to take into consideration the reasons behind the decision-making process the health carers are using, or the expert role we have in our own births.

A woman's health carers may present an intervention as her only option to rectify a particular issue. She may not, however, be fully informed by the health carer. Often, there may have been other options that the woman would have been unaware of and, therefore, it may have seemed to be her only choice available. If this happened to you, then you are not alone.

You did not fail if you agreed to a particular intervention without further questioning your health carer. This is what our entire culture is trained to do, and is expected to do. It can be *very* difficult to ask questions when you are feeling vulnerable and possibly in pain. Even more so if you have a partner who does not know that asking questions is possible, and can be helpful, and feels you are being 'rude' by not just accepting what is being offered.

So, in answer to the initial question, *Why did I agree to that epidural/episiotomy/ caesarean etc.?* (p210), the answer is most commonly, "Because it was the best decision you could make at that time, with the information being offered to you, and with the support you had available, and what most people in the same situation would have done to remove themselves from extreme pain or feeling out-of-control or frightened".

For more on this see our chapter *I feel like a failure* (p227).

## Tools for healing self-blame

- Look at your situation again and determine exactly what you were saying 'no' to. Now might be a good time to do a *Birthtalk Breakdown* (p47) if you have not already, to help you see what feelings were occurring at the time of the decision making. This may give you some insights that allow you to be more kind to and forgiving of yourself.

- Find out more about how women's bodies are designed to work in birth because this information may allow you to see that your body was actually working beautifully in a difficult situation. *See Why wouldn't my body work in labour?* (p230) for essential information.

- Sometimes women seem to adopt a stress response where they become extra-friendly and chatty, or act passively and agreeably towards everyone. This can be confusing when a woman finds herself acting this way towards health carers and give rise to feelings of guilt and self-blame afterwards. However, this behavior may actually be an innate stress response, occurring at a hormonal level, rather than a conscious decision to act in a particular way. To read more about this possibility, see *I kept trying to befriend all the staff. Why did I do that?* (p214).

- If exploring this issue brings up feeling of anger towards your doctor or midwife, turn to our section *I'm so angry with my health carers* (p163) for ideas in how to address these feelings appropriately.

- You may need to directly express your new understanding and empathy to the person you were during the birth. Perhaps write a letter to 'the birthing you' and apologise for blaming her. Explain to her what you know now, and let her know that you understand that she was operating as best she could with the information she had at the time. Forgive her and thank her for working so hard to bring your baby into the world.

# I KEPT TRYING TO BEFRIEND ALL THE STAFF. WHY DID I DO THAT?

*I began to become my super-friendly self. I smiled a lot, I was quiet and meek. A very tired staff member came and tried to cannulate me. He tried five times. I sat there joking with him as my veins began to crawl away. [During the caesarean] I remember feeling so vulnerable, so paralysed, so passive, but I was doing the friendly thing and talking to the obstetrician like he was an old school friend.* **Leonie**

Reflecting on a traumatic birth, some women have expressed that they behaved and spoke differently to how they thought they might in such a situation. They have told us how they could hear themselves being extra-friendly with staff, for example chatting happily about a midwife's recent trip away or new hairstyle, or becoming passive and agreeable to all they encountered. This can feel confusing and bring up feelings of guilt or anger about acting in this way. Sometimes, the mother even worries that she was 'siding with the enemy'; especially if she felt her health carers let her down.

This behaviour can also affect her partner's willingness to support her emotionally afterwards. A partner might express confusion at the conflict between what the woman is saying she felt (trauma, confusion, fear), and how she was acting (friendly, smiling, chatty). This can make it harder to offer support if the partner doesn't understand, and harder for her to ask for it.

It is important to explore this phenomenon, as this 'befriending' behaviour may be explainable at a hormonal level, and actually be more of an innate survival skill on behalf of herself and her child, rather than a deliberate decision to act a certain way.

# Fight or flight?

Most of us are familiar with the fight-or-flight response, which is often considered to be the "prototypic human response to stress".[126] However, until the mid-nineties, most of the research investigating the stress response had been undertaken on males, with females only constituting around 17% of study participants, and the reason for excluding females was due to the inconsistencies in evidence due to women's reproductive cycles.[127]

However, it has been suggested that the confusing data may be due not only to the fluctuations of women's hormones, but also perhaps because "the female stress response is not exclusively, nor even predominantly, fight-or-flight".[128] Instead, it is suggested that females may respond to threat by adopting a stress response described as 'tend and befriend'.

# Tend and befriend

Shelley Taylor is a distinguished professor of psychology at the University of California. She and her colleagues have described 'tending' as "quieting and caring for offspring and blending into the environment" while 'befriending' is "the creation of networks of associations that provide resources and protection for the female and her offspring under conditions of stress". Both of these responses may work better for a woman who cannot easily flee, or fight, because she is pregnant or has young children. In an exploration of female stress responses, Professor Taylor and her colleagues write, "Given the very central role that [being pregnant, nursing or raising young children] play in the perpetuation of the species, stress responses that enabled the female to protect simultaneously herself and her offspring are likely to have resulted in more surviving offspring".[129]

It would make sense then, that in a birthing situation in our modern times, if a woman felt her life or her baby's life were being threatened, or she was stressed about a situation taking place during her birth, that she might resort to 'tend and befriend' behaviour. Even if she does not agree with the medical professionals, or is frightened by a proposed intervention, she may still appear agreeable and friendly, as she attempts to just keep herself and her baby safe.

---

126    Taylor, S. E., Klein, L. C., Lewis, B. P., Gruenewald, T. L., Gurung, R. A. R, & Updegraff, J. A. (2000). Biobehavioral responses to stress in females: Tend-and-befriend, not fight-or-flight. *Psychological Review, 107,* 441 – 429.
127    ibid.
128    ibid.
129    ibid.

## Hormonal interplay

It is possible too, that this stress response of tending and befriending is happening at a hormonal level, rather than as a specific decision to respond a certain way. The basic initial stress response of males and females is similar, involving a release of cascading hormones including oxytocin, adrenaline and noradrenaline. However, Professor Taylor and her colleagues' research into female responses to stress presents the idea that oxytocin, in conjunction with female reproductive hormones (e.g. oestrogen) and the body's naturally occurring opiates such as endorphins, may be at the core of the biobehavioural mechanism that underlies the tend and befriend pattern.[130]

Interestingly, when a woman is in labour, she experiences an interplay of hormones including oxytocin, beta-endorphins (a naturally occurring opiate) and adrenaline. So, perhaps it is this hormonal interaction that is occurring during labour that drives the woman's tending and befriending, rather than any conscious decision to act a certain way. We suggest that perhaps this interplay of hormones, which occur in normal birthing, could more easily predispose the labouring mother to evoke a tend and befriend response when perceiving any stressor or threat while in such a vulnerable state.

## Understanding and forgiveness

Considering this possibility can be really helpful for those struggling to accept how they acted during labour – both in understanding and forgiving themselves for behaving that way, and also in preparing for future births.

> Ben and I had a real a-ha moment [when we found out about the tend and befriend response at a Birthtalk meeting] and could pinpoint when I was trying to befriend my new midwife [during my labour]. Ben walked away from that meeting knowing what to look for next time and I walked away learning something new about myself! **Skye**

We want to reassure you, if you felt this situation applied to you, that your response was normal, was possibly physiologically based, and likely a result of a response to a stressful situation.

---

130   Taylor, S. E., Klein, L. C., Lewis, B. P., Gruenewald, T. L., Gurung, R. A. R., & Updegraff, J. A. (2000). Biobehavioral responses to stress in females: Tend-and-befriend, not fight-or-flight. *Psychological Review, 107,* 441 – 429.

## Tools for healing and moving on

It might just take knowing this information to be able to move on from this aspect.

You might want to write a letter (see *The unsent letter* (p468)) to yourself at the time, expressing your understanding, acknowledging the stress of the situation, and forgiving yourself.

It may be appropriate to share this section with your partner if you feel that they are confused about your actions during the labour.

# I DON'T FEEL BONDED TO MY CHILD

*I had issues bonding with my daughter as a result of my birth, as the labour was too quick. I felt that I didn't want her, or to hold her.* **Sophie**

*I was very numb. I do remember resenting my child as I wanted my pre-pregnancy life back. The panic attacks were a response to not coping, although this was not identified at the time. I started to recognise that I was not bonding with my baby.* **Tina**

*There have been times when I have found it so challenging being her mother that I have hated her for it. But mostly I have felt disconnected with her. I have not, until a year ago, felt 'in love' with her. I have never felt like she is mine; she could be somebody else's baby. I think if I had have been able to feed her from the breast that would have helped with that disconnection. I find this difficult to explain because I do and always have loved her, but I wasn't in love with her. I didn't bond with her and while I would definitely die or kill for her, it doesn't have that substance to it that I can see and feel when I'm with mums and bubs who have had good birth experiences.* **India**

*I felt like I was 'play-acting' when I cared for my baby. I knew what a 'good mother' looked like and sounded like, so I just acted. I assumed every mother must be doing that. When really I was just numb. I would have died for him, I had the whole 'mother lioness' thing going, so I knew I loved him, but I just couldn't feel awash with love like you are supposed to in the pregnancy magazines I read at the time.* **Melissa**

## What you need to know

Struggling to bond with your child is really common after a traumatic, difficult or disappointing birth. But it does not mean that you don't love your child. Most importantly, it does not have to be a permanent state. It is definitely possible to rectify the situation and reconnect with your child.

In our experience there are two main factors that make bonding difficult. Understanding these factors can give you insight into how to restore the bond with your child. The first factor is due to the *hormonal interplay required for bonding* being interrupted or interfered with during the birth or afterwards. The second factor is due to *emotional fall out from the birth* that keeps your emotions on a surface level as a survival mechanism. We will explore both factors, as understanding them can give you clues in how to reverse the damage.

## Interrupted hormones can interfere with bonding

Nature wants us to bond with our offspring. Nature needs us to *want* to care for our babies and keep them alive. In times gone by, if there was no bond, the baby may not survive. In the animal world, this is often the case.

Nature takes care of this by flooding mothers and babies with particular hormones designed specifically to enhance their bonding to each other. One of these hormones is oxytocin, the 'hormone of love' released throughout labour and birth.

However, when a woman has a traumatic birth (that is, she feels frightened or confused or out-of-control), her body releases adrenaline. Eminent French doctor Michel Odent comments that mammals release adrenaline in situations including when there is a possible danger and when they feel observed, and that adrenaline, when high enough, has the effect of stopping the release of oxytocin.[131]

This inhibition of the oxytocin can then mess with the mother and baby's bonding at a chemical level.

Even if the birth wasn't particularly traumatic, the drugs in an epidural can alter the overall hormonal mix that your body was designed to produce, which can also interfere in the bonding process. They indirectly interfere with oxytocin and prolactin (another main bonding hormone) and inhibit the naturally-occurring opiates, beta-endorphins that reduce pain and make you feel good. Dr Sarah Buckley's eBook *"Ecstatic Birth: nature's hormonal blueprint for labour"* discusses the major effects that an epidural has on many hormones of labour, including oxytocin and prolactin. As an example, when a woman has an epidural, there is a decrease in oxytocin levels, and an inhibition of the peak in oxytocin that occurs at birth.[132]

Another factor that can affect the hormonal interplay is any separation from your baby after the birth. One of the main ways that oxytocin and other bonding hormones are released post-birth is via skin-to-skin with a gooey,

---

131    Odent, M. *In-labour physiological reference*. Retrieved from *www.wombecology.com/?pg=physiological*, accessed July 2014.

132    Buckley, S. (2010). *Ecstatic Birth: nature's hormonal blueprint for labour* (eBook). Available from *www.sarahbuckley.com*

messy baby. All those wonderful smells and sensations stimulate the hormones. As Dr Buckley says, "Peak maternal levels of oxytocin in the first hour enhance maternal responsiveness and activate…the brain areas that mediate instinctive mothering behaviours".[133] She adds that this and other hormonal systems are enhanced through skin-to-skin contact between baby and mother straight after the birth.[134]

So missing out on skin-to-skin in the early hours after the birth can have repercussions.

It is so important to know this information, as it can release the feeling of having 'no' maternal instinct or 'being a bad mother', and begin an understanding that it was a physiological lack (due to no fault of your own) and not a psychological failing. Even if you agreed to, or requested, the epidural, we would bet that no one told you that it could affect bonding, or how to fix this situation postnatally.

To explain this further, we turn to the work of Dr Sarah Buckley. With her permission, we have reproduced some excerpts from her article and eBook, *"Pain in Labour – your hormones are your helpers"*. Understanding this may give you an enormous sense of relief, and help you explain the situation to your partner.

> *"…human birth is like that of other mammals – those animals that suckle their young – and involves the same hormones: the body's chemical messengers. These hormones, which originate in the deepest and oldest parts of our brain, cause the physical processes of labour and birth, as well as exerting a powerful influence on our emotions and behaviour.*
>
> *Oxytocin is the hormone that causes the uterus to contract during labour. Levels of oxytocin gradually increase throughout labour, and are highest around the time of birth, when it contributes to the euphoria and receptiveness to her baby that a mother usually feels after an unmedicated birth. This peak, which is triggered by sensations of stretching of the birth canal as the baby is born, does not occur when an epidural is in place. Administration of an epidural has been found to interfere with bonding between ewes and their newborn lambs.*

---

133    Buckley, S. (2010). *Ecstatic Birth: nature's hormonal blueprint for labour* (eBook). Available from *www.sarahbuckley.com*.

134    ibid.

*Synthetic oxytocin is often given by drip – that is, directly into the bloodstream – when labour contractions are inefficient. Oxytocin given in this way does not enter the brain, and so does not contribute to the post-birth 'high', and in fact can lead to desensitisation to the mothers own oxytocin production.*

*The other major birthing hormone, prolactin, is most noteworthy for its effects after the birth. Prolactin is the major hormone of breast milk synthesis. Suckling by the newborn baby increases prolactin levels; early and frequent suckling from the first days makes the breast more responsive to prolactin, which in turn helps to ensure a good long-term supply of milk.*

*Like the other hormones, prolactin has effects on emotion and behaviour. Prolactin helps us to put our babies' needs first in all situations by increasing submissiveness, anxiety and vigilance.*

*When prolactin is combined with oxytocin, as it is soon after birth and during breastfeeding, it encourages a relaxed and selfless devotion to the baby that contributes to a mother's satisfaction and her baby's physical and emotional health.*

*Beta-endorphin (pronounced beet-a en-door-fin) is one of the endorphin hormones which are released by the brain in times of stress or pain, and is a natural equivalent to painkilling drugs like pethidine.*

*During labour, beta-endorphin helps to relieve pain, and contributes to the 'on another planet' feeling that women experience when they labour without drugs. Levels of beta-endorphin are reduced when drugs are used for pain relief.*

*Very high levels of beta-endorphin can slow labour by reducing oxytocin levels, which may help to 'ration' the intensity of labour according to our ability to deal with it. Moderate levels of beta-endorphin help us to deal with pain in labour, as well as encouraging us to follow our instincts. As part of the hormonal cocktail after birth, beta-endorphin plays a role in bonding between mother and baby, who is also primed with endorphins from the birth process".*[135] **Dr Sarah Buckley**

---

135    Buckley, S. (2005) *Pain in Labour: your hormones are your helpers.* (an article & eBook). Retrieved from *http://sarahbuckley.com/pain-in-labour-your-hormones-are-your-helpers*, accessed July 2014.

So, you can see the ramifications of *not* having those hormones. It can begin to make sense that due to certain events of your birth (including perhaps a lack of beneficial support, having pharmacological intervention, or not feeling good emotionally) you were not fully equipped with what other mothers get in preparation for bonding with a newborn. Which is not your fault.

Another way this hormonal balance can be upset is through 'what happens' in the moments post-birth. Receiving a wet, gooey and sometimes bloody baby on your chest may not sound initially appealing to some, but the consequences of *not* having this occur can be far-reaching, especially in the area of bonding.

If your baby was wiped clean, and perhaps wrapped in a blanket before being passed to you after being born, or even bathed before you could hold him, then there can be fall out, hormonally.

We are meant to hold our babies after birth while they are wet, gooey and messy because their smell and feel ignites hormones designed to spark our mothering instincts. A whiff of newborn goo sets off all those hormonal benefits that Dr Buckley talks about – and other mammals seem to need this hormonal support too.

As renowned birth pioneer, Michel Odent, discusses,[136] one study compared two groups of baby monkeys, all born via caesarean. One group (five babies) was swabbed with secretions from their mother's vagina after birth. All of these babies were accepted and nursed (breastfed) by their mother. Another group of eleven baby monkeys were not swabbed with vaginal secretions. Only one of the eleven infants was accepted and nursed by its mother.[137]

Of course, as humans know intellectually that the baby is ours. Even when our baby is cleaned and bathed before we first meet them, we can receive and care for them; however, we need to realise that we might be doing so without the amazing hormonal support meant for us (and that other mothers receive) to make it easier.

## Were you separated?

Perhaps you and your baby were separated after birth. Research investigating women's experiences of medically necessary elective caesarean section, reports that "the separation of the mother–baby dyad was found to have a devastating impact on maternal–newborn attachment that lasted well into the postnatal

---

136     Odent, M. *In-labour physiological reference*. Retrieved from *www.wombecology.com/?pg=physiological*, accessed July 2014.

137     Lundblad, E.G. & Hodgen, G.D. (1980). Induction of maternal-infant bonding in rhesus and cynomolgus monkeys after cesarean delivery. *Laboratory of Animal Science, 30*(5):913.

period".[138] This research was undertaken with women who were having medically necessary caesareans; however, in our work at Birthtalk, we have seen a wide variety of women – however they gave birth – who have been impacted in numerous ways when they were separated from their babies.

In the animal world, this separation is being recognised as a likely hindrance to mother-baby bonding. Understandably, a farmer wants his livestock mothers bonding so they accept and feed their infant, which saves him money and time. On a website called *Making more from sheep* (a Meat and Livestock Australia website), it is recommended that "the longer a ewe stays at the birth site, the greater the chance of the ewe and lamb bond forming".[139]

We find it very sad, and unacceptable, that animals are given more respect in this important postnatal moment than humans. Mothers and babies are designed to be together post-birth.

## An early 'sensitive period'?

A 2009 Russian study looked at early contact between mother and child in the two hours following birth, versus separation, and compared the effects on mother–infant interaction one year later. They concluded, "Skin-to-skin contact, for 25 to 120 minutes after birth, early suckling or both positively influenced mother–infant interaction one year later when compared with routines involving separation of mother and infant".[140] They also found "the negative effect of a two-hour separation after birth was not compensated for by the practice of rooming-in"[141] meaning that having the baby with you in the hospital room after a separation was not enough to make up for the time spent apart.

According to the study's authors, these findings "support the presence of a period after birth (the early 'sensitive period') during which close contact between mother and infant may induce long-term positive effect on mother–infant interaction".[142]

---

138    Bayes, S., Fenwick, J., & Hauck, Y. (2012). 'Off everyone's radar': Australian women's experiences of medically necessary elective caesarean section. *Midwifery, 28*(6).), e900-9. doi: 10.1016/j.midw.2012.01.004.

139    Australian Wool Innovation Ltd & Meat and Livestock Australia. *MODULE 10: Wean More Lambs.* Retrieved from *www.makingmorefromsheep.com.au/wean-more-lambs/procedure_10.3.htm*, accessed June 2014.

140    Bystrova, K., Ivanova, V., Edhborg, M., Matthiesen, A.S., Ransjö-Arvidson, A.B., Mukhamedrakhimov, R. Widström, A.M. (2009). Early contact versus separation: effects on mother-infant interaction one year later. *Birth, 36*(2), 97–109.

141    ibid.

142    ibid.

Dr Sarah Buckley talks about this early time after birth in terms of hormones: "Putting your newborn baby to your breast is the easiest way to increase oxytocin levels, but Michel Odent also emphasises the importance of privacy during the hour following birth. This gives the opportunity for uninterrupted skin-to-skin and eye-to-eye contact between mother and baby – conditions that optimise oxytocin release".[143]

This does not mean, however, that all is lost if you missed this 'sensitive period'. As Dr William Sears says, "Bonding is not a now-or-never phenomenon".[144] He believes 'catch-up' bonding is possible, and we certainly agree. We have seen many women reconnect beautifully with their children, even years after they were separated for a period of time after the birth (see *I don't feel bonded to my child* (p218) for more on this). Remember too, few of the mothers in these studies above likely had access to support or information for healing.

It is just worth noting that it is recognised that a sensitive period may exist, which could help explain why you are struggling if you were separated from your baby, even if that separation was necessary. It can be helpful to know that women can feel impacted by being separated from their baby, even for a relatively short amount of time.

Understanding this information can result in a new picture forming of the reasons you might struggle with bonding, a picture that clearly shows that it was not your fault. We talk about ways to renew the bond shortly, but first we will look at the other main reason for bonding difficulties.

## A traumatic start can interfere with bonding

After a traumatic birth, there is little time to rest, to take stock and to process what just happened to you. New mothers are often in 'survival mode': facing the challenges of mothering a newborn and just managing the basics to keep themselves and their child fed, clean, and safe.

It can feel unsafe to go there and think about the birth, or the myriad of emotions tied up in the experience. Sometimes women are worried that they might start crying and not ever be able to stop. It can seem too scary to even think about the birth. So they don't. It gets locked up somewhere in their mind, or blocked behind a barrier that says 'don't go there'. Emotions are walled up and this can be made worse by well-meaning people telling a woman to "just be grateful".

---

143    Buckley, S. (2005) *Pain in Labour: your hormones are your helpers.* (an article & eBook). op. cit.

144    Sears, W., *Bonding – What it Means.* Retrieved from *www.askdrsears.com/topics/pregnancy-childbirth/tenth-month-post-partum/bonding-with-your-newborn/bonding-what-it-means*, accessed June 2014.

But what this means is that a whole lot of emotions are unavailable. Because a woman cannot risk descending into the deep and heavy emotions of the birth, it means she often cannot access the deep and meaningful emotions of love either. Because she has 'cut off' her emotions, she must stay on a surface level that feels safe, but also a bit numbing.

In addition, women often talk of cutting off emotionally from their body after a traumatic birth, especially if they feel their body failed them. This lack of connection with their physicality can result in even more emotional stifling.

Many women coming to Birthtalk find that by beginning to explore the birth and to process their experience in a safe environment with good support, things change. Gradually, because they are facing uncomfortable or painful deep emotions, and processing them, there is a space to experience the positive deep emotions too. A newfound depth of love can be felt, and a realisation that a bond is now being felt.

## Tools to bond, heal and reconnect with your child

- Having skin-to-skin time with your child can reignite the hormones and create a renewed opportunity to bond. An effective way to do this can be by having wet, slippery, skin-to-skin contact with your child in the bath tub. This can happen even if your child is older too, just by having a bath with them and cuddling in the water. Many Birthtalk mums have found this to be a powerful exercise in reconnecting with their child. One mum said, "Even with my second child, whose birth was not traumatic, we still had showers together when she was quite a bit older, and I cuddled her in the water. I felt an immediate rush of those post-birth hormones, and we emerged feeling connected and content". There's more about this in *Reconnecting with your child* (p409).

- If you were separated from your baby after the birth, you might find some helpful information in *I was separated from my baby* (p250), to support your understanding and healing.

- Play some 'bonding games' to renew the bond with your child, such as those mentioned in our section, *Reconnecting with your child*. This can be a less intense way to begin a new way of interacting and exploring a more connected relationship.

- Do the exercise in the section *Saying the words you couldn't say at the birth: a reconnection tool* (p421). Many Birthtalk women have found this to be incredibly healing, and the beginning of a new chapter in their healing journey and in their relationship with their child.

- Just continue to do the work of exploring the different sections of this book, and facing the issues that arise for you. As we have mentioned, doing this work can enable deeper positive emotions to arise as you acknowledge and process deeper more difficult emotions.

- In the section *How do I heal?* (p61) we share how to go about continuing to do the work. Usually, it comes down to answering a question, "What is bothering you the most right now?" or "How do I feel right now?" The things that are standing out the most are your clues and your gifts. They are your signposts for what needs to be explored next. So ask yourself these questions, and then look up an appropriate section in the table of contents of this book for ideas and further understanding that will help you heal.

# I feel like a failure

## DEALING WITH FEELINGS OF FAILURE

*I was a failure, not good enough, fragile, demoralised, so sad and utterly disappointed. I dreaded it every time my husband had to go home to sleep while I was in hospital. I have never felt so alone in my whole life even though I was surrounded by hospital staff.* **Kerri**

*I felt I was a failure; a failure as a person, a failure as a mother. The constant guilt made me very defensive with people, often for no reason. We just had no bond. It was a vicious cycle of feeling so much guilt and wanting to smother my baby in love to make up for being a pathetic mother who couldn't even birth her own child, but also frustration at not being able understand my baby. Not knowing what she needed and wanted.* **Angie**

*I had one friend in particular who had flown from interstate to see me and the baby. She wanted to visit me in hospital and I had said I couldn't see her because I needed a rest. But actually, I was so sad that I had not given birth like her that I couldn't look at her.* **Skye**

*I felt an incredible sense of failure surrounding the second 'pushing' stage of the birth and I started the whole process of motherhood from a place of extreme vulnerability, which shook me deeply.* **Christy**

## What you need to know

Feeling like a failure is echoed in so many women we meet. In fact, it is one of the most common responses to a bad birth that we come across at Birthtalk, and one that often has the deepest emotional distress.

The fact is, we don't ever see a woman as having failed, because we know that birth is simply not a pass/fail event.

You may be thinking, "Ahhh – but you haven't met me!" And that is true. However, we have met plenty of women over the years who were certain they had failed before they began coming to Birthtalk. Many conversations in our meetings start with, "If only I'd just done this" or, "Why did I do that?" or, "I can't believe that I did that". (See *Why did I agree to that epidural/episiotomy/ caesarean etc.?* (p210))

Women describe themselves as "giving in", or as "not being strong enough". They sit in our meetings mentally kicking themselves, judging themselves pretty harshly, and are often in emotional agony about what they perceive as their failure.

> *I felt a deep sense of failure for a long time after my birth, which pervaded every part of my life. I lost my confidence in social situations, and did not feel confident looking after my newborn, because I felt like I'd 'failed at everything else'. I wouldn't even put my baby in the car seat to come home from hospital after he was born. I handed him to my husband, as I just didn't feel capable anymore. I did eventually move on from this, but the feelings didn't just lift over time. They only lifted because I gained an understanding of what actually happened in my own experience.* **Melissa**

Working through feelings of failure needs to be grounded in facts. It's not just a matter of getting over it, or stopping feeling like that. It's a matter of exploring new information and applying it to your situation, to get to a place where you can see your birth in a new light.

> *I realised that I didn't fail, and my body didn't fail, and my partner didn't fail. As it dawned on me that I didn't fail, a new understanding emerged: that I was failed. I began to understand where I was failed by my health carers, where I was failed by my antenatal education, and where my partner and I were both failed by our culture's understanding of birth. It was just the beginning of the healing journey, but an incredibly important turning point.* **Melissa**

If you felt like you failed and find yourself making comments starting with, "I should have…" or "I wish I didn't…" or similar, reading the sections under this heading of *I feel like a failure* (p227) hopefully will give you a chance to let yourself off the hook once you see the wider picture, learn more about the challenges you were facing, and gather some tools to view your situation anew, with compassion and understanding.

# WHY WOULDN'T MY BODY WORK IN LABOUR?

*I felt like I had been hit by a bus and that I could not catch up with what had just happened to me. I was so sad I did not get to experience the birth I had always imagined and felt like a complete and utter failure. Breastfeeding and attachment went badly too, which added to my great sense of failure and I hated my body ... stupid, useless thing!* **Kerri**

## What you need to know

Most of the women who ask us, "Why wouldn't my body work in labour?" in Birthtalk meetings (including Kerri, above) come to the understanding eventually that their bodies were actually working beautifully. This might seem hard to believe, but in most cases, it's true. To explain, let's look at what a body actually needs to be able to do its job in birth.

The process of birth is driven by a combination of hormones, arriving in just the right amount, at just the right time, in just the right order. It's a very delicate balance and a slight upset of that balance can affect the progression of labour and the feelings that accompany it. One of the most common ways this balance can be upset is via adrenaline.

## Adrenaline's labour-stopping effects

An excess of adrenaline actually inhibits one of the main hormones (oxytocin) from doing its job of contracting the uterus to progress labour. It does this on purpose for a very good reason. Imagine you are a gazelle on the plains of Africa (stay with us – it will make sense). You are in early labour, things are going well, but then you hear or smell a lion heading your way. Not a good time to have a baby!

When you see, hear or smell the lion, you are scared. You need to escape and, as an initial response, your adrenaline (an emergency hormone) picks up, the oxytocin is inhibited and the labour is stalled... until you can move to another safe place, and continue birthing. How amazing mammals' bodies are to be able to do that! And you are a mammal, so your body can do that too for exactly the same reason – to keep you and your baby safe.

So what can bring on an adrenaline response in humans? According to Dr Michel Odent, situations where mammals release adrenaline include when there is a possible danger, when they feel observed, and even when they are in a cold environment.[145]

An important point to know is that you might not actually *feel scared*. However, your body may still respond to factors that tell it that this is *not a favourable situation* for birthing, in which case it can induce an adrenaline response. Further below we will look at what the modern day equivalent of a lion might be to see what could induce the adrenaline response that slows labour for a human mother.

Before we do, we're just going to look at another birthing mammal: a domestic cat.

## Our amazing brain – and what it needs for birth

Have you noticed that cats always look for a dark, secluded place to birth? Often in the back of a cupboard or behind a couch? And with reason. Dr Sarah Buckley has written a wonderful article titled, "Pain in labour: your hormones are your helpers", where she uses the description of a pregnant cat finding her place to birth as a starting point to explore what human mammals need for optimal birthing. She writes, "Your cat has been hunting for an out-of-the way place – your socks drawer or laundry basket – where she in unlikely to be disturbed. When you notice, you open the wardrobe door, but she moves again. Intrigued, you notice that your observation – even your presence – seems to disturb the whole process".[146] This is a key point in why many women's labours may stall.

Michel Odent, an eminent French doctor highly revered in birth circles, has commented, "It is noticeable that they [mammals] all rely on a specific strategy not to feel observed when giving birth".[147] It seems that not feeling observed is crucial for humans, too, in enabling the parts of the brain that release the hormones required for good labour progress to do their job.

Dr Odent describes how the brains of humans have a highly-developed neocortex for talking, counting and being logical and rational. However, it is not the neocortex, but the more primitive brain structures that release the

---

145    Odent, M. *In-labour physiological reference*. Retrieved from *www.wombecology.com/?pg=physiological*, accessed July 2014.

146    Buckley, S. (2005) *Pain in Labour: your hormones are your helpers*. (an article & eBook). Retrieved from *http://sarahbuckley.com/pain-in-labour-your-hormones-are-your-helpers*, accessed July 2014.

147    Odent, M. *In-labour physiological reference*. Retrieved from *www.wombecology.com/?pg=physiological*, accessed January 2014.

birthing hormones. He writes that the "neocortex is supposed to be at rest so that primitive brain structures can more easily release the necessary hormones" and that this implies a basic need of labouring women is "to be protected against any sort of neocortical stimulation".[148]

So, what could stimulate the human neocortex during labour? Dr Odent lists the following:

1. language (particularly rational language)
2. bright light
3. a feeling of being observed.[149]

From this information, Dr Odent's bottom line is that women need to feel secure as a basic need, in order to birth.[150] It just means that when they feel safe, secure, unwatched, away from bright lights and do not have to interact much on a rational level, their bodies can do the job of birth more easily and safely. Just like the cat who removes herself from stimulation when needing to birth her babies, humans, who have a more highly developed neo-cortex, are even more in need of this privacy and security.

## Some factors that can affect labour's progress

Now let's now look at some common situations women find themselves in during a modern birth that could compromise their hormonal balance and slow labour:

a. getting in the car and travelling to hospital;
b. feeling like your health carer does not have confidence in your own expert knowledge about your body, or your ability to give birth;
c. not knowing, or not liking, your health carer;
d. being surrounded by lots of people, or hustle and bustle, or bright lights or not being 'allowed' to move around how you want to;
e. fear of birth – fearing what is happening to your body or fear of pain in birth;
f. remaining cognitive due to various circumstances.

---

148    Odent, M. *In-labour physiological reference*. Retrieved from *www.wombecology.com/?pg=physiological*, accessed January 2014.

149    ibid.

150    ibid.

## a. Getting in the car and travelling to hospital

Suddenly, the woman is not in her home. She is out of her comfort zone, where she had been feeling safe. Plus, there is nothing comfortable about travelling in a car while in labour! She might feel observed, perhaps by passers-by as they drive. She might need to concentrate on things like finding a position that works, putting a seatbelt on in awkward positions, and bracing herself while going around corners. Any of these situations could be interpreted by the mammalian part of her brain as being *unfavourable* circumstances and thus possibly *unsafe* for birthing. She will likely need to come out of 'labourland' (that is, from the primitive part of her brain that produces the hormones for birth), and come into the cognitive thinking part of the brain (neocortex), which can override her hormone production. Her brain, if stimulated, may continue to respond to her surroundings in this manner.

### What this can mean

Even though the woman might not feel particularly unsafe, her body is responding like it is, because her adrenaline is activated. A labour that stalls on the hospital trip is actually the result of a body working beautifully – exactly how it was designed to work, to keep her and her baby safe.

How amazing and wonderful, yet probably frustrating for many couples who don't know this information and are sometimes embarrassed to arrive at the hospital, only to be sent home again when labour has stopped altogether. It is important to know that there are things that you can do if labour stops in hospital: getting in the shower, turning off the lights, leaving the woman to have some space and privacy are all techniques that can facilitate feelings of safety and not being watched, and hopefully allow the birthing hormones to recommence their role, and labour will continue.

## b. Feeling like your health carer does not have confidence in your own expert knowledge about your body or in your ability to birth

It can be an unnerving experience to be labouring in a certain way, only to be told you are not doing it 'right' or managing well, or to have doubts expressed about your body's ability to birth. This alone can be enough to tip those hormones out of balance, again stimulating the part of the brain that responds to doubt, fear or concern as *unfavourable* and therefore *unsafe*. The confusion or concern that can arise from this situation can also lead to the neocortex becoming dominant in trying to make sense of what was said, which can again reduce the level of birthing hormones as nature intended.

Women need someone with them who trusts birth and who trusts a woman's innate knowledge about herself. Sometimes a labour may be unfolding in a less-than-textbook manner, which may not mean something is wrong. It could just be normal for her. Women's paths to birth can vary immensely. However, if the person looking after that woman expresses concern or a lack of trust in birth, then that can easily transfer to the woman. While this may result in the woman registering that she feels slightly uneasy, her hormones could be interpreting and responding to this as an *unfavourable situation*, alerting the body and priming her physiology to respond. This can then disrupt the hormonal balance and the labour may not progress easily.

## What this can mean

Again, it can still mean the woman's body was working beautifully. It is designed to slow down labour in those times when the woman's mammalian brain considers that a situation may not be conducive to birthing, even if the woman's logical brain is telling her that things are fine.

How brilliantly a woman's body responds, yet how often we blame ourselves for just not labouring well when, in fact, we were doing everything we were physiologically primed to do in such a situation.

> *I really feel that my first birth stalled because I had no trust in my obstetrician and was so intimidated when she ended up being there. I hadn't felt supported by my obstetrician from day one. I was supremely confident in my ability to give birth, but I don't think she trusted birth, or thought that I could do it. As my due date loomed closer, I was increasingly frustrated and upset at my antenatal appointments and in desperation seriously considered changing obstetricians at thirty-eight weeks. In the end, I just pinned all my hopes on the fact that the obstetrician wouldn't be there at the birth (that's the way it works out most times, right?).* **Megan**

## c. Not knowing or not liking your health carer

When you think about it, birth is about opening up. Cervix opening, legs opening, vagina opening – a woman is truly at her most vulnerable and 'open' in every sense of the word, physically and emotionally.

Look at it this way: Who do you feel comfortable being open with? Who do you feel comfortable being vulnerable with?

It is usually only with people we truly trust and who we know we will be safe with that we allow to see our 'inner world' and to be vulnerable around.

Do you want to share your inner thoughts and feelings with someone you have never met before? Especially if that someone arrives and proceeds to ask intimate questions, rather than pausing to acknowledge you and introducing themselves and their role. Do you want to be vulnerable around someone you don't like? Would you tell the innermost workings of your mind to someone who you had an uneasy or bad feeling about? Would you want to 'open up' around this person? Our bodies are finely-tuned instruments that respond to our emotional state. If we don't feel comfortable opening up emotionally, how can we expect our bodies to open up physically? Often, in this situation, they don't.

> *Now I know that I didn't want my baby's first intimate moments to take place around this woman. I didn't know her. She did not try to get to know me. She was blunt and not nurturing in the most vulnerable hours of my life. So I shut down. But I didn't know I did. And I didn't know that I was having this response to her, because I didn't really know that it mattered. We had a similar philosophy (I was in a birth centre so felt 'safe' from that point of view) so it was not that I thought she didn't trust birth, or even that she didn't trust me. She was just not kind and didn't enable me to feel that opening up was a good thing. So I didn't.* **Melissa**

### What this can mean

Again, if you did not like or even did not know the person caring for you, then that could have greatly contributed to your labour stalling or being very slow to progress. It's not a little thing; it can be the clincher between a birth that flows and a birth that stagnates.

And it is *not your fault.*

It is very difficult to find this information; many health carers themselves don't know about this.

It is completely understandable if you felt uneasy during pregnancy, and did not change health carers. Being a pregnant woman needing care, and not knowing if you could get care elsewhere if you gave up your current health carer is an extremely vulnerable position to be in.

Knowing this information can be the start of letting yourself off the hook and the beginning of forgiving yourself and your body.

Exploring why you felt unsafe with a previous carer has benefits for the future as well. Your new understanding will mean you have more insight about your own needs in vulnerable situations. This process can also provide you with a wealth of information to help you in choosing a health carer who is right for you if you have another baby. You will have a clearer picture of your needs, and what you don't need, and new information to support your decision making in this situation. For future births, it is important to know that rarely are there no other options. In the event that you feel your carer is unsuitable, there are ways of finding appropriate care without potentially leaving you in a situation where you have no care at all. A section in this book's *Appendix A* titled *Suggested reading for birthing again* lists organisations and individuals who may be able to offer you guidance and support in this process. You can also see our chapter *Birthing again* (p507) for ideas on working towards an empowering birth.

## d. Being surrounded by lots of people, or hustle and bustle, or bright lights or not being allowed to move around how you want to

You may be beginning to see that the hormones of birth are often super-responsive to the environment around you and your emotions. We describe it as birthing women having heightened senses, like a 'radar' that is on high alert looking for danger or anything 'unsafe'.

Anything that takes a woman out of the trance-like state of birth or puts her on alert has the potential to disrupt the progress of her labour.

This distraction can be as simple as asking her to choose her dinner menu, or labouring with an open door when the nurse's station is just outside, or restricting her movement when she clearly wants to move in a certain way, or two people having a conversation over her head. Unfortunately, most of us don't know this before we go into labour.

## What this can mean

Maybe your body *was* working beautifully. Maybe, stimulated by everything happening around you, your body slowed everything down, as it is designed to do, to keep your baby safe.

Even if you didn't feel particularly unsafe, the distractions could have been enough to make you feel 'observed', which is what mammals don't want; it alerts your adrenaline to action stations. So maybe it's not that your body didn't work… maybe it's just that it was not in a situation that enabled it to get the hormones to the right levels for labour to kick in.

## e. Fear of birth – fearing what is happening in your body or fear of pain in birth

Sometimes, the birthing process can feel completely overwhelming. Even before labour, a woman might already be feeling apprehensive or worried about impending pain or frightened of a particular scenario unfolding, perhaps due to her family's birth history or through the experience of friends. Feeling frightened about the intensity of what is happening within your body could result in a similar physiological response to an external threat or fear. That is, adrenaline can surge, the brain goes into 'high alert' mode and the oxytocin is inhibited, slowing labour.

## What this means

Firstly, it doesn't mean you did something 'wrong' by being frightened. There are many justifiable reasons why a woman can be frightened before or during labour. Some of the more common reasons are:

- **Not having your worries addressed antenatally.** For example, perhaps during your pregnancy you might have voiced to your health carers that you were worried about something – and were told to 'just trust birth', or told 'don't worry about it, we'll take care of that'. Imagine, instead, if you had been given accurate, factual information that could have allayed your worries, or if options had been explained to you regarding this situation you were concerned about. Imagine if you then felt calm and more informed and that the fear dissipated. For some women, when a fear goes unaddressed or gets pushed aside by their health carers, that fear just sits there and may rear its head in labour, when the woman is not in a position to gain more information. Her fear is fuelled by the vulnerability of birthing, and it escalates as her imagined scenarios feel closer and more possible.

- **Not receiving adequate reassurance from your health carer during labour.**
  Feeling reassured can depend on who is offering the support. It may not
  be enough if the woman considers that the person reassuring them during
  labour is not the person with the right knowledge base. For example, she
  might be frightened at what's happening in her body and her partner may
  offer reassurance. We find, however, that many women need the voice of the
  person they believe knows about birth or have trusted with their life, and
  their baby's life, in this instance usually the health carer. Women need to hear
  from the health carer that 'everything is okay'. They may reject what others
  offer as they are waiting for word from the health carer.

- **Feeling overwhelmed by the intensity of birth.** Birth, even normal birth for
  a woman who has a detailed knowledge of birth, is well supported and has
  birthed before, can feel raw and rough and exposing and tumultuous. It can
  feel like it is about to consume you with its relentlessness. It can require you
  to draw from the depths of your last reserves of strength and resilience.
  Feeling this raw and vulnerable and challenged by the power of birth can be
  something that requires extremely sensitive, nurturing care from those
  around you. It can require an acknowledgement from those supporting you
  that, yes, this is hard and challenging. That, yes it is intense and painful. But
  that you are okay, and the baby is okay. If you also have access to specific
  information* about birth, then that can support you too, as you can 'check in'
  with your health carers to make sure things are safe, and then turn your full
  attention to moving through each contraction. Unfortunately, many women
  do not have access to such support when they feel overwhelmed and perhaps
  frightened by the intensity of their birth. It's important to know that it's not
  being frightened that affects the labour so much, it's being frightened without
  adequate support to stay centred and call on your inner reserves. This support
  needs to come from those around you and from your information base.

So, any of these scenarios (and others) can create a situation where your body
responds to an understandable and justifiable fear and produces hormones that
slow down or stall labour as your body simply does its job and responds to
the 'threat'.

---

*The specific information we mention about birth can be tricky to find and it is not your fault if it was
not accessible to you. See *Appendix A* for resources that can provide avenues to begin exploring this
information for future births.

# f. Remaining cognitive due to various circumstances

Although it might seem too simplistic, it's important to know that just having to think might have contributed to your labour slowing down. We discussed this above when reviewing Dr Michel Odent's explanation of the importance of reducing stimulation to a part of the brain called the neocortex. Of course, it is important to be able to think in terms of making decisions or asking questions; however, remaining 'cognitive' can be detrimental to labour progress. Examples of this can include:

While labouring:

- being asked what you want for breakfast so they can complete the hospital menu form
- having a health carer engage you in chit-chat about your other children, your work, the baby names you've chosen, and so on
- being told you need to change positions or move rooms
- being asked to complete admission forms
- being asked questions about your early labour
- using 'labour tools': significant conscious focusing on and thinking about learned techniques meant to support your labouring. An over-focus on breathing techniques, positioning, pain distraction techniques, relaxation techniques or visualisation techniques can be detrimental to labour progress. Of course, all of these can be helpful to reduce fear around birth antenatally, and they can be helpful during labour if they happen organically during a labour where the woman feels safe and unobserved and able to follow her body's signals, rather than if they are significantly orchestrated, directed or focused on cognitively.
- Any of these situations can stimulate your neocortex and as a result, over-ride the part of your brain that produces the hormones that facilitate labour, pain relief, endurance and enable you to transcend time.

**What this can mean**

Again, this might be an opportunity to see that your body was simply acting as it is supposed to act, rather than malfunctioning. It might open up some possibilities for healing, releasing some resentment towards your body and yourself. It might also provide some insight into how you could set up the environment for any future births.

# Tools for healing and understanding when you feel your body failed

Sometimes, just reading the information above and understanding how it applies to your own situation can be enough to kickstart some healing.

Many women come to the realisation that they did not fail, but that they were failed:

- Maybe they were failed by a system that didn't provide them with enough information to make informed decisions or an environment conducive to birthing (see *The pitfalls of going with the flow in birth* (p513)).

- Maybe they were failed by our culture, which has a distorted and dysfunctional perception of birth that is cultivated within our community and that undermines confidence and often leads to fear or doubt (see *Why doesn't anyone get it?* (p129)).

- Maybe they were failed by their health carers, who may have unwittingly mismanaged their birth, or failed to listen, or reacted according to their own fears and prejudices (see *I'm so angry my health carers* to deal with this).

You might find some of the following feelings arising:

- **Relief** – to finally be able to see that perhaps you didn't fail. This in itself may be a catalyst for healing, as we can begin to forgive ourselves and be gentler with ourselves and let ourselves off the hook a bit.

- **Sadness** – when we start thinking about 'how things could have been', now we have access to this information. It can set off a spate of 'if onlys', and that's all part of the healing process too. Try our *Tools for your healing journey* (p403), especially *The healing power of rewriting your birth story*, and consider undertaking this exercise, now you know the possibilities of how birth can be. Also allow yourself to feel sad – this feeling deserves acknowledgement and validation. You may have much to be sad about. It is okay to be sad. Try the chapter *I feel sad* (p245) to get some ideas on how to process the sadness.

- **Anger at your health carer** – you might be getting angry with your health carer if you felt that they did not put you in a situation where your body could do its job. This certainly may be justified; it can be important to express this appropriately. Go to the section called *I'm so angry with my health carers* (p163) to get some healthy ideas on how to explore and process your anger.

- **Anger at your support people, such as a partner, friend or your parent** – your anger may be understandable, and made more complicated because your support people most likely had no idea about the issues discussed in this section. They likely did not know the importance of the environment to your hormones or the importance of you not being disturbed. This means that you may have some 'stuff' to process about all that. See *Issues with your partner* (p291) for some ideas (it doesn't matter if it was your partner or other support people, you will still find help in that section for dealing with any anger that has arisen).

- **Self-forgiveness** – the awareness of all the things that can impact on a labour can give you some clarity as to why your body may have responded in a way you didn't expect, rather than feeling it failed. Go to *I feel like a failure* (p227) and *Reconnecting with your body* (p477) to explore this more.

Note: To read more about the interaction between the hormones in mammals and the basic needs of a mammal for birthing, we encourage you to read more of Michel Odent's work. This article is a good start: *www.wombecology.com/?pg=physiological*, accessed January 2015.

# I READ ALL THE RIGHT BOOKS AND DID ALL THE RIGHT CLASSES – WHAT HAPPENED?

*I worked so hard to prepare for this birth. I read all about active birthing, and did empowering birth classes and pretty much read anything I could about birth. I was going to have this active, natural birth with no pain relief. I had stress balls and positions and mind games all planned. I knew so much about birth – but obviously not the right things.* **Melissa**

*I don't know how to recover. Reading more about childbirth just seems to add fuel to the fire. I know more about birth than almost anyone I know and it doesn't help at all.* **Robyn**

## What you need to know

We meet many women who knew *a lot* about birth, and painstakingly prepared for childbirth before their baby's arrival and still had a bad birth.

Many of them have done classes outside regular antenatal classes, learning hypnotherapy for childbirth, active birthing, pregnancy yoga, or classes preparing for a natural birth. Many of them were extremely informed about the birthing process. Some of them were quite informed about the politics and limitations of our maternal health system.

But they had a bad birth.

This can leave you with a feeling of "I'm damned if I do and damned if I don't," about becoming informed before labour. But the truth is, it is unlikely that having this knowledge (or certain expectations) has created your bad birth. It is more likely that you were not in a position to use this knowledge as there were other needs that took priority at the time, often due to the environment you were in.

The truth is, all of this extra information and labour preparation *can* be extremely useful and a wonderful gift for birth. Yet if the woman's emotional needs are not being met, the birth is unlikely to be a positive experience.

In *The foundations of your healing journey* (p37), we talk about a woman's emotional needs and their importance in birth.

A woman's needs are *not* being met if:
- she is not feeling safe
- she is having to advocate for herself without feeling supported
- her health carers are diminishing her confidence by not demonstrating their belief in her birthing body
- her health carers are not acknowledging her important role as an expert in her own body and baby
- her health carers are not respecting her and are talking over the top of her
- her health carers are not seeking her consent before undertaking interventions
- no one is explaining to the woman what is going on
- the woman does not like or trust her health carer.

Any of these situations can affect the physiological process of labour as a woman's birthing body is designed to shut down when it senses it is not safe to birth, and that can happen from something as simple as too many people looking at her. So all her other knowledge and skills and ideas for labour may be thrown out the window, as she is now dealing with issues that can threaten the natural progress of her labour without the woman even knowing it. Being in situations like this can also create a threatening or combative atmosphere in the birth room, which can be a tricky situation in which to use the extra skills these birth preparation programs can offer.

Alternatively, if the woman feels safe and supported and able to 'check out' mentally (moving away from the thinking part of her brain) and to be centered in the present moment, then the chances are that her hormones will work beautifully to choreograph her labour. She may then be in a space to find that the learnings she has received from any birth preparation classes or her own research are now able to come forth and support her as they are designed to, to honour and work with what the body is naturally doing anyway.

Unfortunately, without a safe, supportive and peaceful space, the woman whose birthing needs are unmet has to work too hard against nature for those skills to be used optimally. It is important to know that your extra knowledge about birth can be extremely beneficial. If you decide to have a baby in the future, you can make wonderful use of this prior knowledge – and the new information you are gaining from this book – as you process previous births. Next time, you can take steps to ensure that those around you also understand the importance of your emotional and physiological needs being met. That, combined with your level of understanding about birth, can work together to create a positive, empowering birth, no matter how you are birthing. For a more in depth look at this, read *Why wouldn't my body work in labour?* (p230) to understand how to create the ideal atmosphere for using your skills and knowledge about birth.

## Tools for healing when you've read all the right books and still had a bad birth

- Sometimes, just reading the section above and understanding how it applies to your own situation can be enough to kickstart healing.

- Many women come to the realisation that they *did not fail*, and maybe that *they were failed*. They might have been failed by a system that didn't provide them with an environment and support conducive to birthing or with enough information to make informed decisions. They might have been failed by their health carers, who may have (often unwittingly) inadequately cared for them during birth, or failed to listen, or reacted in response to their own fears and prejudices (see *I'm so angry with my health carers* (p163) to find ways to deal with this).

- You might be getting with your health carer if you felt that they did not put you in a situation where your body could do its job, even though you felt so informed. This certainly may be justified, and it can be important to express this appropriately. Go to the section *I'm so angry with my health carers* (p163) to get some healthy ideas on how to explore and process your anger.

- You might feel anger at support people, such as your partner, friend or parent. This may be understandable; however, it is important to remember that they most likely had no idea about this information. They most likely did not know the importance of the environment to your hormones.
  Or the importance of you not being disturbed, which means that you may have some 'stuff' to process about all that. See our section *Issues with your partner* (p291) for some ideas (it doesn't matter if it was your partner or other support people, you will still find help in that section for dealing with any anger that has arisen).

Reflect on the new understanding about birth that you are developing as a result of reading this book. If you were already very informed about birth, this new information will add to your knowledge. How will this new information be reflected in the choices you make for future births? What are you learning about what you will need or not need? Or, if you are not planning any more babies, how will you share understandings about 'what is important in birth' with your friends, and even your own children, so they grow up with an awareness of birth that will support them when they are ready for their own families?

# I feel sad

## DEALING WITH SADNESS

*I felt so sad that I hadn't picked up my baby girl and loved her and welcomed her into the world when she was born. I really wanted the chance to do this over. I kept reliving this part.* **Sally**

*I felt a deep sadness I did not understand and wondered why I could not shake these feelings of major disappointment. I had to grieve the birth that I missed out on… I had such high expectations that it would be an experience of raw excitement and elation. It took a lot of time to work through when it eventuated differently. I always longed for a normal vaginal birth without even knowing it.* **Kerri**

*In the early days it was hard – especially when all anyone cares about is the baby's wellbeing, especially when they are still in hospital (our baby was premature). Or when, after all the drama, the baby is okay. Then of course it's, "What are you talking about, crazy lady, it all worked out in the end". I have a history of being denied raw grief in my family as well, so it was no surprise to find myself alone when it came to talking about the losses I have suffered.* **Diana**

*I remember when my son was a few months old, we had this happy moment in the car with him, where I was reaching into the back seat and tickling him under the chin and he was bubbling with gurgles of laughter. My husband, myself and my baby were all laughing and laughing. I wrote a poem about it that night, thinking I was going to write about this happy moment. But the last line of the poem was, "His laughter is the salve that heals my pain". I was confused: what pain? I had a healthy son, didn't I? What could I possibly have to be in pain about?"* **Melissa**

*It was my birthday yesterday, and I got all dressed up, picked up my husband from work, was quiet and short-tempered all the way to the cafe. We got to our table in this funky little cafe, sat down, got our menu each – and I burst into tears and could not stop crying. Sometimes I just feel this is just too much to handle, all this grief and sadness and pain in my heart – and I have to hide it from most people, as they don't understand. I feel so isolated from other happy mums, from everyone really; it's as though my actions and reactions are a little out of whack. I feel like I just want some 'time off' from this intensity of sadness. It has really hit me, after lying dormant for two-and-a-half years, all these feelings.* **Jane**

## Dealing with grief and sad feelings

Feelings of sadness are often an undercurrent to a woman's daily life after a traumatic birth. This can be confusing, because everyone keeps telling us we 'should be grateful', and often we ourselves are thinking the same thing, and push the sadness away, unaware of its origins.

Sometimes the sadness is masked by strong anger, and once the anger has begun to be explored and expressed and acknowledged, it melts into deep grief. That is okay – and good. It means you are peeling layers off the onion, and going further along the healing path. The amount of sadness that arises may seem overwhelming initially, so it is really important that you have some tools for handling the grief.

# The big sob

We often have women attend Birthtalk who do not realise just how much sorrow they are holding inside, and it can take a few sessions for it to arise. It can come bubbling up and out, almost without warning, when a woman feels safe and has debriefed a certain amount of her birth, and often when she is beginning to realise just how much she has missed out on. She may begin to sob – deep, harrowing sobs from within – where her body goes limp with the letting go of these hidden emotions. If this happens, just know that it is okay. These tears need to come. They need to be released, and doing so is healthy and healing. We have held many women as they weep, finally feeling the sadness they have been denied by our culture's lack of understanding about traumatic birth.

> *I was at my pregnancy yoga class, working towards a better experience than my previous traumatic birth which ended in caesarean. A woman was invited by the yoga teacher to share her beautiful birth story with the group – a natural birth in a birth centre (which was what I'd planned for my previous birth). Then the teacher read out a story that, perhaps because it followed the telling of a birth story that was exactly how I'd wanted my first birth to be like, struck at my heart. It was a simple but heartfelt piece about lost dreams and changes in plans, with the message that the pain of such a loss is valid, and that it's okay to feel sad. And as she finished reading I felt this desperate sob billow up from deep within me. I folded over, wrapped myself around my pregnant belly and just bawled. It was so raw and open and I was bellowing. I felt a distant sense of slight embarrassment, and also a need to pull back so I didn't freak out the first-time mums-to-be in the class. It was the end of the class, so everyone quietly packed up and left while I curled up on my yoga mat and sobbed and sobbed. The teacher indicated for the woman who had shared her birth story earlier to come and hold me. The teacher held me too, and I felt such a depth of acceptance and love and support. I also felt very strongly their trust in birth, that I was being held by women who had experienced empowering births, and I clung to their strength. I left that session feeling wrung out, but also in a new place. I'd acknowledged the loss, finally. And I'd begun to grieve the loss, at last. And now we could move forward. I was no longer stuck.* **Melissa**

## Why am I so sad?

Sometimes the challenge can be to figure out just what you are sad about.

In our section *Why doesn't anyone get it?* (p129) we talk about why it can be so hard to receive validation for a difficult birth experience in our culture. If we are led to believe that a traumatic birth is a 'normal' birth, and that we should feel grateful if we have a healthy baby, then the reasons for any sadness can be difficult to pinpoint.

An important part of the healing process can be identifying the loss (or losses) you have experienced. It might be the loss of the dream of how you had planned to welcome your child into the world. It might be the loss of a peaceful, calm experience where you felt in control and nurtured. It might be a physiological loss, where you might just know you feel 'empty' or 'like something is missing', which can be a result of missing out on the hormones that are meant to accompany birth, that stimulate breastfeeding, enhance our bonding with our child, and smooth our first steps into motherhood.

## How do I process the sadness?

Sometimes it might get tricky to maintain contact with the pain and sadness so you can access the insights and lessons. This is where our *Tools for your healing journey* (p403) come in. To investigate the origin of your grief, or to explore the impact of it on your life postpartum, you can try any or all of the following:

- Doing a *Birthtalk Breakdown* (p47) to find out the emotions you were experiencing during the birth. It may be enough to enable you to see just what the experience was like for you, which may bring up feelings of grief that you can then acknowledge and process.

- Read *Why doesn't anyone get it?* (p129) to gain more clarity about why it can be so hard to connect with feelings of sadness, when our culture does not understand birth, or acknowledge the significance of a birth experience on a woman's life postnatally;

- Read *I was separated from my baby* (p250) to learn about the 'dance towards motherhood' our bodies are undertaking during birth, and the consequences for us when certain steps in that dance, and therefore certain hormonal advantages are missed. This section is helpful even if you weren't separated from your baby.

- Have a go at *Using art as a healing tool* (p461). This can be a great exercise to pull up feelings and unpack them in a safe situation. It may give you insight about your thinking or your responses that will move your healing forward.

- Try reading *Self-discovery: what's really going on for me?* (p457) Set yourself sentences to explore such as, "I feel sad when I think about my birth because…" Take one of your responses to this, for example: "My baby was left without me for too long" and explore it. "The fact that my baby was left without me for too long makes me feel sad because…" Just keep going, following new paths, exploring new possibilities and opportunities to address the sadness.

- Write a letter to your child where you talk about sadness. Just start each sentence with, "I feel sad about…" or "It makes me so sad that…" or "I am grieving for…" or "I am so sad that…" And if you feel that you want to finish the letter on a more positive note, see the *Shifting from anger exercise* (p433) for further tips on moving through the emotions from sadness to love.

For some more specific issues surrounding sadness, see: *Saying the words you couldn't say at the birth: a reconnection tool* (p421), *Why take the healing journey?* (p76).

# I WAS SEPARATED FROM MY BABY

*We were separated after the birth. It has had a massive impact on bonding and I think it has affected my baby deeply in the areas of trust, attachment, independence and behavioural problems.* **Jana**

*We were only separated for an hour. But it was too long. For a long time after the birth I grieved for that hour… or I would have if I'd known how.* **Melissa**

## What you need to know

Being separated from your baby is *never* a small thing. Even if you were 'only' apart for an hour or less, it is still important. That is, it can be an important loss.

Separation from the baby after the birth is something that often comes up in Birthtalk. It doesn't always come up straight away, as there are often issues of anger and confusion and blame that need to be dealt with first. However, when a woman begins to sort through her birth, and often after she has done a *Birthtalk Breakdown*, she can begin to see other parts of the birth and postnatal experience arising that are painful and distressing.

## Why does it hurt so much to be separated?

Even if you know your baby is being well looked after, even if your partner is with your baby, it is still significant that you were separated. The reason it is so painful is simple: mothers and babies are designed to be together. Australian research found that "the separation of the mother – baby dyad was found to have a devastating impact on maternal – newborn attachment that lasted well into the postnatal period".[151] While this research was undertaken with women who were having medically necessary caesareans, we have seen a wide variety of women, however they gave birth, who have been impacted in numerous ways when the mother and baby were separated.

Physiologically, women are being primed during a birth to become a mother. All the hormones are trying to set you up to mother your child when they are born. This is not just an emotional thing – it is happening at a physical level. So even

---

151    Bayes, S., Fenwick, J., & Hauck, Y. (2012). 'Off everyone's radar: Australian women's experiences of medically necessary elective caesarean section. *Midwifery, 28*(6), e900-9. doi: 10.1016/j.midw.2012.01.004.

if you *know* your baby needs to be separated from you for their best chance of survival, your body is waiting, primed and wanting to care for the baby who is supposed to be there.

## The dance to motherhood

We sometimes explain this using an analogy: imagine if labour, birth and the immediate transitional period following the birth was a beautiful, perfectly choreographed dance for a mother and baby. Each dance is unique and individual, yet all include similar elements: our imaginings; a mother and baby moving and working together; deep instinct; involvement of our body, mind and spirit; inbuilt and newly stimulated reflexes; love; connection; euphoria; joy; bonding; our dreams and hopes; physiological changes; hormonal potions swirling; and a collision (or crescendo) of all the senses – smell, sight, sound, touch, and taste.

This dance usually includes a series of predetermined steps along the way that finalise our preparation for motherhood and allow us to traverse safely, beautifully and seamlessly with ease across the floor into our new role and relationship. Feelings of deep satisfaction, confidence and capability are usually an associated consequence. Imagine that it is this dance that gives the mother and baby the physiological gifts, priming them for an optimal postnatal period.

## When the dance is interrupted

When this dance towards the optimal setting for mothering does not occur, or steps are missed, women know, even if they don't understand it. Many women voice disappointment and a sense of loss of their imaginings of how they would welcome their baby into the world and lovingly hold them. Many women share that they felt a sense of emptiness, like 'something was missing'. Often these feelings are accompanied by guilt, that they 'should be grateful' that it wasn't worse or yearning for 'something more' for themselves or their baby. But usually we have found what's happening is that they have missed out on aspects of 'the dance' – on important steps that occur in a normal undisturbed birth and, therefore, missed the gifts these steps offer to support their transition into motherhood.

Using this analogy, in the hours after birth, a woman's mind and body are trying to complete these steps, with all their resultant benefits (from a physiological point of view), allowing for her to seamlessly move into her role as a mother.

So what are these predetermined steps that seem to occur in a normal, undisturbed birth and what are the results of their interplay?

## The steps of the dance

The following table shows some events that occur in a normal, undisturbed birth. Each event plays its part to produce the optimum hormonal mix that provides safety, stimulates bonding, initiates breastfeeding, brings maternal instinct, supports early mothering behaviours and supports your baby's adaptation to the outside world.

These events occur throughout various stages during labour, birth and the immediate postnatal period igniting the production and interplay of hormones to further aid the mother and baby in their journey.

Some of these events, along with some of the prominent hormonal interactions, are explained.

| Event (or dance step) | What happens for the mother and baby |
|---|---|
| The work of labour (while feeling safe) | The uterus does its work predominantly under the influence of oxytocin, allowing for safe, efficient contractions and also priming mother and baby with the 'hormone of love' to support their bonding and deep connection post-birth. |
| Transition | Hormonal changes allow for strength and safety for the final stages of birthing your baby. They also cause mother and baby to be excited and alert immediately after the birth to allow for bonding, caring, nuzzling, feeding etc. to occur. Hormonal changes also continue to prime the baby to have a successful adaptation to the extra-uterine world by supporting effective heart and lung functioning, stabilising blood sugar levels and maintaining the baby's body temperature to name a few. |
| Vaginal birth | Baby passing through vaginal canal and exiting the mother's body allowing her to see it is HER baby and produces extra surges of oxytocin to add to the feelings of euphoria and love when the mother and baby meet. |

| Event (or dance step) | What happens for the mother and baby |
| --- | --- |
| Slippery baby gathered up onto belly and then chest | Skin-to-skin contact and the exchange of smells stimulate more hormonal interplay including oxytocin and prolactin – the hormone of mothering and maternal instinct. The capillaries in the mother's chest dilate and provide an inbuilt heating system for the baby, keeping them warm. |
| Baby in arms nuzzling and rooting for breast | Oxytocin and prolactin stimulate breastfeeding, further aiding in the delivery of the placenta or the clamping down of the uterus to prevent haemorrhage. |
| Mother examining, touching, exploring every part of her baby | This natural urge is driven by, and produces, further hormonal release supporting maternal behaviour. The hormones give the mother the desire to put her baby's needs first with deep satisfaction. |
| Placenta birthed and seen by mother | Signifying the end of the birth, completion and acknowledgement of the mother's amazing role in growing and birthing their baby. |
| Baby skin-to-skin at the mother's breast and remaining there. | Further hormone stimulation, adds to the woman's confidence in being a mother, promoting a happy family unit, bonding, aids the baby being able to self-attach to the breast and feed, stimulating milk production and beginning the mother's transition to a non-pregnant state safely with controlled blood loss, body fluid changes and further hormonal changes. A further benefit of the hormones to the mother are changes in her sleep cycle and REM sleep, allowing her to feel sufficiently rested on short periods of interrupted sleep, a gift for baby care and the breastfeeding relationship to follow. |

These events are some of the steps we refer to in the 'dance towards motherhood' our body and mind is expecting. This hormonal dance provides the only resources that a woman generally needs to be able to care for her child herself, and for them both to have the best chance of survival. Even though we are living in the twenty-first century and can have a conscious awareness and understanding of what's going on, our bodies still respond as if there are no other resources available to us.

Note: We want to acknowledge the work of Dr Sarah Buckley, which has inspired and informed our own work with women, especially in the area of understanding the hormones involved in birth. For further understanding regarding the hormonal interplay of labour and birth, we highly recommend Dr Buckley's book, "Gentle Birth, Gentle Mothering".[152] She presents this information in a highly accessible manner that invites reflection on how amazing women's bodies are, and respects the complexities going on within us during birth as our bodies strive to prepare the optimal setting for the survival, and thriving, of ourselves and our babies. See her website at *www.sarahbuckley.com*.

## When some steps are missed

IIn many traumatic births, parts of the list of events above will be missing. Whether it's labour that is missing, or that you didn't receive a slippery baby on your chest, or even just missing out on viewing the placenta after the birth, can all have implications for you hormonally, which can affect how you feel.

Missing some steps in the dance may result in a number of things:

- **Bonding challenges:** As many of the hormones have not been stimulated at the optimal levels, there can be a feeling of numbness towards the baby, of robotically caring for the child without the deep affection expected.

- **Breastfeeding issues:** The lack of hormones can also affect the ability to breastfeed and the baby's attachment at the breast, as these hormones were supposed to induce a good let-down of milk, and stimulate the baby to naturally seek and attach to the mother's breast and feed.

- **Reduced hormonal support with newborn care:** Chronic sleep deprivation can be suffered from interrupted nights caring for a newborn without the hormonal support to mitigate it.

- **A lack of confidence in mothering:** You may not feeling any maternal instinct and, again, without hormonal support, begin to feel begrudging when having to continually put your baby's needs ahead of your own. This can also lead to you believe that you are not a maternal person.

- **A sense of confusion:** You may know the baby is yours logically, yet you might feel somehow distant or separated from the baby and not being completely sure that the birth is 'finished'.

- **Baby's wellness challenged:** There is an increased likelihood of issues in caring for your baby, with many babies having challenges adapting to the extra-uterine world without having had the optimal hormonal support to do so, perhaps resulting in respiratory challenges, not maintaining body temperature, low blood sugars, attachment or feeding issues, general unsettledness or agitation.

---

152    Buckley, S. J. (2009). *Gentle Birth, Gentle Mothering: A Doctor's Guide to Natural Childbirth and Gentle Early Parenting Choices.* Celestial Arts, Berkeley CA.

We've found that if most of these steps do not happen, the mind seems to just hover in a holding pattern, waiting for these needs to be met, or for the dance to conclude. So if your baby is separated from you, that is, if they are 'missing', even if you know where she is, your body and brain may respond to that as a loss. You are physiologically primed to receive the baby, so it is significant to not have them with you. It is the final step in the dance towards motherhood. You need to know that this is the way it was meant to be, before you can grieve that it wasn't like that.

## This wasn't how it was supposed to be

When we imagine our baby's arrival, we rarely imagine being separated. In a situation where there is something wrong, being separated may be necessary to ensure your child's survival – and of course that is what you want. You may feel torn between wanting your child to be safe, and desperately wanting your child snuggled up with you.

Or your baby may be separated from you due to hospital protocol, even when there may not be anything wrong with them. You might not actually recognise the significance of the separation at the time, as you are recovering from the birth. It might be only later that you begin to mourn that time apart. Either way, it wasn't how you imagined it would be. This doesn't mean you set your expectations too high – it is natural to expect that you will be with your child. It is the natural order of things. So if that order gets upset, then there can definitely be consequences.

## Loss of control

One aspect of the emotional pain can come from a loss of control. Chances are the decision to separate a woman from her child has been made by someone else. Even when the reasons to do so may be valid from a physical health aspect, a woman is rarely invited to take part in the decision-making process that results in this separation. This might be because it is merely hospital policy, so in the minds of the health carers, there is no decision to be made. Or the woman might be too unwell to be involved. Either way, there is commonly a feeling of being out of control in this situation.

## What was happening to my baby?

Women are (often unknowingly) wanting to fulfill their mothering instinct of being with their baby, and this separation, and lack of control over the separation, can be extremely distressing, especially if you don't know what was happening to your baby. Women often say they wondered things like: Who was touching my baby? Did they cry? Did they need me? Were they fed?

Sometimes women don't even know *where* their baby is, so that becomes distressing in itself – the not knowing. Or seeing photos or video of the baby being held by other family members, sometimes even *before* the mother has had a chance to meet her baby, can bring up enormous feelings of hurt and pain and jealousy. These feelings are completely understandable even though the family probably wouldn't have any idea that they are causing you pain.

## An extra checklist

This leads us to some additional (seemingly small) steps that we have found support women in closing the book on their birth, and feeling like the baby is theirs. They are the final few steps in this dance towards motherhood, and are not often mentioned. Women often miss out on many of these steps when they are separated from their babies.

- Being able to identify and announce the gender of the child.
- Being first to hold the child and to continue to hold or be physically close to child in the hours after birth
- Being the key decision maker in her child's whereabouts and care post-birth
- Being able to commence caring for the baby.

We have found, amongst the women we have worked with over the years, there are some common outcomes when the above additional steps are experienced, and common outcomes when they are not. We have outlined some of these outcomes we have observed below :

### Being able to identify and announce the gender of the child.

A woman may find a strong sense of empowerment in being the first to examine her newborn and to have the opportunity to discover and announce the gender of the child she nurtured and grew and birthed. However, feelings of disappointment and disempowerment can result when this step is taken from the women, or she may even experience merely a vague feeling that it was 'not right', but she is unable to 'put a finger on it'. For some women, having someone else identify and announce her child's gender can be the final disempowering step in a birth where they did not feel like the key player. Not all women feel this. Many are happy that another person announces the gender, but we do get a lot of Birthtalk women who voice this as a true loss.

### Being first to hold the child and to continue to hold or be physically close to child in the hours after birth

This is a final triumph of bearing the fruits of her hard work, as well having the physiological benefits of the mother and baby smelling each other's smells, which stimulates a woman's hormones for milk-production, bonding and has other benefits. (You can read more about this in *Breastfeeding was just so challenging* (p269)). We often work with women who are grieving at being the last to hold their babies. This seems to be such a strong desire, and understandably so, considering the effort and endurance required to grow a baby for nine months, and then to go through any kind of birth scenario. To be the last, or even just not the first, person to hold the newborn can feel somehow 'wrong'.

### Being the key decision maker in her child's whereabouts and care post-birth

This is the beginnings of mothering, when a woman decides where her baby should be, and with whom, whether that is with herself, her partner, a grandmother, or in special care. Making that decision with information and instincts that have been kickstarted by the hormones can promote confidence and a sense of being the 'most important person' along with her partner, in this child's survival. However, feelings of fear, of being out-of-control, of worry, or being 'not important' can result from not being involved in these decisions. Feelings of helplessness and even failure may arise as the mother's primary role is not acknowledged or enabled to be undertaken. Due to not being involved, women may struggle with confidence in decision making surrounding their child.

### Being able to commence caring for the baby.

The steps of learning to care for a new baby, when a mother is supported by those around her and her hormones, gradually leads to confidence and skill, both of which build as she increases in experience. Unfortunately, we've seen that feelings of being useless, a failure, out of control, and lack of confidence in mothering can result due to being deprived of these experiences that build this skill and confidence.

This list above is just an example of how women, and their babies, can be impacted by missing out on the little things. It becomes apparent that they are not little things at all, and could be contributing greatly to why you might be feeling bad. Unfortunately, if you were separated from your baby, chances are you missed out on many of these things. This can lead to confusion and isolation, which is not how we planned the first moments, weeks and months with our baby.

## What can I do now?

There is a lot you can do to mend the broken link in the chain of what was supposed to happen.

## Healing and reconnecting

The first step in healing and reconnecting is understanding why what we experienced is felt as a 'loss', which is why we have explained it above. The next step is acknowledging that it is a loss, and allowing yourself to feel the feelings rather than bottle them up and try and get over it. You were separated from your baby. It hurts. Some tools for getting in touch with those feelings of sadness are outlined below.

## Saying what couldn't be said

We have written a section specifically to support you telling your child those things you could never say due to being separated. Many women find this a particularly powerful exercise. See *Saying the words you couldn't say at the birth: a reconnection tool* (p421) for more details.

## Write a letter to your child that they will never receive

See *The unsent letter* (p468) for more ideas on how to use this tool in your healing. However as a start, consider these prompt questions as you start to compose a letter to your child. Remember this is not a letter you will give them. It is a letter they will never receive.

- However as a start, consider these prompt questions as you start to compose a letter to your child. Remember this is not a letter you will give them. It is a letter they will never receive.

- Tell your child what you had been planning for their arrival, what you imagined it would be and how sorry you are that it did not turn out that way. We want to make it clear that this is not your fault.
- Let them know how it felt to be separated from them.
- If you were not fully conscious during that time, or have no recollection of it, tell them how it feels now when you think about how you were separated.
- If you were apart for days and you had to leave the hospital without them, tell them how that felt. You can tell them how it felt in your body – in your heart, in your head, in your arms – to have to be away from them.
- Tell them what you wish was different. You can ask for their forgiveness if you feel you need to. We do not ever think the woman is to blame, but sometimes it can help to do this step.
- Tell them what you are doing now to work through the birth, so you can be more available and present for them.
- Tell them how you are feeling about them right now.
- Sometimes, it can be really helpful to write a 'reply' from your child. Just write as your baby, and you might be surprised at the forgiveness and willingness to embrace what happened that comes out of this.

## Do some birth art

See our section *Using art as a healing tool* (p461) to find out more about this exercise. However as a start consider the following prompts as a healing exercise:

- Perhaps draw where your baby was when you were separated, and where you were, and how you felt.
- Or just draw you, perhaps with empty arms, or with a weeping heart, or whatever symbolises the loss for you.

These images can portray the impact of that situation so strongly, and enable us to truly acknowledge the significance of grieving for lost opportunities.

## Work to actively *reclaim* those lost hours or days or weeks

Although you can't change what happened, you can give your body and brain a second chance to reclaim some steps in the dance toward motherhood, by using a number of tools and exercises that can mend the hurt, and renew the bond with your child. Many Birthtalk mums use these tools with great effect, and we have witnessed their relationship with their child blossom and take a new direction, as well as ease the pain and intensity around the issue. To see these tools, go to *Reconnecting with your child – games for reconnecting* (p415) and work through any ideas that resonate with you. There are some lovely stories there of women who have worked through similar issues. If you have struggled to bond with your baby, read *I don't feel bonded to my child* (p218) and explore the tools listed there.

## Finally...

Go gently with yourself. These may be very hard issues to face. You may find these letters difficult to write, and these drawings challenging to create, and these emotions all-engulfing as you 'go there'. You may want to reach out for support if there is a lot to process. And we are sending you a huge hug as you journey this path.

Note: It is important to know for future births that if some steps of the dance are missed, you can plan to compensate for this now you know of their importance. There are ways to replicate the hormones, or maximise the available hormones and find other ways to still complete the dance. For example, if a mother is separated from her baby, it can be helpful to keep something with the smell of the baby with the mother (stimulating hormones) and the smell of the mother's breast (perhaps a cloth wiped with some colostrum) with the baby. Minimising their separation and promoting and facilitating as much skin- to-skin contact as possible can also be very beneficial for bonding, feeding and attachment in this situation. You can read more about this in *Reconnecting with your child* (p409).

# HOW DO I DEAL WITH MY CHILD'S BIRTHDAY?

A child's birthday can be a confusing event for the mother when the birth was difficult, challenging or traumatic. It can trigger a roller coaster of emotions ranging from joy that your child is a year older, gratitude that you have made it through another year, relief that you are further away from 'that day' of the birth, and sadness that you still feel so bad even though another year has gone by.

> *The party was meant to be about celebrating my son's first birthday, but how could I when I hadn't actually celebrated him for myself? It was just a reminder that one year ago I felt confused, violated and traumatised by his birth.* **Cora**

## The countdown to a crisis?

Turbulent feelings can begin in the days leading up to the birthday, as the anticipation of getting to 'that date' rises. This can be made more intense if the early labour or pre-labour time was traumatic too.

> *The lead up to my son's [first] birthday started getting hard from nine days before his birthday, as this was when I was admitted to hospital and my whole traumatic experience really started from that day. Each day for the nine days before his birthday, I would catch myself looking at my watch, thinking, "This time last year I was lying in the hospital bed. This time last year they told me they wanted to induce me. This time last year they told me… " and so on, even waking up in the middle of the night recalling memories of what had happened this time last year.* **Kate**

## Cultural void

This situation is made even more confusing by the fact that our culture does not tend to recognise any negative emotions in relation to a birthday, except maybe a tinge of sadness that the child is growing up, with people making comments such as, "We'll have to put a brick on your head to stop you from growing up so fast!" To most people, a birthday is a chance to celebrate the child reaching another milestone, which of course it is and this milestone absolutely deserves to be celebrated.

Unfortunately, because the majority of people within our culture do not understand the importance of our birth experience to everything that comes afterwards, because they do not know that birth matters, we do not have a place within the celebration of a birthday to honour that it is the mother's day of birth too.

## Is it bad to feel bad about this special day?

A lot of the distress around a birthday can come from feelings of confusion and guilt about feeling so bad on what is supposed to be a day of celebration. So it is important, firstly, to understand and separate the feelings.

Contrary to what you might hear, a woman's acknowledgement that she feels bad about her baby's birth does not make her a bad mother. It is not a reflection of her love for her child. It is simply a statement of fact – she found the situations surrounding her baby's arrival distressing.

Understanding this is so important, yet can be so difficult to grasp as we tend to assume the good feelings of birth come from actually getting your baby, and nothing else matters. We assume that if you get your baby, you must be happy. But that is only part of it.

The other part involves how we felt when we were meeting our baby, which depends not only on what happened during the birth, but also on factors such as: if we felt cared for, how safe we felt, how we were treated, whether we felt we were being listened to and what information we were given. Feeling safe, acknowledged and respected is important for us to feel good about any major life event (think first day of school, first foray into dating, first sexual experience). Yet these feelings of safety, acknowledgement and respect are often lacking or absent in birth within our culture.

It is actually possible for a woman to celebrate her child's birthday milestone at the same time as acknowledging she doesn't feel good about what happened during the baby's arrival. However to do so, she needs to be supported in understanding that they are separate issues and that birth does have an impact.

## Are you still upset about that?

It is unlikely that a woman will receive the understanding and nurturing required from the people around her, who may not realise that she still struggles with her birth. We find that most people expect that by the time the baby is six-months-old, any grief around the birth will be forgotten, and that a mother will have moved on. This is rarely the case when there has been a traumatic birth.

We find that once the baby is older, that's actually when the feelings of trauma can arise. It makes sense as there is more emotional 'space' when the baby is no longer a newborn with such high needs. Many people respond with surprise to hear that a woman is still recovering emotionally from a traumatic birth – even the woman herself may find it surprising. This can make it hard to access appropriate support to deal with an upcoming birthday. One woman reveals:

> *My husband was supportive when I spoke with him and relived the memories with him, but I didn't really feel comfortable telling anyone else what I was thinking; I knew they would all tell me that it was a year ago and he was here and healthy so it was time to forget about all that! On my son's birthday, nobody acknowledged my birth experience or any of the things I had experienced in the lead-up and post-birth. Family and friends seemed to just want to 'celebrate' and nobody mentioned his birth at all.*

However, the anniversary of a birth, any birth, is worthy of reflection and pause. It is a mighty event in a woman's life for herself, not just in terms of meeting her baby. Understanding and honouring this is essential in the journey to healing.

## When the impact of birth is understood

Through our work with Birthtalk, we know many women who have a very different view of birthing to the mainstream view.

These women have access to information about birth that is not readily available to most women…information that enables them to understand the importance of birth to what follows. As a result, they tend to see birthdays differently.

Even before the baby is born, these women are treating the mother differently. They often do not have a baby shower, where the baby is the focus and showered with gifts such as nappies, musical mobiles and blankets. Instead, they often opt for a 'blessingway', a celebration where the focus is on the mother and the mother's journey through birth to meet her little one is honoured. The gifts are symbolic, usually beads or trinkets to signify strength, courage, determination, surrender – qualities needed for labour, birth and postnatal parenting. The mother wears these beads during labour to remind herself of the emotional strength she has for this task and of all the women who have taken this journey previously.

We have noticed that when these women announce a child's birthday on Facebook, it is often accompanied by a brief account of their birth experience. Their friends on Facebook usually make two comments: one for the child to wish them a happy birthday, and one for the mother in acknowledgement of her anniversary of her birthing day. If the mother has had a traumatic birth, then that is acknowledged too. There is understanding and compassion that it might be a difficult day, as well as talk of the woman's strength and determination.

When birth is seen as the woman's rite of passage, there is space to understand the gravity of the situation if that passage is traumatic. Sadly, in our wider culture, this is not usually the case.

## Unwanted questions

Ainslea came to our *'Healing From Birth'* support group nervously anticipating her child's first birthday in a week's time. She shared with us that she had thirty-five people descending on her house for birthday celebrations, and she was feeling overwhelmed. Her biggest worry was two-fold: that she would get questions about when they would start trying for another baby, and that she would get jovial comments about her birth experience, which unfortunately took place quite publicly during a natural disaster.

She worried that she wouldn't cope with the questions, as she truly wasn't sure if they would have any more children after the trauma of their firstborn's arrival, and she felt too vulnerable to share where she was with that issue. She worried that she might 'fall apart' at the party, which was not at all what she wanted.

She did manage to get through the day unscathed, partly due to the healing path she was already on after attending our sessions for a few months and partly with the help of some prepared answers that enabled her to feel she was staying true to herself, without putting her heart on her sleeve. We share more about Ainslea's experience in our tips section below.

## Dealing with 'that' day

> *The birthday was a big 'celebration'. Nobody mentioned his birth at all. I got myself as busy as possible decorating, cooking, setting up and cleaning so that I tried not to give myself too long just to sit and think about it. I did have a lot of flashbacks that day, and was staring at my watch a lot, remembering every single thing that had happened and reliving some of the experiences in my head.* **Kate**

So how can you manage any growing feelings of dread and panic that arise as a birthday approaches? How can you deal with the people around you, who likely will not understand that this is a difficult day for you? And how will you deal with the actual day?

Fortunately, there are a lot of things you can do to pave the way for an easier birthday period, and working through them can actually be extremely helpful in the overall healing process after a traumatic birth.

As Ainslea found, it can be really helpful to take steps to actively prepare for the birthday itself. There is also much value in using the strong emotions arising as an opportunity to process aspects of the birth, and gain new insights about what happened to you. It can be a chance to take a few more steps along the path to healing.

## Tips for a better birthday

- **Acknowledge the situation.** It is important to acknowledge that you are dreading or feeling uneasy about an approaching birthday, and also that you know why. It is not because you are a bad mum; it is because you have unresolved feelings about the situations surrounding your child's birth.

- **Separate the issues.** It's important to remember that you are dealing with two different things: firstly, your feelings about the birth and secondly, your feelings about your child. You feel bad about what happened at your child's birth, and don't want to celebrate the experience of that. This is understandable, and reasonable considering your experience. This is also separate to how you feel about your child. If you feel that you can't separate your feelings about your birth from your feelings about your child, that's okay too. It is just an indicator that you have some work to do in your healing journey, to unravel your birth experience so you can separate the issues.

- **Honour yourself.** You may not find the support you need or an understanding of the magnitude of the birthday for you from the people around you. So it may be up to you to honour your own milestone. You've made it through a whole year. You've been through so much. Honour the birthday as your birth day. It is special, not just because it is the day your child arrived, it is also the day you, as a mother, arrived. This is important and worthy of honoring. Can you give yourself something symbolic to represent an honouring of how hard you've had to work to overcome this birth? Maybe a little potted plant to symbolise new growth, or a smooth shiny precious stone that symbolises strength and determination, or a fresh journal to document your healing journey, or even a new dress! One woman honoured her experience by acknowledging that there were very valid reasons to grieve:

> *I also re-watched the video of my son's birth with my husband the night before his birthday – we cried a lot and saw all the things we had been trying to forget had happened. But I think watching it again helped us grieve too, because it reminded us that all the grief and sad feelings we had felt from time to time in the year since his birth had been legitimate. We really did have reason to grieve. When we went back and watched the birth video with all the knowledge of what birth could and should be that we have gained from Birthtalk since, it was a huge step for me to realise that night that I wasn't crazy; I really did have these reasons to be sad.*

Note – This woman had been attending Birthtalk for a number of months, and had explored her experience intensely. She had released feelings of failure, guilt and grief and had gained more information and understanding about what had taken place in her birth. Her husband had attended Birthtalk as well, and had a clearer understanding of his wife's experience and his own. It was due to this work that she felt she could look at the video at this time. It may not be right for other women to look at their birth video until they have reached a certain place in their healing and have appropriate support.

- **Take time to grieve.** The birthday party is probably not an appropriate place to debrief the birth, so if you have not already, it might be helpful to write an account of the birth to just clear it from your head enough to get through the party. Perhaps this also might be time to write in your journal, maybe do some exercises such as writing a compassionate letter to the woman you were, on the day of the birth. What would you say to her? How do you wish she had been supported? What does she need? The process of answering these questions may give you more insights into how your birth has affected you, what feelings you have about yourself and the birth now, and what you have learned. It can also offer some ideas on where you need to focus your attention in the healing journey. Keep in mind you might need some emotional support to undertake this exercise: from a counsellor, or your partner if they are open to this, a good friend, or an understanding birth worker. And go gently with yourself.

> *At Birthtalk, I learned about the power of journaling and letter writing, and used these skills to deal with my feelings in the lead-up. Then, on my son's birthday, when I got home from the party I wrote him a big, long letter telling him what I wished his birth had been like, and what I wished my memory was full of*

*instead of what I did remember. This was so helpful! As I wrote to
my son of the birth experience I had wished for him, I felt such a
release of all the grief I had felt all day.* **Kate**

- **Prepare for tricky questions.** While your birth may not have been
  empowering, you can certainly now plan for an empowering birthday event.
  As Ainslea discovered, thinking ahead and being honest about what you
  fear can give you insights into what you will find helpful on the big day.
  Ask yourself, "What am I most afraid of being asked/people saying?" When
  trying to compose a ready-made response, focus on the love you have for
  your child as a way to deflect an unwelcome comment, as Ainslea did below.
  When she brought up her fears at our *'Healing From Birth'* session, we did
  some troubleshooting as a group, coming up with some ideas of what to say
  to fend off unwelcome, prying questions that she did not feel comfortable
  answering. Ainslea reported back that she survived the party, and only had
  to fall back on the answers she'd prepared a couple of times. She was able to
  answer a comment of, "I bet you're wanting another one!" with a casually
  delivered, "Actually not really... we're just enjoying watching him grow at
  the moment".

  > *To survive the party and family, I went for an in-between of the
  > two extremes of grinning and bearing it and being upfront that
  > I wasn't completed happy or satisfied. I came out and said to a
  > few people that I hadn't really seen since the birth that, "My son's
  > birth wasn't at all how I imagined it, I wasn't planning a C-section
  > and I felt ripped off having one. I may have a happy and healthy
  > baby, but I am not happy and healthy yet".* **Ainslea**

Ainslea's new understanding about traumatic birth is evident in her answers
and importantly she knew that there was nothing 'wrong' with her for having
mixed-up emotions about the birthday. Her healing journey continues.

## A personal account

Melissa, one of the co-founders of Birthtalk, shares her own difficulties
embracing the birthday of her child as a celebration.

> *I experienced the lead up to my son's first birthday as a confusing
> mish-mash of emotion. At this stage I did not know I'd had a
> traumatic birth – I still thought I had just not coped with birth
> and had failed. I did not recognise a connection between how
> I felt about the birth, and how I handled the first anniversary of
> such a challenging experience.*

*After planning a big party carefully, I worried unnecessarily about trivial things and really worked myself into a tizz. I felt nervous about being the centre of attention, and felt a lot of pressure to display my mothering success. I found myself focusing a lot on my appearance – it felt incredibly important to look good and, I realise now, to display the semblance of a coping mother. On the day of the party, I changed my outfit feverishly a number of times before everyone arrived; I was as stiff as a board with tension and stress with my mind whirling the whole day. I was saved only by my son's sweetness, my husband's patience, and a fair bit of cake.*

## It really does get easier

Melissa continues:

*I can speak from experience – it really does get easier over time as each birthday approaches and it gets even easier if you do the work. It can be so hard to go there and begin the healing journey, but the benefits can be far-reaching.*

*After the debacle of the first birthday, I felt so much guilt and sorrow and even embarrassment that I was so messed up. Until I began the healing journey, with much support from Deb (who was a midwife, my sister-in-law and later co-founded Birthtalk with me). The process of exploring the birth, and beginning to understand the notion that the birth was having this impact on me and my family, really helped pave the way for some much better birthdays.*

*I became able to focus on the celebration this day was – the day my child arrived. I could join other people in truly enjoying the day as his birthday. It became a day of joy.*

*In private, I would also reflect and honour and take myself back over the years since his birth. There is acknowledgement from myself and my partner and other women I have since met who understood that this birth was significant for me for reasons beyond presenting me with this gorgeous son. But these reflections no longer overshadowed the day. They were simply an acknowledgement of who I'd become and of all the gifts my son's arrival has given me for the journey of being his mother. I couldn't see them until I'd begun to heal, but they were there. It was a birthday gift to me; a Happy Birthday at last.*

# Breastfeeding was just so challenging

*I felt very frustrated when the midwife was acting like I wasn't trying to feed my baby. Of course I wanted to feed her! Of course I wanted to feel like I could do something right after such a disaster during the birth!* **Katie**

*I felt like everything else had gone so very, very wrong, that maybe I could do this one thing. I NEEDED to feed my child from my body. I needed to salvage that one thing, and it was going terribly.* **Megan**

*I just hated my body and was angry at myself for not being able to birth him or breastfeed him.* **Kerri**

*I said sorry to my baby a million times. I was sorry that I'd let him down, sorry that I couldn't get him out properly and sorry that I couldn't even breastfeed him properly.* **Skye**

*My self-esteem had been wrecked [by the actions of a midwife during the birth, and the resulting consequences] and I truly didn't believe I was good enough to feed my son. It's taken me a long time to reconcile with that. I feel my traumatic birth denied me the chance to feed.* **Barbara**

After any birth – even a positive, empowering one – there can be challenges with breastfeeding. Each baby feeds differently, each breastfeeding relationship between mother and child is different, and even for seasoned breastfeeding mums, there can be obstacles and difficulties along the path when establishing feeding with the newest baby.

Add a traumatic or difficult birth as a starting point and those challenges can compound into a very difficult situation, for reasons that are usually completely out of the mother's control. This can raise some very intense emotions, as a woman struggles to deal not only with the birth, but also with feeding her baby.

## Feelings of failure and dogged determination

> *I was completely devastated. I felt like I had failed to go into labour naturally and, while having resisted some interventions, did not achieve the peaceful, calm, un-injured birth I wanted, and [I] had now failed to exclusively breastfeed my child.* **Rosemary**

Failure is the most common word we hear at Birthtalk surrounding breastfeeding. Many women already often see themselves as having failed at birth, and then if breastfeeding does not work out, it becomes a double blow. They might feel compounding grief or anger that the circumstances surrounding their birth put them in this situation. Additionally, women often see their breastfeeding difficulties as another sign that their body doesn't work, and can spiral further into feelings of despair and confusion. It can even affect how a woman sees herself as a mother.

> *When I walked in the doors of the lactation consultant's office I burst into tears and explained that I was sure I was a failure as a mother. I mean, I couldn't give birth without surgery and now I couldn't breastfeed. How could I be a good mother?* **Skye**

> *I felt like such a bad mother – every other baby in the ward was calmly asleep next to their mother and mine was just screaming his lungs out till he was too tired to scream any more. I really started to question if they had given me the wrong child. It made my feeling of being useless so much worse because I couldn't even give birth to my child like everyone else, and now I couldn't even feed him.* **Kristie**

Often, this perceived failure at birthing is channelled into a fierce and dogged determination to salvage some remnants of control over a vastly out-of-control birthing experience, and to 'succeed' at breastfeeding. Professor Cheryl Beck and Sue Watson, in their study of the impact of birth trauma on breastfeeding, report that part of some mothers' tenacity to succeed at breastfeeding was due to their need to prove themselves as mothers.[153] They also reported an unyielding resolve in some mothers to make atonement to their babies, to 'make up' for the birth.[154]

> *I felt like everything else had gone so very, very wrong, that maybe I could do this one thing. And it was excruciating; I was punch-drunk. I was exhausted and failing at feeding my child. Everyone around me, from my husband to my mother to the lactation consultant were all telling me that it was okay to stop. It wasn't though; I could not stop. I NEEDED to feed my child from my body, I needed to salvage that one thing, and it was going terribly.* **Megan**

While this is an understandable response, it increases the chances that the woman will feel more failure, if breastfeeding does not establish in spite of her determination. This is especially difficult if she hears about other women who voice similar determination after a traumatic birth, and are ultimately able to breastfeed. She may wonder was she not determined enough, did she not try hard enough, and is her body just that much more of a failure. Which is such a difficult position to be in, and of course, untrue.

## Not really a failure

A delayed onset of lactation is defined as having more than 72 hours between the birth and when copious milk is secreted.[155] This delay, which for some women may be normal*, is, according to Dr Jennifer Lind and colleagues, associated with women breastfeeding for a shorter amount of time.[156] Most women are not aware that having a caesarean, psychological stress or pain, or a stressful labour and delivery, or even a delayed first breastfeed are known risk factors for this delayed onset of lactation.[157]

If a woman is struggling, for example, because her milk hasn't yet 'come in', she is rarely told of the possible link between this and aspects of her birth, so unfortunately, women often see themselves as failing. However, really, they are often in a situation where it is very challenging to initiate and sustain breastfeeding, through no fault of their own.

---

153    Tatano Beck, C., & Watson, S. (2008). Impact of Birth Trauma on Breast-feeding: A Tale of Two Pathways. *Nursing Research, 57*(4), 228–236.

154    ibid.

155    Lind, J.N., Perrine, C.G., & Li, R. (2014). Relationship between use of labor pain medications and delayed onset of lactation. *Journal of Human Lactation, 30*(2), 167–73

156    ibid.

157    ibid.

*We want to point out here that a delay in the onset of lactation may not mean that something is wrong and may not indicate that you will breastfeed for a shorter length of time, as suggested by the literature. Deb's personal breastfeeding journey included an experience with her second child, where, after a positive, undisturbed water birth, breastfeeding on (high!) demand, her milk took longer than 72 hours to come in. With excellent support from her private midwife and a thriving baby, Deb worked through this challenging situation and went on to feed her daughter into toddlerhood.

## The complexities of breastfeeding

The lactation process and the act of breastfeeding are quite complex, with a woman's ability to breastfeed governed by various factors in both her internal and external environment.[158]

Her internal environment includes her physical and mental health, and her external environment includes support of her spouse, family and the hospital.[159] Most importantly, "the quality and quantity of maternal–infant interaction during the early postpartum period… sets the stage for a successful breastfeeding experience".[160] That is, there is a delicate balance of factors needed for the best environment for breastfeeding to occur. A traumatic birth can upset this balance in a number of ways, leading to a situation where breastfeeding is very difficult or at times, even impossible.

## Why is breastfeeding so challenging after a bad birth?

There are many reasons why it can be so hard to breastfeed after a traumatic birth, and none of them are the mother's fault. Some of them are a result of the emotional fall out from the birth, others are physiological – that is, the hormonal fall out from the birth. These are compounded by issues such as lack of support from those around the woman, not just for breastfeeding but also in response to her birth experience. These reasons can all intertwine to result in difficulties in feeding.

Here, we explore some common factors we have seen that can make breastfeeding difficult, or simply not possible, after a traumatic birth.

---

158    Hurst, N.M. (2007). Recognizing and treating delayed or failed lactogenesis II. *Journal of Midwifery and Women's Health, 52*(6), 588–594.

159    ibid.

160    ibid.

## Emotional fall out

Many women we meet after a traumatic birth feel they have lost their confidence in themselves, experiencing turmoil from emotions such as guilt, shame or grief, sometimes alongside flashbacks and severe anxiety. This combination of strong emotions can put a woman in a compromised position to develop a breastfeeding relationship with her baby. If a woman did not feel central to the birth experience, which is part of our definition of a good birth, then she may not have gained a feeling of her own importance in her baby's life. This may translate to a lack of confidence in caring for her baby ("I couldn't even birth him…how can I care for him?").

Breastfeeding requires a woman to try new things, attempt a new skill and use unfamiliar methods of caring for another person. It is a lot to ask of anyone, to develop a new skill in the throes of a life-changing event. This is especially the case after she has perhaps been in an experience where she feared for her life, or felt belittled or manipulated without being able to leave the situation, or had invasive procedures undertaken on her body. When developing this new skill has the added pressure of providing nutrition for another human, it can be very stressful indeed.

If a woman has just experienced a birth where she felt disempowered, degraded, out of control or unable to ask questions, she may not suddenly feel overly confident in asking for help and advice when breastfeeding. She may be feeling overwhelmed, shocked or that her 'voice' was taken from her during the birth. She may struggle to find that voice when attempting the task of breastfeeding, and feel unable to seek the help she needs.

> [After being separated for three hours after the birth, then being sent out of the Special Care Unit without her baby after a first unsuccessful breastfeeding attempt] I felt helpless and my anxiety was really starting to build. Plus I was completely drained from the long labour, two nights with minimal sleep and the difficult birth. **Emm**
>
> Two hours later [after my traumatic birth] my son was forced onto my breast despite me saying I wanted him to be coaxed gently. The problems started there. He wouldn't latch very well and, as I was in a private room, I had to ring for help at every feeding. I was in a state of shock and feeling really detached from everything, including him. **Barbara**

No wonder emotions are running high as women attempt to feed their babies, with so much riding on it and so much fall out behind them. Unfortunately, the high levels of anxiety and strong emotions can compromise the situation further, by impacting on the very hormones required for breastfeeding. This leads us to the next factor: adequate hormonal support.

## Lack of optimal hormonal support

In our sections *Why wouldn't my body work in labour?* (p230) and *I don't feel bonded to my child* (p218), we discuss the hormonal cocktail necessary for a normal, vaginal birth and for solid bonding to occur. This same hormonal cocktail also provides the optimal situation for breastfeeding to establish.

Dr Sarah Buckley notes there is an "elaborate interplay between these hormones of labour, birth and breastfeeding".[161] Dr Buckley explains that labour and birth involve the hormones oxytocin and prolactin at peak levels. Oxytocin is known as the hormone of love, while prolactin is the major hormone of breast-milk synthesis, and is known as the 'mothering hormone'. Another hormone of labour and birth, beta-endorphin, helps the body release prolactin, and plays a role in bonding.[162]

However, this delicate interplay of hormones can be interfered with in a number of ways that can impact on breastfeeding.

## 1. Not feeling safe during birth

All mammals can release adrenaline, an emergency hormone which, when high enough, has the effect of stopping the release of oxytocin.[163] It is interesting to know that mammals release adrenaline in situations when there is a possible danger, when they feel observed, and even when they are in a cold environment.[164] Dr Michel Odent notes that, "Since humans are mammals these physiological considerations suggest that in order to give birth women must feel secure, without feeling observed, in a warm enough place."[165] (You can read more about this in *Why wouldn't my body work in labour?* (p230)) So, if a woman simply did

---

161    Buckley, S. (2005) *Pain in Labour: your hormones are your helpers.* (An article & eBook).
        Retrieved from *http://sarahbuckley.com/pain-in-labour-your-hormones-are-your-helpers*, accessed July 2014.

162    ibid.

163    Odent, M. *In-labour physiological reference.* Retrieved from *www.wombecology.com/?pg=physiological*, accessed July 2014.

164    ibid.

165    Odent, M. *In-labour physiological reference.* Retrieved from *www.wombecology.com/?pg=physiological*, accessed July 2014.

not feel safe or supported during birth, the adrenaline she will likely release can impact on her oxytocin release and tip the balance of the overall combination of hormones to one that is less optimal for breastfeeding.

> *No one even mentioned that with a three-hour labour, my daughter's birth was considered precipitate and no one acknowledged that this could be a traumatic, frightening, overwhelming experience in and of itself, regardless of the further feelings of disempowerment and failure engendered by the way some of the staff treated me. No one ever mentioned that milk and even colostrum production can be delayed by the shock and trauma of a fast, scary, birth. No one said, 'I know this has been hard but this doesn't mean you won't go on to have a very happy and breastfeeding experience and this doesn't mean you won't meet your breastfeeding goals'.* **Rosemary**

For some women, the emotional fall out from a traumatic birth includes flashbacks, and some flashbacks can be triggered by breastfeeding. Professor Cheryl Beck and Sue Watson found that, understandably, for the women in their study, these uncontrollable flashbacks had "a detrimental domino effect on women's breastfeeding experiences".[166]

## 2. Having pharmacological intervention during birth

If a woman has pharmacological intervention in the form of synthetic hormones (for example, morphine, pethidine, Syntocinon), it can interfere with her body's natural hormone production, which can then impact on breastfeeding. This is absolutely not a judgement about any decision to have pain relief; it is just an explanation of how it can impact on breastfeeding, to help you understand reasons why breastfeeding may have been difficult – reasons that nobody may have mentioned to you before now.

One recent study found that "mothers who received labor pain medications were more likely to report a delay in the onset of lactation, regardless of delivery method".[167] If a woman experiences this delay, and is not made aware that it may be connected to the pain relief she was given in labour, then she can easily see herself, incorrectly, as having failed.

---

166    Tatano Beck, C., & Watson, S. (2008). Impact of Birth Trauma on Breast-feeding: A Tale of Two Pathways. op. cit.

167    Lind, J.N., Perrine, C.G., & Li, R. (2014). Relationship between use of labor pain medications and delayed onset of lactation. op. cit.

## The hormonal effects

Natural hormones, such as oxytocin, are produced in the brain and have follow-on neurological effects, such as feelings of love. The synthetic counterparts, such as Syntocinon or Pitocin, administered into the blood stream, cannot replicate the same effects as they can't cross back from the blood into the brain. As Dr Sarah Buckley notes, "This means that Pitocin, introduced into the mother's body by injection (IV), does not act within her limbic system as the hormone of love, and may interfere with the labouring woman's own oxytocin system".[168] The end result is not optimal, hormonally, for breastfeeding.

Epidural pain relief has a major effect on the hormones of labour: the release of beta-endorphin (a hormone important in breastfeeding) is dramatically inhibited, oxytocin levels decline and the oxytocin peak that occurs at birth is also inhibited when an epidural is in place.[169]

Dr Buckley says that epidural drugs may affect a mother's breastfeeding physiology, citing research that found "women who had received an epidural plus Pitocin during labour had a marked reduction in their oxytocin release during breastfeeding… [and] the more Pitocin the mother had received during labour, the lower her breastfeeding oxytocin release, two days after birth".[170]

## Mental alertness affected

The woman's and baby's mental alertness can also be affected by the pharmacological intervention, which means they are not primed to start their breastfeeding relationship. As we mention in *I had a caesarean under general anaesthetic* (p365), one Australian research study[171] found that women emerge more quickly from a general anaesthetic than men, but take twenty-five per cent longer to recover, despite the women opening their eyes and obeying commands more quickly.[172] Women were also found to be "more likely to suffer from side effects such as nausea, vomiting, headaches, backaches and sore throats".[173] According to Associate Professor Paul Myles, who led the research, "Women recover more slowly, suggesting they are more sensitive to the side-effects of the drugs, or recover more slowly from the effects of surgery itself. We have

---

168    Buckley, S. (2010). *Ecstatic Birth: nature's hormonal blueprint for labour* (eBook).
       Available from *www.sarahbuckley.com*

169    ibid.

170    ibid.

171    Myles, P.S., McLeod, A.D.M., Hunt, J.O., & Fletcher, H. (2001). Sex differences in speed of emergence and quality of recovery after anaesthesia: cohort study, *British Medical Journal, 322*, 710–711.

172    BBC News. (2001). *Anaesthetic's Effect on Women*.
       Retrieved from *http://news.bbc.co.uk/2/hi/health/1236380.stm*, accessed July 2014.

173    ibid.

known for some time that women have higher rates of nausea and vomiting after surgery; but [this] study has found they also have more headaches, and backache. Importantly, their overall quality of recovery is worse".[174]

> *I was taken off for a tear repair under general anaesthetic, and my daughter went to my husband's chest for skin on skin. I saw my daughter again about two hours later in the postnatal ward. I was very groggy and felt cold. I don't remember this, but as soon as I saw them my husband offered for me to hold her, and apparently I said, "Not yet". While I had been away, she had been very alert, eyes open and had found my husband's nipple and tried to latch onto it. By the time I saw her, she was sleepier and unsettled.* **Rosemary**

## Effects on baby

The baby can also be affected by the mother's labour pain medications, with many studies showing an association between the mother receiving these medications and "suboptimal infant breastfeeding behavior, including diminished early sucking".[175] This can potentially affect the onset of lactation, as these suboptimal behaviours can affect the ability of the baby to effectively latch on, extract milk, and stimulate the breasts.[176]

We want to make it really clear that this in NO way is an indication that you made the wrong decision if you had pain relief medication or other interventions. Firstly, we would take a guess that no one mentioned that these interventions could impede your breastfeeding, so you were likely not making that decision with the information you needed to receive (and this is not your fault). It's not likely you were told, "It would be reasonable to consider an epidural, but did you know that this may impact on breastfeeding so you may need some extra support, guidance and information to establish your baby's breastfeeding?" For more on this, see our section *Why did I agree to that epidural/episiotomy/caesarean etc.?* (p210).

It is also important to know that this does not mean that you cannot choose pain relief in future births. Being fully informed and aware of the possible hormonal challenges means you can create more options. You can take steps as part of your postnatal plan to stimulate those hormones in other ways, to

---

174    Myles, P. in BBC News. (2001). *Anaesthetic's Effect on Women.*
       Retrieved from *http://news.bbc.co.uk/2/hi/health/1236380.stm*, accessed July 2014

175    Lind, J.N., Perrine, C.G., & Li, R. (2014). Relationship between use of labor pain medications and delayed onset of lactation. op. cit.

176    ibid.

promote a more optimal breastfeeding environment should you require pain relief medication. You can read about other ways of stimulating these hormones in our section *Reconnecting with your child* (p409).

## 3. Mode of delivery?

It is worth noting that some studies have focused on the mode of delivery and its impact on breastfeeding. One study found that women who had caesareans had lower levels of prolactin and a less pulsatile oxytocin release pattern when breastfeeding a couple of days postbirth, compared with women who had vaginal births.[177] Knowing that both prolactin and oxytocin are critical for successful lactation,[178] it is understandable that a woman recovering from a caesarean might need special support to overcome these hormonal discrepancies for a more optimal breastfeeding situation.

It is not just caesarean mums who struggle with breastfeeding after a traumatic birth. Beck and Watson report on other studies reflecting this, for example, a vacuum extraction in a vaginal birth was a significant predictor of stopping breastfeeding early.[179] In another study on Guatemalan women, stress during labour and delivery was identified as a likely significant risk factor for delayed onset of lactation,[180] and stress during labour has also been shown to reduce women' plasma concentration of the hormone prolactin.[181]

We suggest that, really, any birth where there are significant levels of stress has the potential to send the delicate balance of hormones into disarray, and upset the perfect environment for mother and baby to initiate a healthy breastfeeding relationship.

177     Nissen, E., Uvnas-Moberg, K., Svensson, K., Stock, S., Widstrom, A.M., & Winberg, J. (1996). Different patterns of oxytocin, pro-lactin but not cortisol release during breastfeeding in women delivered by caesarean section or by the vaginal route. *Early Human Development, 45*(1–2), 103–118.

178     Tatano Beck, C., & Watson, S. (2008). Impact of Birth Trauma on Breast-feeding: A Tale of Two Pathways. op. cit.

179     ibid.

180     Grajeda, R., & Perez-Escamilla, R. (2002). Stress during labor and delivery is associated with delayed onset of lactation among urban Guatemalan women. *Journal of Nutrition, 132*(10), 3055–3060.

181     Onur, E., Ercal, T., & Karslioglu, I. (1989). Prolactin and cortisol levels during spontaneous and oxytocin induced labour and effect of meperidine. *Archive of Gynaecological Obstetrics, 244*(4), 227-232. As quoted in Nissen, E., Uvnas-Moberg, K., Svensson, K., Stock, S., Widstrom, A.M., & Winberg, J. (1996). Different patterns of oxytocin, pro-lactin but not cortisol release during breastfeeding in women delivered by caesarean section or by the vaginal route. *Early Human Development, 45*(1-2), 103–118.

## 4. Lack of skin-to-skin or separation from baby post-birth

It is well known that early mother–infant skin-to-skin contact increases the rate of exclusive breastfeeding.[182] As we discuss in our section *Reconnecting with your child*, skin-to-skin contact at birth has many benefits for the mother–baby bond. According to Dr Sarah Buckley, "Skin-to-skin contact… benefits the mother, who releases high levels of oxytocin, the hormone of love, when skin to skin with her newborn".[183] Dr Buckley explains that oxytocin has also been called the hormone of calm and connection, and switches on the mother's instinctive mothering behaviours. She says, "It actually alters our brain… to switch on those areas that we need for mothering".[184]

Oxytocin plays a major role in lactation, says Dr Jennifer Lind and associates, being "essential for the milk ejection reflex and milk removal from the mammary gland".[185] And both prolactin and oxytocin can be released in the brain by close physical contact such as that which occurs when breastfeeding.[186]

So, whether you were separated from your baby, or just not given the opportunity to have skin-to-skin contact, it makes sense that, in these cases, your body may not have been prompted to produce the hormones that increase the likelihood of successful breastfeeding. Even seemingly harmless hospital routine measures such as wiping or bathing babies after the birth can reduce the prompts a woman's body needs to produce the hormones required for breastfeeding.

The following is reproduced from our section *I don't feel bonded to my child* (p218). We recommend reading that entire section for more information about the work of hormones in the moments post-birth.

We are meant to hold our babies after birth while they are wet, gooey and messy because their smell and feel ignites hormones designed to spark our mothering instincts. A whiff of newborn goo sets off all those hormonal benefits that Dr Buckley talks about – and other mammals seem to need this hormonal support too.

---

182    Mahmood, I., Jamal, M., & Khan, N. (2011). Effect of Mother-Infant Early Skin-to-Skin Contact on Breastfeeding Status: A Randomized Controlled Trial. *Journal of the College of Physicians and Surgeons. Pakistan, suppl. 21*(10), s. 605.

183    Buckley, S. *What are the benefits of skin-to-skin contact upon birth?* Retrieved from *http://canaustralia.net. s150349.gridserver.com/%E2%80%A8what-are-the-benefits-of-skin-to-skin-contact-upon-birth%E2%80%A8-%E2%80%A8/*, accessed July 2014.

184    Your Baby Booty. *Interview with Dr Sarah Buckley: The Silent (but insanely powerful) Impact Hormones During Pregnancy Have On Helping You & Your Baby at Birth.* Retrieved from *http://yourbabybooty.com/interviews/ hormones-baby-body-birth-interview-with-dr-sarah-buckley/*, accessed July 2014.

185    Lind, J.N., Perrine, C.G., & Li, R. (2014). Relationship between use of labor pain medications and delayed onset of lactation. op. cit.

186    Hurst, N.M. (2007). Recognizing and treating delayed or failed lactogenesis II. op. cit.

As renowned birth pioneer, Michel Odent, discusses,[187] one study compared two groups of baby monkeys, all born via caesarean. One group (five babies) was swabbed with secretions from their mother's vagina after birth, and all of these babies were accepted and breastfed by their mothers. Another group of eleven baby monkeys were not swabbed with vaginal secretions. Only one of these eleven babies was accepted and breastfed by its mother.[188]

Of course, as humans know intellectually that the baby is ours. Even when our baby is cleaned and bathed before we first meet them, we can receive and care for them; however, we need to realise that we might be doing so without the amazing hormonal support meant for us (and that other mothers receive) to make it easier.

This separation from the baby can be exacerbated by the fall out from the birth. Avoiding external reminders of the traumatic event is a symptom of posttraumatic stress,[189] and, as Beck and Watson explain, this avoidance can have the effect of distancing mothers from their babies because the babies can be constant reminders of the trauma of the birth.[190] This distancing, while understandable, can also potentially impact on the production of the required hormones required for breastfeeding.

Many of the challenges of breastfeeding after a traumatic birth are strongly related to the situation, rather than to the woman's actual ability. It is the situation that has compromised the hormones a woman's body requires to promote breastfeeding, and that is not the woman's fault.

It is important to know for future births that even if the birthing situation has resulted in compromised hormonal levels, there are many ways to stimulate hormonal help to support breastfeeding. Unfortunately, most women do not have access to this information and support, but if you know about it for future births, you can take action and set up a supportive environment to increase the chances of more successful breastfeeding.

---

187    Odent, M. *In-labour physiological reference*. Retrieved from *www.wombecology.com/?pg=physiological*, accessed November 2013.

188    Lundblad, E.g. & Hodgen, G.D. (1980). Induction of maternal-infant bonding in rhesus and cynomolgus monkeys after cesarean delivery. *Laboratory of Animal Science, 30*(5):913.

189    American Psychiatric Association. (2013). *Diagnostic and statistical manual of mental disorders* (5th ed.). Washington, DC: Author. P.271

190    Tatano Beck, C., & Watson, S. (2008). *Impact of Birth Trauma on Breast-feeding: A Tale of Two Pathways*. op. cit.

## Rough handling

Even after a positive birthing experience, it can be very difficult to accept strangers grabbing your breasts, shoving a baby's head onto your nipple, and poking and handling these (usually) private parts of your body. This is even more relevant if you have just undergone a birth experience where you felt a strong sense of powerlessness, loss of dignity and the feeling that your body was not your own. As Professor Beck and Sue Watson describe in their study on the impact of birth trauma on breastfeeding, mother's breasts become "just one more thing to be violated".[191]

> They came to 'try and help me attach her' which amounted to watching her failing to latch, and then rushedly trying to forcefully make her attach by pushing her head onto the breast. The forceful, hands-on approach of the midwives wasn't working and was upsetting both of us, but I didn't know what else to do. **Rosemary**

> During that admission [re-admission for jaundice] I had many more frustrating encounters with different opinions and approaches to feeding, many of which I now know were simply wrong (e.g. more than one nurse pushing my baby's head onto my breast while she cried!). **Emm**

Some birth workers can, unfortunately, be less-than-gentle in their handling of a woman's breasts when trying to teach breastfeeding. When a woman has had a traumatic birth, is in a lot of pain from the breastfeeding process or as a result of the birth and is possibly feeling helpless and vulnerable as she recovers, then this invasion of her person can elicit severe anxiety and distress. The release of both oxytocin and prolactin is inhibited by stress,[192] so a stressed mother who is feeling poked and prodded and roughly handled (thus raising her stress levels) is not in an ideal situation for breastfeeding. This, again, is not the mother's fault.

---

191    Tatano Beck, C., & Watson, S. (2008). *Impact of Birth Trauma on Breast-feeding: A Tale of Two Pathways.* op. cit.

192    Nissen, et al. (1996). Different patterns of oxytocin, pro-lactin but not cortisol release during breastfeeding in women delivered by caesarean section or by the vaginal route. op. cit.

## Unwell baby or mother

When the mother is unwell, or the baby is sick, there are often even more obstacles to breastfeeding. Perhaps the baby was premature and does not yet have an established suck reflex, or the baby is too sick to be touched or stimulated, or the mother is struggling to recover after surgery and is not coherent enough to be with her baby. There might be challenges with supporting the mother and baby to receive ample time together if they are dependent on staff making this happen. There might be difficulties with holding and positioning the baby when either mother or child has a physical injury or wound and has treatment paraphernalia such as an IV drip pole, catheter or monitor attached.

> *[The day after my son was born at 30 weeks] I started pumping for my son that I hadn't even met yet. Pumping was very difficult; I had a hard time sitting up straight enough to pump without spilling all the milk I was pumping on myself. I was able to pump enough to fill a syringe to send to the Neonatal Intensive Care Unit. By the end of my five-day hospital stay I had spent more time pumping than I had with my baby. I wasn't able to hold him until he was 11-days-old, and even that was difficult with all the tubes and wires.* **Janelle**

> *[After a caesarean under general anaesthetic] I was never offered skin-to-skin and was too tired and out of it to hold him any more than a few minutes.* **Kristie**

> *She was four-weeks-old, going limp in my arms and had refused all feeds for almost six hours. We were told to rush to hospital. Once there, they placed a very tiny oxygen mask on my tiny little girl, and a cannula in her invisible vein. But she kept on turning blue. So we were rushed to the Neonatal Paediatric Intensive Care Unit. My little girl was taken away from me for well over an hour. We called our priest. I geared myself up to say goodbye to my perfect little baby. Finally, a nurse came to tell us that they had stabilised her and that the hospital priest had been informed to be on standby in case things take a turn for the worse. They were not going to feed her for a few hours, so I had to sit next to my precious girl and listen to her whimper with hunger, unable to hold or touch her. Finally, the nurse suggested we feed her a few drops of milk by finger just to soothe her. I diligently whipped*

*out a boob and squeezed, but nothing came out. Nothing. Not a
drop. I was told later that my milk had stopped with the shock
and as a means of coping with potential loss.* **Becky***

These situations, and more, provide challenges that understandably may be very
difficult to overcome, especially when it is likely that the woman's hormones
have already been compromised from situations arising during the birth, for
example, pain medication, separation from the baby or high levels of fear.

## Lack of good support or information

Three factors that are associated with higher rates of breastfeeding initiation
and duration are (a) positive social support, (b) the confidence and attitude
of the mother and (c) health carers who are knowledgeable and supportive.[193]
After a traumatic birth, a woman's confidence may be low and her attitude
may, understandably, be one of fear, distrust in others and distrust in her own
body's ability to work. If she is also dealing with low levels of social support, or
inexperienced or unsupportive health carers, then the odds are further stacked
against her for breastfeeding.

## Advice from health professionals

Receiving conflicting advice is often voiced as being a huge deterrent to
successful breastfeeding by the women we meet. Many women tell us about
their experiences in our hospital system, where they reported receiving
contradicting information and advice from each midwife who entered the room
postnatally.

Women have reported that this conflicting information is confusing and
distressing and even undermining of any positive steps a woman may have been
making with prior knowledge or a particular tip she has learned.

This situation is not limited to women who have experienced a traumatic
birth; however, these women may be more vulnerable to confusion and feeling
dependent on the 'expert', as they may not have their own instincts ignited via
their hormones as a result of the birth or separation post-birth.

---

*To read a postscript to Becky's story, see the end of this chapter.

---

193    Hurst, N.M. (2007). Recognizing and treating delayed or failed lactogenesis II. op. cit.

*I felt like a serial number whose checklist needed to be ticked so I could be sent on my way. Few of the midwives seemed to have time to be there, let alone understand why I felt so fragile. Breastfeeding advice was conflicting.* **Kerri**

*I still feel a lot of guilt that I went along with the [expressing and formula] plan even though I felt so uncertain about it and that I couldn't stand up to a system I thought I knew so well (it's all about bed numbers!).* **Emm**

Sometimes this situation is a result of a communication breakdown: often it is not explained that any feeding advice is merely a suggestion; that it may be helpful or may not. It can be presented by the health carer as the only or best way. Plus, as each midwife is seeing a different snapshot of what is going on at that moment in time, often they may be without the full context of all that has happened. They also may not have the ability to follow up with after a shift-change. Continuity of breastfeeding support with the same midwife or lactation consultant can help to remedy this situation; however, even then, it is important that the information and rationale are presented in a way that encourages women to feel confident to be able to consider, try or decide to dismiss suggestions based on their and their baby's individual situation.

We want to add that we know there are some amazingly skilled midwives, lactation consultants and other health carers supporting women every day with breastfeeding. We want to acknowledge their hard work and unfailing support of women. Many of the women we interviewed talked about a particular health carer who made all the difference in their quest to breastfeed, and this support cannot be underestimated.

## Support from partner and family

There also may be a lack of support from the woman's partner or family, which can further exacerbate her chances of being able to breastfeed. The woman's perception of her partner's attitude towards breastfeeding can impact the initiation and duration of breastfeeding.[194]

Even if her partner is supportive of breastfeeding, if they do not understand the possible emotional impact from a traumatic birth, then they may not respond appropriately to her needs. If the woman is feeling unheard, confused, in shock, or even violated, then she may need support for this, before she can feel ready and comfortable to tackle breastfeeding. A focus on breastfeeding without addressing the fall out from the birth can add to the woman feeling

---

194    Hurst, N.M. (2007). Recognizing and treating delayed or failed lactogenesis II. op. cit.

unimportant and distressed, which can impact on her hormonal levels, which can then also impact on her breastfeeding. This may leave her feeling further isolated and with less support for her breastfeeding as often partners, family or friends may believe the emotional fall out they are seeing is from breastfeeding, not the birth, and they may suggest that stopping breastfeeding is the answer, which often it is not. We do not blame partners for being unable to offer support for a traumatic birth. We know that they, like most people in our culture, are unaware of the implications of a traumatic birth, or how to help. See our chapter *Issues with your partner* (p291) for more. Usually, there is no one offering information to the couple that encourages understanding of the fall out of a traumatic birth.

Partners are also usually not informed that breastfeeding after a traumatic birth may actually benefit the mother and baby via an increase in helpful hormones. As an example, according to Dr Sarah Buckley, "All the time that we're breastfeeding our babies, we're getting a hit of this hormone oxytocin, which rewards us, which makes us calm and connected, which increases our bond with our baby, and makes us feel good".[195] The women in Beck and Watson's study who were able to breastfeed reported that breastfeeding after a traumatic birth helped them to heal, restored their self-esteem and also restored their faith in their bodies.[196] Perhaps if partners were given this important information about the benefits of breastfeeding, it could enable them to offer more support for establishing feeding, even in the turbulent postnatal period that often follows after a traumatic birth.

## Forgiveness and new understanding

Whether you were ultimately able to continue breastfeeding, or needed to move on to other forms of feeding, it can be helpful to understand why it was such a challenging process. This understanding might help to take the pressure off you, and also give you some insights and confidence for planning for breastfeeding future babies.

We wanted to share a postscript from Kerri and Skye, who shared aspects of their stories above. Both women had traumatic caesareans and experienced many difficulties with breastfeeding with their first babies. Their second babies were also caesarean-born. Both Kerri and Skye attended Birthtalk before their second birth, not only our Healing From Birth sessions, but also our antenatal

---

195    Your Baby Booty. *Interview with Dr Sarah Buckley: The Silent (but insanely powerful) Impact Hormones During Pregnancy Have On Helping You & Your Baby at Birth*, accessed July 2014.

196    Tatano Beck, C., & Watson, S. (2008). Impact of Birth Trauma on Breast-feeding: A Tale of Two Pathways. op. cit.

course. Here they learned how to have an empowering experience regardless of the situation unfolding, including how to negotiate to get their needs met, how to stay central to the experience and how to optimise their hormones should they be compromised as a result of the birth. As a result, their subsequent births, while not 'textbook' or easy, were still empowering and ultimately positive. The same could be said for their breastfeeding journey.

> *My second birth – a 16-hour labour and unplanned caesarean birth – was the hardest challenge of my life, both physically and mentally, but also my proudest achievement! Even though it did not go as hoped, trying for a VBAC was so important and being given a fair and decent opportunity to birth with staff I trusted and who listened is something I will always appreciate. The feeding was very painful again but the midwives were fantastic. They said to buzz them every feed so they could sit with me and just be there, especially in the night. I really needed that. And we had a breastfeeding plan that every midwife had read before visiting me so they already knew my past situation, what had already happened this time and gave me consistent advice on the next step. However, I found breastfeeding very difficult for each of my babies and I eventually went to formula, so I guess it doesn't always work out. But what a better introduction to motherhood!* **Kerri**

> *When my second baby was being born via caesarean, I actually felt like I released and gave birth as he came out. I was attached to the birth (if that makes sense) and talked him out. This time around, breastfeeding was relaxed and amazing, no latching problems, no pain. I was more confident, happier, and I knew I could work through any difficulties. Ultimately, I was well bonded; I smelled my baby boy and knew everything was okay between us. He was taken away after the birth for observations and antibiotics due to poor Apgars, particularly breathing. But because we asked all the questions and had time with him before he was whisked away, I felt happy that we were doing everything we could. I guess one last thing I should say is that my experience has certainly proven to me that it's not 'what happens', it's 'how you feel' that matters. And how empowered you are. I had two long labours, two difficult experiences, two caesareans, two post-birth separations. But the difference was immense. The first time around, I felt panic, scared, a failure and cried a lot. Second time, I still worried (it's my nature) but felt reassured, supported, understood (mostly,*

*as at least I got my needs across) and patient. However, despite all my knowledge and confidence that every child is different, I was still a bit surprised that breastfeeding worked so easily the second time around! (Very pleasantly surprised). I'm tearing up just thinking about this – what an amazing experience.* **Skye**

\* We wanted to share the rest of Becky's story (from the section above about unwell mothers and babies) to illustrate how, sometimes, women can regain their milk. Becky's daughter stabilised and luckily was able to feed from stored breast milk that Becky already had. Becky began taking supplements, having as much skin-to-skin and close contact with her daughter as possible, and fed her daughter with her own expressed breast milk, while expressing at the end of every single feed, in a very challenging regime. They were released from the hospital and she kept up this regime for a month. Then, "We hit a growth spurt. And boy did I have a hungry little girl. In one day, my frozen reserves were depleted because I simply could not physically pump any more. At the end of the second day, I was at my wit's end. [The] baby could not stop asking for more milk and I just had no more expressed milk to give. I prayed. And then I picked her up and put her to my breast. I had never, and have still never, felt my milk let down like I did that day. I had milk spewing out of me. [The] baby was laughing and guzzling it all up, sometimes taking breaks and ducking away from the spurt. I think I called everyone I knew because I could not contain my sheer joy". Becky went on to feed her daughter (with other breastfeeding challenges along the way) until she was 23 months. She says, "I know first-hand how society does not encourage breastfeeding. I know first-hand how little support there is. I know first-hand how much support is needed. I know first-hand the myriad of challenges one can face. I know first-hand that every mother feeds her baby with love, be it from her breast, her milk in a bottle, or formula in a bottle".

## Tools for healing after a challenging breastfeeding experience

- Hopefully, reading this chapter will give you some insight about the reasons that breastfeeding was so challenging for you – reasons that go way beyond your actual ability, such as the emotional fall out, and the hormonal fall out of a traumatic birth.

- You may find it helpful for your healing to extend your understanding of the important part hormones play in our response to our birth overall, by reading *I don't feel bonded to my child* (p218) and *Why wouldn't my body work in labour?* (p230).

- If you have not already done so, now may be the time to complete a *Birthtalk Breakdown* (p47), so you can see more clearly the emotions you were experiencing or the physical separations that occurred, which could have affected breastfeeding.

- If your birth was recent, and breastfeeding is not working out yet you would like to work towards breastfeeding, you can take steps to support your body to replicate many of the hormones from the birth, which could increase your chances of getting things going. We highly recommend contacting a qualified lactation consultant and gaining professional support as you take these steps.

- Even if breastfeeding did not work out, and your baby is a bit older, it still is sometimes possible to revisit breastfeeding now you have this new information about hormones, and are taking the healing journey. This is called relactation. Pinky McKay, an International Board-Certified Lactation Consultant (IBCLC) and well-known parenting and breastfeeding author, says, "It is possible to relactate. It can be hard work but is absolutely possible, whether this means you fully breastfeed or mix feed. It would be good to get support from a lactation consultant to explore the reasons you stopped breastfeeding and what help/support you may need. Snuggle your baby skin-to-skin lots, see if he will take the breast – bottle feeding requires a different sucking action but you can retrain and some babies switch easily from bottle to breast. You can use a nursing supplementer device to feed milk through a fine tube while he is at the breast so he associates the breast with milk (if you don't have milk or very little at the moment). This will also stimulate your breasts and encourage milk production". Pinky offers breastfeeding support and information on her website at *www.pinkymckay.com*. You can also see this article for information about relactation: *http://theleakyboob.com/tag/breastfeeding-again-after-stopping/*. We would also recommend working with a qualified lactation consultant to support you.

- If your child is older, or if it is not appropriate or desirable to attempt to re-establish breastfeeding, it is important to address any grief or sadness or even anger that may have arisen from reading this chapter. See *I feel sad* (p245), *Using art as a healing tool* (p461), *Self-discovery: what's really going on for me?* (p457) and the *'Shifting from anger' exercise* for some ideas on working through these important emotions.

If you are a breastfeeding counsellor or midwife supporting women postnatally after a traumatic birth, you may find it helpful to share appropriate segments of this chapter with them in order to empower them towards understanding and healing. This information may support them when considering trying a different approach or tip, once they understand the reasons behind it. We also like this advice from Dr Kathleen Kendall-Tackett, an IBCLC, author of numerous books in the fields of trauma, women's health, depression and breastfeeding, and President-Elect of the American Psychological Association's Division of Trauma Psychology. She recommends that health carers "recognise that breastfeeding can be quite healing for trauma survivors, but also respect the mothers' boundaries,"[197] and acknowledges that "some mothers may be too overwhelmed to initiate or continue breastfeeding".[198] She believes that a mother may be able to handle breastfeeding with gentle encouragement, but that if she can't, the health carer must respect it, suggesting that "even if a mother decides not to breastfeed, we must gently encourage her to connect with her baby in other ways, such as skin to skin, babywearing or infant massage".[199]

We recommend contacting your country's breastfeeding support organisation for ongoing support with any challenges with breastfeeding. See a list below of organisations that may be able to help.

## Breastfeeding Support Organisations

Australian Breastfeeding Association
Website: *www.breastfeeding.asn.au.*

National Breastfeeding Helpline: 1800 mum 2 mum (1800 686 268)
Email counselling available for members.

La Leche League
Breastfeeding support in the US, UK, NZ and Canada (and other countries)
Website: *www.llli.org.*
Section on breastfeeding assistance: *www.llli.org/resources/assistance.html.*

La Leche League New Zealand
Website: *www.lalecheleague.org.nz.*

UK National Breastfeeding Support
Website: *www.nationalbreastfeedinghelpline.org.uk.*
Helpline: 0300 100 0212

---

197   Kendall-Tackett, K. (2013). *Childbirth-Related Psychological Trauma: It's Finally on the Radar and It Affects Breastfeeding.* Retrieved from *www.scienceandsensibility.org/?p=6821,* accessed July 2014.
198   ibid.
199   ibid.

# Issues with your partner

## DEALING WITH UNRESOLVED FEELINGS ABOUT YOUR PARTNER

*I blamed my husband for not saying anything and not asking questions during the birth. I felt he wasn't there for me.* **Sophie**

*I resented him for everything. Still do in many ways, but it has improved. I hated that he got to leave every morning and would even fantasise about him sitting in the car, pumping the air, saying, "Yes, I'm free 'til four!" I hated that my daughter seemed to love him more than me, that he got to touch, meet and talk to her before me. I resented that his life had on the surface barely changed at all, whereas mine had completely changed. I resented her looking at him lovingly when he fed her my milk out of a bottle like he was taking credit for it. This sounds so childish and I think in many ways it is almost like a sibling rivalry fighting over her attentions, but it was only me doing the battling. I have treated my partner appallingly; I have made him crawl over broken glass, I have been punishing him relentlessly for nearly five years over something that wasn't his fault. We are still working on this.* **Nina**

*I thought I was angry with my partner because we moved from Sydney to Brisbane when our baby was three-months-old. It was a move we decided on in a hurry, when things were so difficult after the birth. A job came up in Brisbane almost immediately and, before I knew it, we were on a plane back to our hometown. I thought it was his fault that I wasn't coping, because if he hadn't agreed to the Brisbane idea, we'd just have stayed in Sydney and I could have sorted out the breastfeeding/lack of sleep/hours of screaming that occurred after we moved. It was all his fault. Oh, and I was a mess. If anyone asked me how I was, I'd say, "Fine". But if anyone asked me how I was coping, I'd start crying. It all came to a head a few weeks later, when he got up at four in the morning to watch the Rugby World Cup on TV. It just ripped me to pieces that he would get up to watch the football, but not to help me deal with a screaming baby that I didn't know what to do with. Each scream seemed to signify further what a failure as a mother I was. I couldn't even soothe my own child. I wrote my feelings down in my journal – one of my first entries as a new mother – and couldn't believe the angry, bitter, resentful words that flowed off my pen towards the man I had loved since I was twenty-two. That was when I realised how jealous I was that his world had only changed slightly, while mine seemed altered forever, turned on its head. And I felt totally alone.* **Melissa**

*I felt my husband was a better parent than me and had a lot more patience for our son. He played and talked with him, which is something I always struggled doing. If anything, I was jealous of how good he was with our son and how much our son adored him.* **Tina**

*My wife had been on the receiving end of the majority of the experience, and she was clearly upset by it. I felt that I had in some way let her down, had failed in my duty as her protector. At the same time, we had done what we felt was a lot of preparation – so I also felt that I had been stupidly naive, had failed to grasp just how much we didn't know and hadn't prepared for.* **Ben**

*The more overdue Ang became, the higher the risks were and so I caved in, leaving Ang with no real support. She got tired of fighting and agreed to an induction. We had agreed that if it didn't get things started that we would just go back home, but I completely forgot about that and really Ang had no fight left in her to begin with. So when we were told she was failing to progress and that the baby's life was in danger, I believed it. Ang was in a world of emotional and mental pain, which amplified her physical pain and felt she had no choice but to have a caesarean. I felt that I'd failed Ang for that birth, and I know she was deeply traumatised.* **Dale**

## Issues with your partner explained

Relationships with partners often suffer in the fall out of a traumatic birth. There is so much emotion swirling in the air, often combined with sleep deprivation, shock, confusion, difficulties breastfeeding, adjusting to life as new parents, or as parents of more kids. Throw in the lack of understanding in our culture (see *Why doesn't anyone get it?* (p129)) and no wonder our partners are the first to feel the brunt of our pain, sometimes while struggling to deal with their own.

In this chapter are some common themes shared among women and couples who have attended Birthtalk.

We want to stress here that it *is* possible to heal relationships that have been shattered by a traumatic birth. Melissa from Birthtalk herself underwent huge relationship issues that have not only been resolved, but also instigated a wonderful new depth to her connection with her husband. We have witnessed many couples working through the emotions and situations presented here as they mend their relationship. We have seen their connection enhanced and their family blessed by their new respect and understanding for each other.

It can be hard to start the process, but what a beautiful gift for a child – parents who have allowed themselves to be vulnerable and opened up in love.

*Attending Birthtalk helped the situation of our relationship issues, as now I had found my release and the pressure at home started to ease.* **Tina**

*He understands now that I'm not the only one that feels this way – that I'm not being a self-indulgent drama queen. Adrian coming along to a Birthtalk meeting was really helpful for this. A big moment for us has been just the simple validation that, yes, we have been through a traumatic experience with our children, the loss of dreams and all the fall out was huge for us. We have been able to take it easier on our relationship because of this. We are currently going through an 'a-ha moment' regarding abandonment and Birthtalk has been extremely helpful in providing tools to help with being constructive with the emotional fall out of it (especially the Shifting from anger exercise).* **Leonie**

The issues with our partner after a traumatic birth can take on different forms, depending largely on the situation that unfolded in your birth. Sometimes our partners are relatively untouched by the birthing process, and the challenge involves sorting through our own intense feelings towards them about certain aspects of the birth.

We might feel resentment or anger towards them, or simply not have words to reframe 'what happened' in a way that will enable them to offer support. Our bitterness towards them may feel all-consuming, without them even having any idea about what's going on.

Other women see that their partner may be traumatised too, which can raise issues such as the mother not being able to accommodate her partner's intense and confused feelings amid her own.

Whatever the issue, many Birthtalk couples have found solace in the information in the following sections, and used the tools to rebuild their relationship and move forward with clarity about the situation and a way through it.

# WHY DIDN'T MY PARTNER RESCUE ME?

## What you need to know

Your partner probably didn't rescue you for a number of reasons. Firstly, look at what is needed to have a 'good birth' (from the section *Why does it matter? And isn't a live birth a good birth?* (p40)).

To have a good birth, a woman needs to feel during the birth:

- empowered, central to the experience, and 'doing' birth not having birth 'done to' her
- safe
- supported by those around her and supported by her knowledge base
- respected
- nurtured
- able to ask questions
- that her expert knowledge about herself and her baby was acknowledged and respected.

Did your partner know that these things such as feeling safe, being able to ask questions and being included in the decision making are important for you to feel strong and healthy afterwards? For that matter, did you? These good feelings are in strong contrast to a bad birth, where a woman's experience includes feeling powerless, confused, fearful, abandoned or unacknowledged.

- Now look again at some of the possible consequences of these feelings that arise in a bad birth:
- disappointment, a feeling of emptiness or that there was something missing from the birth
- a lack of confidence with mothering and an unawareness or rejection of your mothering instincts
- hypervigilance in your care of your baby
- feelings of failure, which can impact on your general confidence in life
- anger with your partner who's a close and easy target, especially if you felt that you should have been rescued by them, whether or not they really could have done that
- feeling so constricted by the trauma of the birth that you cannot fully express your love for your baby.

Did *your partner* know that this was the possible result of the situation you were in? And again, did *you*?

When you think about it, if you – and most of our culture – did not know the importance of feeling safe, central to the decision making and acknowledged and the damage that is possible if these needs are not met, how could your partner?

We imagine your partner probably read less about birth than you before the baby was born. If you did not come across this information, how could your partner?

They just didn't know. Most partners tend to have a single focused outcome for a birth: to take the mother and baby home alive.

Often, they don't have an awareness of the huge significance of your emotional wellbeing during birth and afterwards on how you experience motherhood. Neither do many, many health carers – many obstetricians and midwives and anaesthetists and physiotherapists and child health nurses and so on – are predominantly focused on the best way to keep you both alive and well.

Most people think that if the baby's healthy and you're physically healthy, then everyone is happy. Your partner, like most people in our culture, has been encouraged to put this trust in these people as the experts, because what else would they know to do?

Many partners may think something like this: "These people are professionals – they've studied for years, and they do this every day, so how can I stand up to them, or even question them, when they know *way* more than me. I just want my partner and child to be okay. I must trust their judgement to keep my family alive and well".

This is actually a very helpless position to be in and is quite scary for many partners.

As we share in *How to have a better birth next time* (p507), there is much a partner can do to support a woman towards an empowering birth. Unfortunately it's very difficult to access this information, which is partly why we wrote this book!

• Another reason why your partner may not have jumped in to support you may be because they may not have been able to read the signs that you needed help. Sometimes women seem to adopt a 'tend and befriend' response in times of stress, where they instinctively try to gather support from the people around them (in this case the health carers) by being extra-friendly. This can be confusing for both the woman and her partner, particularly as it may have a hormonal basis. So, while the woman may have felt under a lot of stress, her actions may have indicated otherwise to her partner. To read more about this possibility, see *I kept trying to befriend all the staff. Why did I do that?* (p214).

## Tools for healing and reconnecting

- Explore the idea that your partner, like most people in our culture, knew little about the importance of birth, and so could not possibly have supported you if they simply did not know. Is it possible to forgive them for not knowing stuff that *you* did not know?

- Keep in mind, a partner's primary goal is often simply to take their partner and child home alive and healthy. They are not likely to know about the importance of the mother feeling safe. They may often assume you felt safe because you were with the experts.

- Use the *Shifting from anger exercise* (p433) to begin to understand exactly what you are angry about and how it is affecting your relationship, and develop ideas for reconnecting and renewing your love.

- Ask your partner (after you've written the letter above and got your intensity out on the page rather than in your body) what their goal was for the birth. Ask them why they made particular decisions and comments – not in an accusing way, but in an 'I am interested because I love you' way. You may get to a point where you say things like, "You probably didn't know this, but when you said that, I felt…" without needing a particular response from them.

- Make all your interactions about this come with the aim of moving towards more connection. This will show in how you approach things, and will put them at ease. You can even tell them, "I am talking about this because I love you, and I love our baby, and our relationship is important to me. My aim from this conversation is working towards reconnecting." This can take your partner off the defensive, and enable them to open up and not only share, but begin to really hear what it was like for you.

# MY PARTNER THINKS I'M 'TAINTING' THE BIRTH BY TALKING ABOUT IT NEGATIVELY

*When Melissa expressed how differently she had experienced the birth to me, and how different this was to how I thought she had experienced it, I was taken aback, perhaps even a little angry. The birth process had really elevated her in my eyes to this strong, amazing, powerful woman. And here she was telling me otherwise. The whole thing, while hard and not the way we wanted it, had been empowering and validating to me. I thought I had provided the support she needed and that we all 'did well'. When she told me what really happened for her, all of that positivity I had experienced felt destroyed. I thought, "So, I didn't do a good job? Why are you telling me this now? We're all fine, move on! You're wrecking my memories!"* **Rem** (Melissa from Birthtalk's husband)

## What you need to know

It can be hard for a partner to hear how difficult or traumatic the birth of their child was for you, especially if it was a different experience for them. There are a few reasons for this. Firstly, if it was a good birth for them, yet you're saying otherwise, it can feel like you are 'wrecking' their experience, and taking away from their wonderful memories of the day they met their baby – which of course you're not. You're just saying how it was for you. They are unlikely to know that it is possible for two people to feel different (and even opposite) ways about a birth. Secondly, they may worry that by talking negatively about the birth, you are talking negatively about your child, which are two completely separate things. They may worry that it means you do not love the baby, and move quickly to 'talk you around' to preserve their family. This effectively closes off another outlet for you to have your feelings validated, and induces more feelings of guilt. (They don't know this, of course – they're just trying to protect you all and to move on.)

### There are important things for you to know and to then express to your partner:

It can be a good birth for them and a bad birth for you. Your experience of it does not taint theirs. However, your side of things does need acknowledging and processing so that you are able to see the gifts from your child's birth. This processing also opens up a space to be able to honour your partner's experience as well as your own and maybe share some of their 'good feelings'. This can't really take place until you have had your own experience valued and given attention and processed, which you can do by working through this book.

If your partner can grow to understand the important issues of traumatic birth, that how a woman experiences birth can affect her life postnatally, and that many, many women go through this, then this can give them space to be able to see how things were for you.

They may need to grieve for the fact that your experience was so bad; it may be where you can meet in the middle, and connect. You can say something like, "It would be okay if you felt sad that I did not have the same great experience that you did. I know I feel sad that it wasn't like that for me. But I also know that by acknowledging this, I am moving onto another stage of healing, and finding the good things from our child's birth".

### Melissa's husband, Rem, shares his experience:

*I felt on top of the world after the birth of our first son. It had been a really long and hard labour – thirty hours in the end. I had been actively involved in supporting Melissa throughout it and it was one of the hardest things I have ever had to do emotionally and physically. I was stuffed by the end of it. Sleep deprived, aching hands and fingers from massaging for so many hours and, emotionally, pretty well 'put through the wringer'.*

*The whole thing felt like a big test for me, something I had to get through no matter what, as I knew Melissa was going through so much more and had no way out. In the end, I felt I had passed that test and that Melissa had done so too with flying colours. She had gone through so much and her strength astounded me. I felt so proud of her, proud of myself for the way I supported her and absolutely smitten with our new son. Because he was born by C-section, I got to spend forty-five minutes alone with him while his mum was getting stitched up. That was one of the best moments of my life, looking into this beautiful trusting face looking up at me.*

*In the week that followed before bringing him home, I had negotiated to stay in the hospital with my wife and child. Melissa was pretty groggy and sore, so I took care of the baby – bathing him, changing him, helping her. I felt like husband and dad of the year. I felt that Melissa must be feeling great also, aside from her pain and exhaustion of course. I had no idea what was really going on for her. I had this new perspective of her as this amazing, strong woman. I had always thought she was amazing, but had never seen her go through something like this before. So I imagined she was feeling the same way – strong, proud, and capable of anything. I had no idea of what was going on, or what lay ahead.*

*I had found parts of the labour very difficult – hard to watch or hard to endure. Hearing your wife moaning, straining and crying for hours on end isn't easy. There were times when I was physically aching too. Watching her in pain as she had to lay still through contractions while the epidural was put into her spine was horrific. I also remember feeling really sad (crying to myself) in theatre because I knew how much she wanted and worked towards a natural birth. I really felt for her. I also recall at one point in theatre not caring about, or even thinking about, the baby. I just wanted my wife to be okay. She had been through so much. I couldn't bear her going through much more. But once the baby arrived, all of this was gone for me. I was elated. I'd got through it. I felt proud of myself. I felt proud of Melissa and completely in love with our new baby.*

*I think my outcome from the birth was quite different from Melissa's. I felt really empowered and validated. I felt I had performed my roles as husband and father really well. It was like emerging on the other side of a 'rite of passage' empowered. I felt I had grown as a person. I never realised that the time I spent bathing and changing the baby in hospital, cuddling him to sleep and looking after my wife was not necessarily a good thing. I didn't realise that her confidence and sense of capability as a parent were suffering.*

# Tools for healing and reconnecting

- Explore the idea that your partner may not be 'against' you. They may have simply had a good experience of the birth, and not be able to (yet) understand how you can have had such a different experience.

- Perhaps continue your own healing journey, until you are in a position to be able to explain things in a way they can understand. If you don't understand what happened to yourself yet, you can't really explain it. You can perhaps tell your partner that you are struggling, and beginning to see there is a whole aspect of birth you did not know about. You could share that this is helping you to gain clarity about your situation, and that you would like to talk to them about it in a while.

- If you haven't already, then it may be helpful now for you to do a *Birthtalk Breakdown* (p47) *to be able to see exactly how you did* experience the birth. Even this information can be enough for a partner to begin to see the vast differences between your experiences. Or, if you are not ready to share that yet, it might be time to do some grieving for what happened to you – and what didn't happen (see *I feel sad* (p245)).

- Use our *Shifting from anger exercise* (p433) to begin to understand exactly what you are angry about and how it is affecting your relationship, and develop ideas for reconnecting and renewing your love.

- It might be helpful for your partner to read *Birthtalk Breakdown – a new tool* (p47) and *What is a traumatic or bad birth anyway?* (p42) so they can understand the implications of the feelings from the birth for both of you and why your experiences differ so greatly.

- Ask your partner exactly how they experienced each aspect of the birth. You may need to wait until you have worked on your own healing first. You can even make up a *Birthtalk Breakdown* page for your partner, with just the 'What happened' side filled out already, and ask them how they felt at each of those stages.

- Or, they might need to do their own *Birthtalk Breakdown* where they fill in the 'What happened' side, as they might have experienced a different series of events to what you. Perhaps to kickstart the process, you can write in the basic progression of events, and invite them to include the things that happened that you don't know about. This might be another way for them to express what the birth was like for them.

- A comparison between your own *Birthtalk Breakdown* and theirs may reveal insights for you both. It may illustrate to them more about why you are feeling the way you do and give them insights into the reasons you are struggling. This process can also allow you to learn more about and acknowledge their experience as well.

- Perhaps ask them to read the quotes in this book – it can sometimes be helpful for a partner to read about someone other than their own partner experiencing similar things. This is a benefit for many couples attending our *'Healing From Birth'* meetings, as they can sit outside another couple's experience, and see their story echoed in their stories. This can be a powerful way for a partner to learn more about what is happening for you.

- Make all your interactions about this come with the aim of moving towards more connection. This will show in how you approach things, and put them at ease. You can even tell them, "I am talking about this because I love you, and I love our baby, and our relationship is important to me. My aim from this conversation is working towards reconnecting." This can take your partner off the defensive and enable them to open up and not only share, but begin to really hear what it was like for you.

# MY PARTNER WANTS ME TO 'JUST GET OVER IT' AND MOVE ON

*I think because the birth hasn't had such as marked an impact on him, he has found it difficult to understand why it's not something I could talk about once and be done with it.* **Leonie**

*My thoughts towards Melissa were, "We got through the tough times. Everything is fine now. Enjoy it. Don't bloody wreck it by filling perfect days with dredged up horrors of the past". I wanted to move on and leave the bad birth experience behind.* **Rem**

*My husband and I would have these hissing arguments while our son slept in the next room. I would be trying to share my feelings, and that I was struggling to cope. This was more than two years after the birth. He would hiss and point wildly, "But you're fine and he's fine!" And then I'd almost explode, and hiss even louder, "He's fine, but I'M. NOT. FINE!" And then I'd burst into tears. Again. And then he'd say, "But my mother had two caesareans, and she was fine!" And I'd say (trying to keep quiet but sounding more and more hysterical), "How do you know that? Have you ever asked her?" Which did stop him in his tracks, but each argument left us feeling frustrated and angry. Late one night after one of these fights, I lay alone in our bed wondering how I could possibly stay with a man who understood me so little. We'd been best friends for ten years, and now here he was unable to accept or understand the hugeness of the situation I was in. I felt miserable, bereft, and even more completely alone.* **Melissa**

Melissa would like to share that they moved through this stage, and used the techniques and ideas in this book. Now, thirteen years later, their relationship is stronger than ever.

## What you both need to know

Your partner wanting you to move on is very, very common, and a really difficult situation for a couple to be in – we probably don't need to tell you that! And if the issue were just sadness, then time would mend the pain.

Unfortunately trauma – if left unprocessed – does *not* go away. It stagnates and just sits there, colouring your whole life. Research has shown that women do not spontaneously recover from post-traumatic stress (after childbirth).[200]

So wanting to 'get over it' is understandable, but not really possible until processing of the experience has taken place. With a bad birth, *the only way out is through*. What this means is: it is possible to feel better, to reduce the intensity and move on – and this is more likely when you undertake the process of working through and exploring 'what happened' and are able to make sense of it all. This process is easier with *good support*. So what is the best way to support your partner to be able to support you?

Firstly, they need to *understand* what is happening for you. And secondly, they need to know that by supporting you through this, they are potentially (a) giving themselves the gift of a healed partner and (b) giving their child the gift of an emotionally recharged mother – which is what they really want anyway.

How, then, can you enable your partner to understand? It is important, firstly, for you to have an understanding of what's happening. So if you haven't read *The foundations of your healing journey* (p37), now's the time! The sections in this chapter will give you insights to gain clarity about your own experience, and a foundation for building your own knowledge base about traumatic birth.

For your partner to increase their own understanding, we recommend inviting them to read pertinent sections of this book. Reading a book about the issues, as opposed to hearing it from you, has the benefit of (a) coming from someone else so it can be less threatening and more likely to be heard and taken seriously (unfortunate, but true) and (b) this is the only place where your partner will find this information collated together, along with other people's experiences, to form a good understanding of the issues.

200   Söderquist, J., Wijma, B., & Wijma, K. (2006). The longitudinal course of post-traumatic stress after childbirth. *Journal of Psychosomatic Obstetrics and Gynaecology, 27*(2), 113 – 119.

Parts of the book that could be especially helpful for your partner to read include:

- The very page you have just read, above!
- *What is a traumatic or bad birth anyway?* (p42)
- *Birthtalk Breakdown – a new tool* (p47).
- *How do I heal?* (p61)
- *Can you get PTSD after childbirth?* (p83)
- *Why wouldn't my body work in labour?* (p230)
- Couple's quotes within the chapter *Issues with your partner* (p291).

## How to get your partner involved

Partners can often be quite keen to help; they just don't know *how* and they want it to be *over*. Sometimes they feel there is a stigma attached to not moving on.

> When I first told my husband I was still struggling with our son's birth after two years, he did not handle it well. He admitted to me much later that he had felt it was a sign of weakness and that he didn't want to see that in me. Now he knows just how strong I am, and doesn't feel that way anymore. **Melissa**

We have found that many partners just need an entry point, a 'way in', in order to be able to begin to offer support. Many partners relate well to facts, statistics, and tangible evidence, which we have found often works well to enable them to begin to offer support.

> For my partner, after many long arguments (see the quote at the beginning of this section), he found his 'way in' to be able to understand. He ended up calling Deb, his sister, who was a midwife and went on to form Birthtalk with me. He was in desperation, after one particularly bad fight about the usual stuff ("Why can't you just get over it? You're fine, the baby's fine. What's the problem?").

*Deb handled it from a physiology point of view. She gave him the facts of what I had missed out on hormonally, and how that could affect a woman's behaviour, the ease of her transition into motherhood and her bonding with her baby. And suddenly 'the light went on' for him. He could see factually that there were things I had missed out on, which enabled him to offer support. And, as my understanding of what had happened to me grew, I shared it with my partner and we made much of the journey to healing together.* **Melissa**

These facts about the physiology of birth that are often missing in a bad birth are shared in the section *Why wouldn't my body work in labour?* (p230). This, along with the other recommended sections, can be very eye-opening for a couple to read together as they can begin to pinpoint why certain things occurred in the birth and why it is understandable for there to be fall out afterwards. What a relief to realise that there is an explanation.

*I didn't realise at the time that Melissa would need to process the trauma properly before it would be remotely possible to leave the bad birth behind. I didn't even realise that she had experienced 'birth trauma' or that such a thing existed. I do now though and when I think about the experience, there is no other word for it than trauma. She was in excruciating pain. She was unsupported and felt abandoned by her midwife. She was misinformed by her doctors. She went through hell.* **Rem**

# Tools for healing and reconnecting

- Explore the idea that your partner may not be 'against' you; they may simply not be able to (yet) understand about bad births, like most of the population.

- Perhaps continue your own healing journey until you are in a position to be able to explain things in a way that your partner can more easily understand. If you don't understand what happened to yourself yet, you can't really explain it. You can perhaps tell your partner that you are struggling, and beginning to see there is a whole aspect of birth you did not know about. You could share that this is helping you to gain clarity about your situation, and that you would like to talk to them about it in a while.

- Use the *Shifting from anger exercise* (p433) to begin to understand exactly what you are angry about and how it is affecting your relationship, and develop ideas for reconnecting and renewing your love.

- If your partner is unsure about the benefits of processing your birth experience for yourself and your family, encourage them to read *Why take the healing journey?* (p76) for information and insights from other women and men who have been there.

- Ask your partner exactly how they experienced each aspect of the birth. You may need to wait until you have worked on your own healing first. You can even make up a *Birthtalk Breakdown* (p47) page for them, with just the 'What Happened' side filled out already, and ask them how they felt at each stage. A comparison between your own *Birthtalk Breakdown* and theirs may reveal more about why you are feeling the way you are and allow you to acknowledge their experience. It might be helpful for them to read *Why does it matter? And isn't a live birth a good birth?* (p40), and *What is a traumatic or bad birth anyway?* (p42) so they understand the implications of the feelings from the birth for both of you, and why your experiences differ so greatly (or you may find you actually feel the same about certain areas).

- Make all your interactions about this come with the aim of moving towards more connection. This will show in how you approach things, and then put your partner at ease. You can even tell them, "I am talking about this because I love you, and I love our baby, and our relationship is important to me. My aim from this conversation is working towards reconnecting". This can take your partner off the defensive, and enable them to open up and not only share, but begin to really hear what it was like for you.

# MY PARTNER IS TRAUMATISED AS WELL, BUT I HAVEN'T GOT SPACE FOR THAT

*I didn't want to hear anything about how my husband viewed our birth because I felt like such a failure and I didn't want to hear about how he viewed me, or hear him say anything that could make me doubt myself any more.* **Sharona**

*I wasn't aware of the time passing, but my husband held on to our baby for close to six hours after the birth, while the staff worked on bringing up my core temperature, blood pressure and heart rate. He doesn't want to remember that time – it's too much for him – but with his wife basically unconscious, hooked up to machines and covered in silver blankets, he must have been terrified. The emotions surrounding the birth and the first few months were almost enough to destroy our marriage. We both needed to cope with them in different ways, and those ways were not complementary. Trying to cope with the emotions the way we needed to drove us further apart, not closer together.* **Michelle**

## What you need to know

It can get very tricky when both partners are impacted by a birth. When both of you are reeling and struggling to cope, it can be very difficult to know how to move through this, especially when you are both crying out for support and understanding. This is made even harder because usually neither one knows what is going on, or how to heal.

For some partners, it can be hard to find an outlet to talk about their experience of the birth (For men, especially, it's not generally something that comes up over a couple of beers!) And often, you are unable to hear your partner's pain – because you are drowning in your own.

# Tools for healing and reconnecting

- In a situation where both partners are traumatised, sometimes things begin to move when the mother is undertaking her own healing journey, and begins to talk about her new understandings, so we encourage mothers to focus initially on their own healing. Continuing on this healing journey until you are in a position to be able to explain things in a way your partner can understand is helpful and important. If you don't understand what happened to yourself yet, you can't really explain it. Explore the idea that your partner may not be 'against' you, but may have simply also had a bad experience of the birth, and not be able to go there (yet) for themselves or for you.

- Use the *Shifting from anger exercise* (p433) to begin to understand exactly what you are angry about and how it is affecting your relationship, and develop ideas for reconnecting and renewing your love. While you are on your healing journey, you can perhaps tell your partner that you are struggling, and beginning to see there is a whole aspect of birth you did not know about. You could share that this is helping you to gain clarity about your situation, and that you would like to talk to them about it in a while.

- Your partner may benefit from reading certain parts of this book as well – obviously the above section, and also the section titled *My partner is traumatised. How can I help?* (p314). They will likely also find the beginning sections of this book helpful (*What makes a birth good or bad?* (p37), *Why does it matter? And isn't a live birth a good birth?* (p40), *What is a traumatic or bad birth anyway?* (p42), *Birthtalk Breakdown – a new tool* (p47), and *How do I heal?* (p61)), so they understand the implications of the feelings from the birth for both of you, and why your experiences can differ so greatly.

- It may be advisable to seek a professional for support to begin to wade through some of the issues.

- When you feel you have more emotional space to turn your attention to your partner's experience, read *My partner is traumatised. How can I help?* (p314) to explore ways to support them in their own journey towards healing.

- Importantly, make all your interactions about this come with the aim of moving towards more connection. This will show in how you approach things, and put your partner at ease. You can even tell them, "I am talking about this because I love you, and I love our baby, and our relationship is important to me. My aim from this conversation is working towards reconnecting". This can take your partner off the defensive, and enable them to open up and not only share, but begin to really hear what it was like for you.

# I'M ANGRY THAT MY PARTNER ISN'T AS AFFECTED BY THE BIRTH AS I AM

*There's been lots of resentment and sideways comments from me. I've felt abandoned for not really valid reasons in the present, but it stems from feeling abandoned in the beginning of the birth (this understanding has only just happened as an 'a-ha moment'). Like whenever my partner goes out in the evening after being at work all day, it sends me into a spin. I become really defensive and horrible. I have been unable to be even slightly vulnerable with him since our child's birth. It has placed huge amounts of strain and stress on our relationship.* **Gemma**

*In the months after the birth, I became furious that my partner's life had only marginally changed (in my eyes) since our son's arrival. Here I was feeling pulled and pushed around by my emotions, like I was constantly on a roller coaster, being pummelled by the effects of little sleep, a colicky baby, the emotional and physical impact of the birth, oh and moving cities! I felt like I was drowning, while he seemed the happiest he'd ever been. It just brought up such resentment and probably jealousy, too.* **Melissa**

*I found parts of Melissa's labour very difficult – hard to watch or hard to endure. Hearing your wife moaning, straining and crying for hours on end isn't easy. There were times when I was physically aching too. Watching her in pain as she had to lay still through contractions while the epidural was put into her spine was horrific. I also remember feeling really sad (crying to myself) in theatre because I knew how much she wanted and worked towards a natural birth. I really felt for her. I also recall at one point in theatre not even thinking about the baby. I just wanted my wife to be okay. She had been through so much. I couldn't bear her going through much more. But once the baby arrived, all of this was gone for me. I was elated. I'd got through it. I felt proud of myself. I felt proud of Melissa and completely in love with our new baby.* **Rem**

## What you need to know

The same birth can be experienced completely differently by every single person present. What was a traumatic and horrific journey for you may have been a wonderful and exciting trip for your partner. And if they're saying it was a positive experience for them, that's generally not because they are nasty, cruel, unfeeling or blind. It's more likely because they might genuinely have had a different experience to you.

They may have had different conversations with health carers, seen and felt different things, taken different interpretations of the process, and arrived at a different emotional outcome.

If, during this experience they felt: empowered, safe, supported, respected, nurtured, and able to ask questions (that is, they felt the feelings we describe in our definition of a good birth), then they can move into parenthood with confidence, strength, and positive feelings.

> *I think my outcome of the birth was quite different from Melissa's. I felt really empowered and validated. I felt I had performed my roles as husband and father really well. It was like emerging on the other side of a 'rites of passage' empowered. I felt I had grown as a person.* **Rem**

This can be hard for the mother to hear, especially if her partner finds it difficult to acknowledge that perhaps the mother felt unheard, confused or powerless. This can be particularly hard for the mother if her partner felt gratitude for the health carers, whom they may see as having protected or saved their family, while the mother is, at the same time, feeling violated or mistreated by the same health carers.

It can feel to the mother like her partner is fraternising with the enemy, sending an unspoken message that what happened to the mother was 'okay'. This can leave her feeling even more alone and isolated, as if there is no one on her side.

> *It felt like I was the only person who had 'collateral damage' after the birth. Like everyone else was able to leave it at the hospital. My husband was feeling so grateful to the midwives and doctors; we'd got through the birth with a live baby, we'd overcome hurdles to get breastfeeding established. The only way was up, right? Meanwhile, I was in complete turmoil. I was grateful, of course, but confused, bitter and fragile and just so deeply jarred. My husband's cheerful disposition only made me feel more desolate and inadequate – and angry.* **Melissa**

It can be hard to let go of the anger, once you begin to realise that your partner may not be the unfeeling, heartless person you might have judged them to be and that they may, genuinely, have had a more positive experience of the same birth. It can hurt to know that they got the good feelings and you didn't. However, once you know that it likely isn't their fault, there is room for healing, reconnection and forgiveness. Before your partner is able to acknowledge and validate your own experience of the same birth, they may need to increase their understanding of birth and birth trauma. They might not be aware that how you felt during the birth could be different to their own experience, and that these feelings can impact on you postnatally.

Most of our culture, and even most of our maternity health carers, don't know how much your experience of birth matters. So it would make sense if it was new information to your partner. Many people don't know that a healthy baby doesn't 'clear the slate' after a traumatic birth. They might need more information to be able to understand this. Many people don't know that how you feel during the birth can have repercussions for years afterwards if left unaddressed. This might be an opportunity to begin to be able to acknowledge your partner's experience, while still grieving your own, and for them to gather new information that might enable him to offer a new kind of support to you.

## Tools for healing and reconnecting

- Explore the idea that your partner may not be 'against' you; they may have simply had a good experience of the birth, and not be able to (yet) understand how you could have had such a different experience.

- Perhaps continue your own healing journey, until you are in a position to be able to explain things in a way your partner can understand. If you don't understand what happened to yourself yet, you can't really explain it. You can perhaps tell them that you are struggling, and beginning to see there is a whole aspect of birth you did not know about. You could share that this is helping you to gain clarity about your situation, and that you would like to talk to them about it in a while.

- It may be helpful now to do a *Birthtalk Breakdown* (p47) to be able to see exactly how you did experience the birth. Even this information can be enough for a partner to begin to see the vast differences between your experiences. Or, if you are not ready to share that yet, it might be time to do some grieving for what happened to you – and what didn't happen (see *I feel sad* (p245)).

- Use the *Shifting from anger exercise* (p433) to begin to understand exactly what you are angry about and how it is affecting your relationship, and develop ideas for reconnecting and renewing your love.

- Ask your partner exactly how they experienced each aspect of the birth, although you may need to wait until you have worked on your own healing first. You can even make up a *Birthtalk Breakdown* page for them, with just the 'What happened' side filled out already, and ask them how they felt at each of those stages. A comparison with your own Birthtalk Breakdown page may reveal to your partner more about why you are feeling the way you do. It might be helpful for them to read earlier sections of this book, so they understand the implications of the feelings from the birth, for both of you, and why your experiences differ so greatly. Suggested sections for this include: *What makes a birth good or bad?* (p37), *Why does it matter? And isn't a live birth a good birth?* (p40), *What is a traumatic or bad birth anyway?* (p42), *Birthtalk Breakdown – a new tool* (p47)

- Or, they might need to do their own *Birthtalk Breakdown* where they fill in the 'What happened' side, as they might have had a different series of events occur to what was happening for you. Perhaps to kickstart the process, you can write in the basic progression of events, and invite them to include the things that happened that you don't know about or remember. This might be another way for them to express what the birth was like for them.

- Make all your interactions about this come with the aim of moving towards more connection. This will show in how you approach things, and put your partner at ease. You can even tell them: "I am talking about this because I love you, and I love our baby, and I care about our relationship. My aim from this conversation is working towards reconnecting". This can take your partner off the defensive and enable them to open up and not only share, but begin to really hear what it was like for you.

# MY PARTNER IS TRAUMATISED. HOW CAN I HELP?

*I thought I was prepared for the birth, but I was not prepared for what the experience ended up being at all. I was diagnosed with depression a couple of months after my son's birth, and this is something I have never had to deal with before.* **Mike**

*When our baby was in the intensive care unit, my husband often thought about the survival rate of prems. Myself? It didn't even cross my mind as there was too much else going on. His main emotion was helplessness towards either myself or our baby. While our son was in hospital, my husband felt a huge inability to help him, yet at the same time had confidence in the medical profession looking after him. My husband's helplessness was extended once we were all at home and I started to not cope.* **Tina**

*My partner was traumatised too – not to the extent that I have been, or for the same reasons. His experiences have been around watching me and feeling powerless to do or say anything. Like a lot of men he needs to fix things – he can't sit in despair or anger or pain or sorrow for too long without doing something to fix or avoid it.* **Leonie**

*I had a mental image of what to expect, which was completely thrown out of the window. It was not like the books, classes or anything I'd seen or read. I was left with no information, I didn't know where my wife was, how she was, what had happened, where our baby was, or even whether he was alive or dead, until he was rushed passed me to go to special care. I wasn't included in any decision making; it was like I wasn't there. I didn't know what to do. I probably wasn't much good for my wife at the time because I was just as frightened as she was.* **Craig**

"If fathers are witness to a traumatic birth, as they perceive it, they need resolution."[201] ***Professor Gillian White,*** *Massey University, New Zealand*

---

201    White, G. (2007). You cope by breaking down in private: Fathers and PTSD following childbirth. *British Journal of Midwifery, 15,* 39-45.

## What you both need to know

The most important thing to know is that you both have your own experience of your baby's birth. Sometimes, the reasons a partner is traumatised or affected by the birth are quite different to the birthing woman's, yet they still fall into similar categories; that is, they fall under our definition of a bad birth, where the partner also experiences powerlessness, confusion, fear, isolation or abandonment.

## What happened for your partner?

Remember the *Birthtalk Breakdown tool* (p47), where we ask you to describe your birth using two columns: 'What happened', and 'How I felt'?

In both the 'What happened' and 'How I felt' columns, two partners often report vastly different accounts of the birth to each other. For example, in the 'What happened' column, it is quite possible your partner had different things happening for them, such as being required to field incoming information from health carers, engaging in conversations that you might not even have been aware of. Or gowning up for an emergency dash to theatre. Or having to sign papers you did not know about.

And the other possibility is that, even if you both had identical 'What happened' columns (that is, you both experienced similar events) the corresponding 'How I felt' columns (that is, your responses) could be entirely different.

## Missing important information

It can be hard for a support person to stand outside of a situation, not knowing what's going on in the birthing woman's body. They may have been missing essential information that you yourself were aware of, that meant that you did not feel as out-of-control as they did, for example when you felt sure the baby was fine, or you could feel the baby moving, and they did not know this.

Another scenario might be a situation where their knowledge of birth or experience in hospital situations may be less than yours. A lack of knowledge about these areas can lead to very scary thoughts and concerns.

## What did they mean?

Sometimes, all it can take is a health carer to give a certain look, or say something with an unnecessary sense of urgency, for a partner to feel fear and concern for the birthing woman's wellbeing. The health carer may be expressing urgency about a situation that has little to do with the safety of the woman or baby. The urgency may be more related to the practicalities of running a healthcare institution, for example, where certain hospital policies and protocols are expected to be met.

An example of this might be a situation when there are expectations about certain equipment being set up, or certain staff being present for the birth. The baby might be arriving faster than anticipated, without posing a threat to the health of mother or child, with the birth progressing smoothly. Yet meanwhile the midwife may be concerned that she may be in trouble with her superiors due to not having time to set up the equipment or alert certain staff as outlined by hospital protocol, and may be panicking about possible repercussions for her from this situation. Unfortunately the partner does not know this and assumes the panic is in response to the situation from a point of view of the health and safety of their partner and child.

> *Our experiences were traumatic in different ways. My wife's account of what was traumatic wasn't really what I noticed, such as the way people spoke to her, or the way examinations were done. The things that were scary for me were things that I saw happening to my wife, and things the doctors were doing to my wife and son that I didn't know why they were doing it, and they ended up being things that she hadn't even noticed because she was so deep in the experience of labour. We had very different versions of what was traumatic in the birth.* **Mike**

> *My experience of the birth was different from my partner's. I saw the happy healthy baby at the end. I didn't have the extra feelings of not having had a baby naturally or not being there when the baby was born or more of the other mother emotional stuff. I was just as scared though, when I didn't know what was happening and decisions were made without us.* **Craig** (whose partner was under a general anaesthetic for the birth)

# Birth as a traumatic event for the partner

The Birth Trauma Association (UK) describes Post-Traumatic Stress Disorder (PTSD) as, "The term for a set of normal reactions to a traumatic, scary or bad experience. It...can occur following the experience or witnessing of life-threatening events."[202] It is important to note that the diagnostic criteria options for PTSD include the situation of witnessing in person an event where someone else was being exposed to death, or the threat of death, or actual or threatened serious injury.[203]

In a new book called Traumatic Childbirth[204] (with Professor Cheryl Beck as a co-author), a chapter is devoted to fathers and traumatic childbirth. Here, the authors review research from Norway, the UK and New Zealand that investigate PTSD in fathers. They report that in a Norwegian study,[205] 18% of the fathers, who all had healthy babies, reported moderate to severe intrusive stress in the months after the birth. Meanwhile in another study in the UK,[206] 11.6% of the fathers, who also had healthy babies, experienced clinically significant symptoms six weeks after the birth on at least one of the three dimensions of PTSD. The fathers in the New Zealand study,[207] according to the authors of Traumatic Childbirth, shared feelings of alienation, sensing they were perceived not as participants, but as spectators. The fathers described feeling excluded in the process of childbearing, as they "were not acknowledged as a vital component of the family unit",[208] and reported intense psychological and physiological distress during sexual activity due to this triggering memories of the traumatic birth. These men also shared that they experienced humiliation, shame and helplessness due to suppressing emotional distress during the labour and birth.[209]

Another important point here involves the issue of perception. The US Department of Veteran Affairs reports on evidence showing that "the perception of threat (distinct from the level of actual threat) is an independent

202     Birth Trauma Association, UK. *What is Birth Trauma?*
Retrieved from *www.birthtraumaassociation.org.uk/what_is_trauma.htm*, accessed January 2014.

203     American Psychiatric Association. (2013). *Diagnostic and statistical manual of mental disorders (5th ed.)*. Washington, DC: Author. P.271

204     Beck, CT., Driscoll, JW., & Watson, S. (2013). *Traumatic Childbirth*. London and New York: Routledge.

205     Skari, H., Skreden, M., Malt, U.F., Dalholt, M., Ostensen, A.B., Egeland, T., & Emblem, R. (2002). Comparative levels of psychological distress, stress symptoms, depression and anxiety after childbirth--a prospective population-based study of mothers and fathers. *British Journal of Obstetrics and Gynaecology*, 109(10),1154–63 PMID: 12387470

206     Bradley, R., Slade, P., & Leviston, A. (2008). Low rates of PTSD in men attending childbirth: a preliminary study. *British Journal of Clinical Psychology*, 47, 295–302. in Beck, CT., Driscoll, JW., & Watson, S. (2013). Traumatic Childbirth. London and New York: Routledge. P. 206

207     White, G. (2007). You cope by breaking down in private: Fathers and PTSD following childbirth. *British Journal of Midwifery*, 15, 39-45

208     Beck, CT., Driscoll, JW., & Watson, S. (2013). *Traumatic Childbirth*. London and New York :Routledge. p. 205

209     ibid.

predictor of PTSD symptoms".[210] Translated to a childbirth scenario, we have supported partners who have experienced a situation as traumatic, even when the mother or baby were never in danger, because they *perceived* the situation as threatening to their loved ones, based on what they were seeing, or being told, or interpreting about the event. That is, even if everyone else in the room knows that it is not a dangerous situation, what the partner *thinks* is going on is *what matters*, in terms of their experience and its effect. This can also be experienced at some level by other support people present, including health carers.

Some of the more common situations we have worked through at Birthtalk are:

- **Having medical staff rushing around the partner, sometimes seemingly in a panic, and not explaining the situation to them.** It can be very frightening to believe your loved ones are in danger, and even more so if you feel powerless to act. Unfortunately, this trauma may be avoided, if even one person stops to explain what is going on. Sometimes, the panic is just the rush by the staff to get things in place – things that are expected of them – rather than a current threat to the mother and child. For someone who is not familiar with such situations, the looks on the staff's faces can portray a very different story.

- **Witnessing procedures being done to the birthing woman.** It can be horrifying for someone to see their partner lying flat on a bed, having things done that look like they hurt, especially if there is blood, and especially if the birthing woman is expressing that she is not happy with the situation. What a helpless situation for the person looking on. This is not to invalidate the experience of the woman on the bed; we are just saying that this is a situation commonly reported to us, which can have repercussions for the partner.

- **Being excluded from the event.** Occasionally, partners are pushed aside altogether. Sometimes curtains are pulled around the bed with them on the outside and their loved one and medical staff on the inside. Or they are moved to the back of the room, witnessing things helplessly from afar. Or a 'cast of thousands' descends on a previously intimate birth, and they feel like they have no voice in the experience and are unable to support their partner.

## Initial steps for men

It can be a different process for men after a traumatic birth, as they tend to handle things differently to women. Some men do not want to talk about their situation, and will not admit they are affected by the birth. Others will become

---

210   Department of the Army Headquarters, United States Army Medical Command. (2012). *Policy Guidance on the Assessment and Treatment of Post-Traumatic Stress Disorder (PTSD)*. Retrieved from *http://cdn.govexec.com/media/gbc/docs/pdfs_edit/042312bb1.pdf*, accessed November 2014.

angry if it is implied that they might be affected by the birth, as they may feel there is a stigma attached to this and that they are 'being weak'. Some may feel that they 'shouldn't' need support as it didn't happen to them and they need to focus on their partner's wellbeing.

As a result, it may be challenging to find a way of explaining things that he can connect with. Our recommendation is to perhaps approach it once you have traversed the path to healing yourself, or at least once you have explored the nature of traumatic birth (this book is designed to help with this). These steps will hopefully increase your understanding and confidence in your approach.

Sections of the book that could be initially helpful for your partner to read include:

- The very page you have just read above
- *What makes a birth good or bad?* (p37)
- *Why does it matter? And isn't a live birth a good birth?* (p40)
- *What is a traumatic or bad birth anyway?* (p42)
- *Birthtalk Breakdown* (p47)
- *How do I heal?* (p61)
- *Why wouldn't my body work in labour?* (p230)
- Couple's quotes throughout the chapter *Issues with your partner* (p291).

## Tools for supporting a partner who is traumatised

We recommend completing your own *Birthtalk Breakdown* first, and working on your own healing so you can support your partner.

- Perhaps you can make up a *Birthtalk Breakdown* page for him, with just the 'What happened' side filled out already based on what you know, and ask them how they felt at each of those stages, which could give you both insights into exactly how your partner experienced each aspect of the birth.
- Perhaps your partner can add in the things that happened that were different to what you experienced. A comparison with your own *Birthtalk Breakdown* page may reveal to them more about why you are feeling the way you do, and why they feel the way *they* do.
- A comparison between your own *Birthtalk Breakdown* and theirs may enable you to acknowledge your partner's experience.

- If they are willing to read the sections mentioned above, they will support your partner to explore and understand the implications of the feelings from the birth, for both of you, and why your experiences differ so greatly. Or you may even find you actually feel the same about certain areas.

- If you are feeling overwhelmed by your partner's trauma due to struggling with your own traumatic experience, read *My partner is traumatised as well, but I haven't got space for that* (p308), which is designed to support you through this.

- Read *Can you get PTSD from birth?* to increase understanding and awareness of the nature of Post-Traumatic Stress Disorder and its impact. Note that this section also applies to partners witnessing a birth.

- It may be advisable for your partner to consider a counselling session with an appropriate health carer. This might be helpful for a number of reasons, for example, if there is a situation where your partner needs to discuss things they might not want to share with you that need to be expressed and explored for them to be able to move on. It may also be helpful if the whole situation feels too overwhelming for you as a couple in general. As much as a woman may want to 'be there' for her partner, it may be beneficial to seek professional support to take the pressure off the relationship. The partner is responsible for their own healing, and while a woman can offer her support, there may be benefits to seeking professional guidance.

- It might be helpful for them to read the partner's quotes throughout this book, so they can receive some of the validation they may need to be able to begin to process their own experience.

- Give them the opportunity to explore other chapters of this book according to where they are at, whether it is anger, guilt or sadness. They may find just reading through the book gives them insights into what happened, which may enable you both to chat about things further.

- Importantly, make all your interactions about this come with the aim of moving towards more connection. This will show in how you approach things and put them at ease. You can even tell your partner, "I am talking about this because I love you, and I love our baby, and I care about our relationship. My aim from this conversation is working towards reconnecting". This can take your partner off the defensive and enable them to open up and share, leading to new conversations and awareness of the situation for both of you.

# Special circumstances

## MY BABY WAS VERY UNWELL

*In the quietest and darkest hour of the night, when bone weary parents have laid their heads, the machines continue their unrelenting tango with delicate souls. The tiny children with whom they dance have arrived into this world with something missing: their chance to share a lusty cry, to suck with fervour at their mother's breast, to look into their father's loving eyes… lost.* **Caylie Jeffery, from 'The Baby Artist'** [211]

*Somebody yelled out, "Don't forget to show mum on the way through," and my baby was rushed past me (they slowed ever so slightly when going past me). My baby was a fair distance from me and I was so shocked when I saw him. He had a huge tube down his throat and was all covered up. I could only see a bit of skin around his mouth and eyes. I started vomiting as soon as I saw him.* **Freya**

*After a very straight forward, no complications pregnancy, we took for granted that we would have a 'normal' birth and meet our new little girl and have all those newborn moments that you expect and- hear about. Instead, we crashed into a world we didn't understand, had never experienced or even knew much about.* **Kathryn**

---

211    Jeffery, C. (2013) *The Baby Artist*. Retrieved from *www.cayliejeffery.com.au/2013/06/06/thebabyartist/*, accessed September 2014.

*I had experienced such a peaceful pregnancy and beautiful labour only to birth a very sick baby. No one prepares you for having a very unwell full term baby. I just remember crying and crying.* **Rebecca**

*It was incredibly lonely. No one we knew had ever been through something like this, I didn't have anyone to talk to and felt like I needed to be strong for everyone else when all I wanted to do was curl up into a little ball and cry.* **Kathryn**

*I have been obsessed with the birth for over two years now. It has haunted me and I have examined it from every angle – everything that I did, everything that others did, different choices I could have made, what I should have been told during the pregnancy but wasn't.* **Freya**

*I first saw her on a photo which the staff took for us. It was about five hours before I met her for the first time. She was critically ill and still on a ventilator. I have never felt so completely heartbroken and overwhelmed as I did when I met her.* **Kathryn**

The impact of a traumatic birth is difficult enough to deal with when your baby is healthy. But when your child is born at term and is unexpectedly very unwell, there is a whole new set of difficult issues, more opportunities for feeling isolated and unacknowledged in your pain.

If your baby began their life in a tenuous position, you may have felt like you were walking on a very high tightrope. Women we have spoken to report dealing with strong feelings of guilt, failure and isolation, often while being judged by others and consumed with worry over their child's wellbeing, finding themselves in a very distressing situation.

This section explores some of the emotions that women with very sick babies often face, and shares the stories and feelings of three strong women, who have also been through this experience: Freya, Rebecca and Kathryn.

## Why do women with sick babies need specific support?

For many women who have had a traumatic birth where the baby emerges healthy, it may not be evident why the woman is distressed just by looking at the situation. This can make it challenging for her to find support. When a baby is compromised, however, reasons for the mother's distress are usually immediately obvious. Yet that doesn't tend to make it any easier for her to find support for the complexity of her situation. There is a lack of understanding around the intricate layers of feelings that can accompany such a challenging event as having an unwell baby, which can create even more trauma. She may be told she should feel grateful – not for the baby's health, but merely for the baby's survival. But issues may have occurred within the birth separate to the situation with her baby. These issues need addressing; however they are often lost amid the trauma of the baby's health. She may struggle herself to deal with a rollercoaster of emotion at different stages in the weeks and months post-birth, which is why we have invited Freya, Rebecca and Kathryn to highlight the key issues facing women in this situation.

## Why is it different for women with an unwell baby?

For many women who've had a traumatic birth, it might not be evident why they are distressed just by looking at what happened in the birth and postnatally. That is not the situation for these women. Most people can see straight away that it would be a traumatic event. How the woman feels about the things that happened outside of the traumatic event can often get lost in the trauma of having an unwell baby.

## Our stories

It is important to know you are not alone. We have asked Freya, Kathryn and Rebecca to share their birth stories to give you more insights into their own journeys:

> My baby suffered shoulder dystocia during his birth. He was eleven pounds and I am a Type 1 diabetic. Ventouse was used and his head was born. Shortly thereafter, there was utter panic in the room. There were a *lot* of people there, all screaming at me to push. I knew my baby's head had been born as I heard the doctor say it at the time and I was aware that it was taking far too long for the rest of him to come out. I knew if I didn't get him out then he was going to die and I was afraid he might already be dead. The whole room screamed at me to push and eventually (over five-and-a-half minutes later) he was finally born. At that point I felt very relieved and thought everything was going to be okay. Time went on and I couldn't hear any crying. I asked my husband if it was a boy or girl and he said it was a boy and kept telling me how I'd done exactly what they said and pushed our baby out. I started getting worried that I couldn't hear any

crying. My husband was told to go out of the room (to go to the neonatal intensive care unit [NICU] with the baby). I knew at this point I was being stitched up. The baby was whisked past me and I didn't then see him for another twelve hours. He had been born flat and required resuscitation. When he was taken to NICU, they thought he was breathing okay and pulled the tube out. He stopped breathing and they had to intubate him again. They couldn't get the tube in and it took three attempts and an anaesthetic to get it in again. This resulted in a collapsed lung, air escaping into my baby's chest cavity and a week heavily sedated on morphine while a visit to theatre was arranged (at day four) for a check of my baby's airways. On top of this, my baby had suspected meningitis and after several lumbar punctures, was treated for it. He also became addicted to the morphine he was on. When he finally came off it at a week old, his eyes were rolling back in his head and he was clearly agitated. This was the first time I had seen his eyes open and I had not held him at this point in time. He ended up being put back on the morphine and it took another two weeks to wean him off it very slowly. When my baby was about five days old it was also realised his right arm wasn't moving at all (this was missed until this point due to the morphine). It transpired he had suffered a brachial plexus palsy as a result of the way he was pulled out when he was stuck. He had a five-hour nerve graft surgery for this when he was four months old. This involved nerves being taken from the backs of both his legs – resulting in big scars down his legs – and transplanted into his brachial plexus in the neck area. **Freya**

The labour itself was a peaceful, beautiful experience as I was able to stay at home in comfortable surroundings and go with the flow. About eight hours into the labour I started to feel like the contractions were getting on top of me and I was feeling a pushy sensation. At this point we decided to go to the hospital. I arrived at the hospital, a CTG monitor was put on me and the midwife did a vaginal examination, which found I was ten centimetres dilated. At this point, Emily's heart rate appeared fine. I got into position for second stage. After fifteen minutes of pushing, I birthed my baby Emily. Emily flopped out and I heard the midwife swear and Emily was taken out of the room. I was facing the opposite direction so didn't actually see her. I heard an emergency bell go off outside the room. A paediatrician then came in and asked me about all the medications I was on and

*if anything had happened with the labour at home. She then
left the room. I then started to haemorrhage as I had a retained
placenta. After what seemed like forever the midwife came and
told me Emily had a very low heart rate at birth and required
resuscitation. Emily was not breathing at birth and required
immediate resuscitation. Her Apgar score was 1:1:3. It took
two attempts to intubate her and forty-five minutes for her to
take a breath. Emily was diagnosed as having possible hypoxic
ischaemic encephalopathy (HIE) grade 2 and underwent brain
cooling for seventy-two hours. She was intubated, ventilated
and cooled to thirty-three degrees for seventy-two hours in the
intensive care unit (ICU). She suffered two seizures and was
placed on anticonvulsant medication. Twelve hours after her birth
the consultant came to visit me in recovery. I was told she had
suffered a severe brain injury due to hypoxia at birth and would
likely have severe brain damage. On day five Emily was weaned
off the ventilator and was breathing on her own. She moved from
ICU to the special care unit. She had an MRI on day five which
showed no signs of hypoxia or brain damage. On day eight we
were able to commence breastfeeding and ten days after birth
Emily was discharged from the special care unit.* **Rebecca**

*I went into spontaneous labour at term and, after a very long
labour and second stage, had a vacuum delivery. During the
delivery, Grace's shoulders got stuck for four-and-a-half minutes
(a severe shoulder dystocia requiring internal rotations and
delivery of the anterior arm) and she came out completely flat (no
heartbeat). She was immediately taken away from us and required
full resuscitation. It took nearly five minutes for her heart to start
beating and twenty minutes for her to take a gasp. Her Apgar
scores were 0:3:3:3:3. For over twenty minutes after the birth we
didn't know whether she was going to survive. Once Grace was
stable, they took her to the NICU. Grace had asphyxiated at birth
due to shoulder dystocia, and as a result, most of her system had
shut down (including kidneys, gut, heart and lungs). She started
having seizures soon after birth as well. She was diagnosed with
severe hypoxic ischemic encephalopathy (HIE III), and initial
blood results also indicated that she had group B streptococcus
(GBS) sepsis. Grace was, at this point, given a guarded prognosis,
and we were told that we would know very little about her
condition and long-term prognosis for at least two or three
days, and that a multitude of tests and scans were being ordered*

*(including further blood counts, continual brain monitoring, cranial ultrasound, lumbar puncture, EEG and MRI – which showed damage to her occipital, parietal and frontal lobe). Grace continued to be ventilated for forty-three hours and was placed on a cooling mat for seventy-two hours. Although her seizures continued, they decreased in intensity and frequency and by day three had almost abated. Grace's organs slowly recovered and began to function normally as well, however, her neurological assessments showed that she was not responding appropriately to a number of newborn tests and her long term outcome was suspect. I didn't get to hold her until she was five days old and, all up, she spent seventeen days in hospital (twelve in the NICU and five in special care).* **Kathryn**

Although all of these babies survived, the impact of their births would continue to be felt in the days, months and years afterwards. These women faced not only the usual recovery from birth, but also an uncertain prognosis for their baby, the challenge of understanding new medical terms and hospital protocols, and dealing with the rest of the world. This is mirrored in many women we meet who experience similar birthing situations.

## The early days

The first few days after the shock of a traumatic birth with an unwell baby can be extremely overwhelming. Devastation, grief, confusion and exhaustion can swirl around, all the while with the woman and her partner struggling to grasp the situation.

*Initially I felt exhausted and confused. I didn't understand exactly what had happened during the birth and it was only when my baby was a few days old I realised the term was actually 'shoulder dystocia'. I didn't know if my baby was at risk of dying in the early hours and days and I was too scared to ask. I began to dread going in to NICU because every time I went in, there was a new concern and something else to be worried about. I felt very shocked and a little bit emotionless in the early days, like I was just trying to keep my head above water. After a few days I started feeling like I just wanted to forget it had all happened, go home to my other baby (my older boy was only twenty-one months old) and do it all again 'properly'. I felt very guilty about what had happened.* **Freya**

*The overwhelming feeling was grief – with guilt and loneliness not far behind. For the first few days we couldn't hold her or stroke her, just rest our hands on her cold little body and talk to her. I felt heartbroken that I hadn't been able to bring her safely into the world, and shattered that we had missed out on everything that we'd thought we'd have when we welcomed our little girl into the world.* **Kathryn**

*The main emotion I experienced during the first few days was overwhelming devastation followed by grief and loneliness. I had experienced such a peaceful pregnancy and beautiful labour only to birth a very sick baby. No one prepares you for having a very unwell full-term baby. I just remember crying and crying. I was so worried about Emily and whether she was going to be okay. I felt so alone in hospital – most people thought we had tried to have an unassisted home birth and that's why Emily was so unwell at birth (which was untrue).* **Rebecca**

## Feeling out of control

With a baby in Neonatal Intensive Care Unit (NICU), there is often not a lot for a parent to do. This can intensify the feelings of helplessness and isolation. The baby's care is predominantly performed by specialist nurses, midwives and doctors. Many parents report feeling that their baby does not yet 'belong' to them. These babies can seem to "belong to the machines, the humidicribs, the doctors and the nurses before they belong to anyone else".[212]

> *While my baby was in NICU and SCBU [Special care baby unit] (for about nineteen days), I really felt like he was not my child. Even though he was my second baby, I felt I had to ask the nurses if I could do things like change his nappy.* **Freya**

> *It was so hard just sitting there, knowing that she was having seizures, knowing she was critically ill, feeling so incredible helpless that we were unable to 'fix her'.* **Kathryn**

> *I went into NICU one morning when my baby was about three or four days old, and during the night his hair had all been shaved off apart from a Mohawk down the back. Apparently, the staff were having trouble getting lines into him. In the end it was all*

*a waste as they couldn't get them into his scalp anyway. I was so shocked when I saw him, but I just pushed the tears away and accepted that it had had to happen.* **Freya**

## Disconnection from your baby

With any traumatic birth or separation, difficulties with bonding often arise. This can be intensified when your baby is whisked away, if you are unable to hold, feed or care for your baby or if you fear for their wellbeing.

*I felt really disconnected from Emily for the first five days of her life. I was unable to touch her or hold her in those first few days. She needed to be maintained at a thirty-three degree temperature and my touch would heat her up. Once I held her on day five I felt the strong connection we had during pregnancy and that close bond has remained between us.* **Rebecca**

*I felt quite removed from him and didn't get any instant feelings of love when I saw him, as my first sight of him being rushed to NICU with a huge tube mounted about his face was so shocking that my reaction after first seeing him was to vomit. My baby was so big, but also so swollen from his birth that he looked as far removed from the normal newborn baby images as is possible. I was unable to hold him for over a week and didn't hear him cry or see his eyes open for over a week. When he had his breathing tube removed at one week old, I was really excited that I would see his eyes open for the first time. When I saw him his eyes were rolling back in his head, he was making dry scratchy gargling noises from his throat and he was clearly very agitated. It turns out he'd become addicted to the high dose of morphine he'd been on for over a week, but I didn't know that. I was so shocked that I spent very little time with him and went back to the postnatal ward, where I spent the night awake thinking I should go and see my baby but not wanting to. I kept thinking that the nurses would surely tell me if he was dying. I didn't go into NICU at all during the night to see him. I felt deflated and just wanted to forget I had a newborn.* **Freya**

The feelings of disconnect can then add to any guilt that is already there, which makes for a big confusing swirl of emotions, day after day. Sometimes this can create tensions between partners, as they struggle to rise above the intensity of the experience.

## Dealing with your partner

It can be so frightening to deal with the aftermath, when a baby is unwell, and our partners have their own journey to take alongside us. Sometimes this can be a connecting experience, and for others, due to the situation they face, it can sorely test a relationship.

> *I was very angry with my husband because he got to see Emily at birth and was able to be with her while she was being intubated and ventilated. I was left alone. I was too unwell to see my baby until eight hours after the birth (post-partum haemorrhage followed by manual removal of my placenta in theatre). My husband had left during the labour so I think he felt like something had gone wrong while he wasn't there. I felt alone because he was, at the time, very angry with my support person (because he couldn't get his head around how such an uneventful labour could go so wrong while he was not there) whereas I needed her as she was the only one I could talk to about the shock of Emily's birth after such an uneventful labour.* **Rebecca**

> *My partner was very supportive. I think we were both just running on adrenaline and trying to get through the difficult period. My husband had a lot on his shoulders as our older child was only twenty-one months and was very confused about his mother suddenly disappearing for over two weeks (the time I was in hospital with complications). We felt relatively close in the post-birth period as we had both experienced the awful birth and were going through the post-birth/NICU trauma together.* **Freya**

## Bringing your baby home

Once the hurdle of your baby being well enough to come home has been overcome, it is likely that many people would expect your fears and worries to abate. However, as Kathryn, Rebecca and Freya share, although the baby might be home and 'stable', the old concerns may not have gone away and new concerns may also have arisen.

> *I was very overprotective of Emily when she came home. I did not want to leave her side. I was constantly worried about her health and kept waiting for something to go wrong with her. Over time, this feeling has reduced in intensity, however, has not gone completely.* **Rebecca**

*I felt very overprotective once she was home and didn't feel comfortable with other people holding her. It probably took a few months before it got easier. I felt really uncomfortable leaving her and hated being separated from her. There were times when we were apart where I'd start to feel sick because I just needed to 'connect' with her again. There was also an element of fear that she wouldn't be okay in the long term, that something would happen to her or she'd get sick again.* **Kathryn**

*It all got progressively worse once I got home. As time went on and after my baby's surgery at age four months, I had more time to ponder what had happened. It ate me up to the point I became suicidal. I really hit rock bottom about fourteen months after the birth.* **Freya**

## Guilty feelings

After a traumatic birth many women express feelings of guilt. When your baby has been impacted physically from the birth, these guilty feelings can be foremost in a woman's mind as she replays the birth, wondering if there was something that she did – or didn't do – that could have changed the outcome. Or sometimes, there can be guilt for feeling good feelings too, in a situation where the labour itself was positive.

*I have spent a long time going over the birth, reading my notes, researching shoulder dystocia, GBS and HIE. I needed to do this to try and understand what happened and I guess in part to see whether I did or didn't do something that might have changed the outcome.* **Kathryn**

*I felt like I failed my baby. It was my job as her mother to bring her into the world safely and I failed to do that. I felt it was my fault.* **Rebecca**

*I feel guilty because of some of the feelings I had towards my baby in the early days.* **Freya**

*There were lots of times where I felt that I'd failed Grace as her mother; the birth in particular, but then also when I couldn't produce enough milk while she was in NICU and they had to top her up with formula. That broke my heart as I'd been so determined to breastfeed my baby and felt like I couldn't even get that right.* **Kathryn**

*I felt guilty about the joy I felt when I thought about the labour at home. I felt like that empowering feeling had been taken away by birthing such an unwell baby. Everyone in the hospital was so focused on what must have gone wrong for Emily to have been born not breathing.* **Rebecca**

## Unhelpful responses from others

In a situation where a baby is very unwell, with an uncertain prognosis, it can be hard for the people around the parents to know how to act. Most people have not been in such a position, so they are not sure of what to say, and everyone wants to find a 'silver lining' for the mother. The resulting comments can feel like barbs to the heart of a struggling woman.

*It seemed that no one really knew what to do or say. I don't blame them for that; before I had Grace I wouldn't have known either if it'd happened to someone I knew. Sadly, I don't think many of them realise just how much of an impact it had on me, my husband and our family. We didn't have a lot of people visit us while Grace was in the NICU – only our mums, my sister and our doula saw her. Many people didn't meet her until she came home. I think that's the reason that a lot of people don't really appreciate just how critical Grace's situation was.* **Kathryn**

*The least helpful thing that someone has said? Being told that since my daughter is 'fine', I should move on from the birth trauma.* **Rebecca**

*I had my Mum say to me that she only wanted to hear 'happy things'. As a consequence I have, since that time, not said a word about my feelings about the birth, my Post-Traumatic Stress Disorder, etc.* **Freya**

When your baby is recovered and doing well, there can be a misperception that you and your partner will now be completely okay, too. It can be difficult for other people to understand that your trauma can be ongoing, and that your grief does not end simply with a positive outcome.

*People say that because Grace is now healthy and fine, I mustn't think much about the birth anymore. I've had a few people comment on how well Grace is doing and how we spent so much time being 'worried about nothing' and the like. It seems that because she is doing so well and so completely 'normal' it's easy for others to dismiss her condition when she was born and almost expect that because everything turned out so well, that we should be able to get over it and move on. I find that incredibly difficult. Grace's birth will always be there; the fact that she was born still will always be there; the HIE will always be there; having her taken away from us at birth will always be there; the moments we lost will always be there. We can't turn around and dismiss what we went through just because we have been so blessed to have a positive outcome. And that's what I wish everyone would understand – it will never go away and I strongly doubt that my grief will ever go away entirely either.* **Kathryn**

## Responses from your health carers

It seems that the response of health carers towards a mother, after a traumatic birth where a baby's health is severely compromised, can range from extremely supportive to dismissive to even making jokes around the event. The reaction of health carers in the days, weeks and months after such a birth may have a marked impact on a woman's ability to move through this experience and to begin to process what happened.

*Support from health carers? Pretty much a big no all round. Initially, I felt really isolated and even judged. The two midwives who were at the birth never came to see me postnatally, even though I was on the ward for six days. The NICU staff were better in terms of support, but there were huge gaps in the emotional support and I felt that very few of them really understood just how traumatic this experience was for us. The doctor who was at the birth came to see me a few times on the ward; we talked a little about the birth but I was still too shocked in the early days to really comprehend what had happened. A couple of months later when I'd hoped to talk to the doctor, I was told they were no longer at the hospital. I wish I'd been able to talk to that doctor again as I had questions and also wanted to say thank you for visiting Grace in the NICU. I found out from a nurse that the doctor had gone in before or after each shift for over a week to see how Grace was doing.* **Kathryn**

*My medical notes had been changed and stated that I had been warned of the risks of shoulder dystocia when I was never given any such warnings. I had never, ever heard of shoulder dystocia and reading that in my notes really sent me off the deep end. I felt so violated that professionals could lie and fabricate notes to try to protect themselves.* **Freya**

*On the ward, most midwives weren't supportive. I had one midwife who got annoyed with me because each time she wanted to do my check up I was down in the NICU; it was almost like she couldn't understand why I wasn't staying on the ward waiting for her to see me. That really pissed me off 'cause it's not like I chose to have a critically ill baby. Many of the midwives just didn't seem to know how to communicate with me and said very little – it was quite isolating to be left alone and feel like they didn't see it as a big deal to have a baby in the nursery. Overall, I think that most of them just simply didn't get it and how much of an impact it has to have a critically ill baby.* **Kathryn**

*I had one person say to me that if I had controlled my blood sugars better then my baby wouldn't have been so big. I had another doctor stand in front of me and tell another doctor that my baby was the "eleven-pound baby of a Type 1 diabetic, supposedly in good control – hahahaha". I had another doctor ask me very suspiciously why I think it was that my baby became addicted to the morphine he had been on for a week (clear implication being I must be a heroine user!).* **Freya**

*I had really good support from my birth support person. She validated my feelings of grief over the birth. I also had great support from a counsellor with experience in birth trauma. My support person also linked me to another mother who had experienced the same birth trauma with her daughter. It was such a relief to meet someone else who shared the same experience as mine and who allowed me to talk openly about my experience.* **Rebecca**

*The midwife who was present at Emily's birth came to see me several times to talk about what had happened with Emily at birth and to clarify any questions I had. She was very kind, supportive and non-judgemental about what had happened with Emily. She also visited Emily everyday she was in hospital to check on her progress. The midwives who looked after me in hospital were very kind to me. However, they made several derogatory remarks about my support person, implying it was her fault we stayed at home too long and, therefore, held some responsibility for Emily's condition at birth (However this was completely inaccurate*

*and an unfair accusation considering her role was purely that
of emotional support). This further increased my feelings of
isolation.* **Rebecca**

*About eight months after Grace came home I was referred to a
psychologist, which was a waste of time in the end. After the third
visit she told me that it was time I 'got over it' and moved on with
my life.* **Kathryn**

## Separating the traumatic event from the rest of the birth

As established in the section *What is a traumatic or bad birth anyway?* (p42),
there is a hidden web of feelings underlying a woman's experience of her birth
that drives her response postnatally. When you experience having an unwell
baby or a baby who requires assistance, this is obviously a very overt, traumatic
experience, often filled with immense horror and helplessness. However, you
too, like all other women, will have feelings about your experience separate to
the traumatic event (before or after). These feelings, whether good or bad, are
important to acknowledge and may need processing.

In the case of bad birth feelings, it is common and understandable for it to
be very difficult to recognise or process these feelings while your baby's health
needs are the priority. This can leave a mother with underlying feelings that she
may not understand, which she may need to acknowledge and make sense of
when she is able.

In the case where these feelings are positive, it is important for women and those
around them to understand that it's okay to have positive feelings alongside
the trauma of having an unwell baby. In fact, recognition of these feelings can
provide a woman with added strength to help her with the challenges she is
facing. Because Kathryn and Rebecca were able to access different information
and support from what is regularly available, each was in a situation where their
births, prior to the traumatic outcome, were very empowering and positive.
That is, they felt safe, nurtured, able to ask questions and the other feelings
that accompany a good birth (see *Why does it matter? And isn't a live birth
a good birth?* (p40)). They also both found that experiencing these positive
feelings brought positive consequences including empowerment, confidence
and strength. Both discovered that it was hard for others to find understand
that there could be some positive on-flow from the birth, in conjunction with
struggling with grief and trauma.

*The birth was amazing, up until the delivery and the shoulder dystocia and the flat baby. People don't get how I can say the birth was amazing and yet the delivery and post-partum was traumatic. Health professionals didn't get it at all. People seemed to think because I referred to the birth as really positive that the deep grief and trauma of the delivery and post-partum events weren't really there. While Grace was in hospital, the depth of grief and fear was, at times, all-consuming; however, we were able to draw on the amazing and empowering experience of labour, the knowledge and faith we'd gained that we were incredibly strong and capable, and that together we would face this challenge and come through it. Grace's birth gave us the courage and confidence to negotiate for her during her time in hospital and her eventual early release to come home. I can't begin to imagine how much harder this journey would have been had we not had an amazing labour experience, or the beautiful support from those around us (both during labour and especially in the months and years that have followed her birth). A good birth isn't about the 'what happened' but about how you feel. I feel incredibly blessed that even with a traumatic birth outcome, we were able to have an empowering birth and as a result face the associated challenges with love and confidence, and it made the sad moments a lot easier to cope with.* **Kathryn**

*The labour and birth up until delivery was a beautiful, empowering experience. The love and safety I felt during my labour at home helped me get through the trauma of having an unwell baby. It also gave me the strength to insist on Emily's early discharge from special care. Most people did not understand these as separate issues. My husband, especially, could not understand why I wanted to maintain a close connection to my support person. The health professionals at the hospital could not understand my description of a peaceful, uneventful labour as they felt something must have gone wrong in order for Emily to have been so unwell at birth.* **Rebecca**

## Dealing with ongoing health issues

The children of all three of these women have had ongoing assessments, as they grow. At the time of writing, Rebecca's daughter, aged three, had passed all her developmental assessments so far. Kathryn's daughter was formally discharged from the hospital's follow-up clinics aged 24 months, and at the time of writing was continuing to meet all age appropriate milestones.

Unfortunately Freya's baby, now aged two, has ongoing issues as a result of his birth. Freya explains:

> *We have recently found out he will shortly need more surgery. He has required intensive physiotherapy and occupational therapy since he was born as a result of this injury. He needed physio sessions six-to-eight times a day up until age one and since then two to four times daily. He will need physio and occupational therapy every day until he stops growing, and even then he will need some. He has some arm function but, given he had a very bad injury, he will have permanent problems with his arm. As well as the surgery on his brachial plexus, he has had six procedures to check his airways due to the narrowing of them caused by the multiple intubations when he was born.* **Freya**

If your child is permanently affected by their birth trauma, it can be particularly challenging. Every day, you may be reminded of the birth, and to see your child dealing with ongoing pain and surgery can increase the feelings of guilt and sadness.

> *I have had counselling to try to deal with my feelings of guilt about the birth and the fact my baby now has a lifelong disability. I am left with an overwhelming feeling of having both been failed (by the professionals) but also having failed my baby. My baby has had, and faces, a regime of physiotherapy and occupational therapy daily. I feel a little hard done by – mostly because my baby now has a burden to carry through life arising from this birth, but also because I have such a burden to carry and so many memories I cannot shut out. I spend a lot of time wondering if my baby will later blame me for his disability. I do feel very lucky that my baby survived and that he is not brain damaged as was initially feared, but I resent that as a mother I have to feel lucky for those things. I worry a lot about the impact all of this has had on my older boy too, who was still only a baby when his brother was born and who was forced on the sidelines as we rushed our baby to countless medical appointments and surgeries and carried out physio multiple times daily.* **Freya**

## Advice for healing

All the women we interviewed here stressed the importance of finding support, especially support that is relevant to your child's particular issues, so you can share your journey with someone who understands. They also express the benefits of being able to share their experience with friends and family.

> *The most helpful things in my healing journey? Finding the HIE group I'm part of and meeting other parents who've been on this journey as well. Being able to share my experience with close friends I've made since the birth and also writing a blog in the earlier days. Coming to Birthtalk's healing groups were a huge part of my healing journey as well. Overall, time has been the biggest healer as well as having my son. Finding my own support network and being open about the experience with people who 'get it' [also helps].* **Kathryn**

> *Going to Birthtalk and telling my story without judgement has been a big part of my healing journey. Connecting with other parents who have had a similar experience through the HIE support group, and seeing a counsellor regularly helped with the healing process.* **Rebecca**

> *One of the most helpful things in moving through this has been the support of the Erb's Palsy Group and the ability to write messages on their message boards and have a group of people who know exactly what I am talking about and who face, or has faced, the same issues.* **Freya**

We asked Kathryn, Freya and Rebecca to share the advice they would give to another woman in a similar situation as themselves:

> *I would encourage her to contact relevant support groups and stress that she should try, if possible, not to blame herself. I would encourage her to get formal help and counselling if she thinks this would be beneficial.* **Freya**

> *Speak up, don't be afraid to ask questions and find the supportive people you need to help you get through the experience.* **Rebecca**

> *Find the support you need – this might take some time, but don't give up. For us, the hospital wasn't very supportive and didn't refer us to any support groups beyond the preemie groups or specific health conditions. Sadly there still seems a big gap in referring parents to HIE-related support. Be open with your family and friends. I wish I'd broken down more in the early days and opened*

*up more about what we went through. I tried to be strong and
I think by doing that some people thought I was coping fine,
even though inside I was falling apart. Let yourself grieve and
rant and express the emotions, whatever they are. Know that you
aren't alone, even if it feels like it at first. Somewhere, someone
knows what it's like to go through this – I hope that you find that
someone and find support in your shared experience. And know
that you will get through this; somehow you'll find a way. It won't
be easy but you'll realise that you have a strength you never
knew existed, and with time, hopefully, you'll find peace and the
emotions won't be as all consuming and overwhelming.* **Kathryn**

## The healing journey with Birthtalk

Kathryn and Rebecca attended Birthtalk's *'Healing From Birth'* sessions after
their births, and Kathryn had been to Birthtalk's antenatal course before
the birth as well. We asked them what they found helpful from coming to
our group:

*It was at Birthtalk that I was finally able to share my story, to cry
and question and feel safe to be able to open up about my grief.
Simply being able to talk about what had happened and being
able to cry without feeling like I was being judged was more
helpful than I can ever explain. I ended up finding something
that was suggested during one of the meetings incredibly powerful
and healing. Once it was suggested, I thought about it for a long
time and planned to go there at some stage – but as circumstance
had it, I ended up doing it one afternoon with no thought or
planning. Grace and I were sharing a very quiet moment together
and I just began to tell her the story of her birth. I didn't try to
sugar coat it, I just told her what her journey had been. I told her
how sorry I was that she'd gotten so sick, that she'd been taken
away at birth, that we hadn't been together and we'd missed
out on so much; how hard it had been; how proud I was of her
strength and courage. And then I told her all the things I had
hoped to say to her when she was born – welcoming her, telling
her how loved she was, how beautiful – all the words I was never
able to actually say to her. And I cried and held her and felt more
connected to her than ever before. To me, this was a huge turning
point in my healing journey.* **Kathryn**

(This exercise is in *Supporting your relationship with your child* (p409).)

*The most helpful thing about Birthtalk was having my feelings validated; that it was okay for me to grieve the birth I wanted but didn't get. It was okay to talk about my labour as an empowering experience despite my baby being born so unwell. It also helped to think about how, if the same thing happened in my next birth, I could change the way it made me feel.* **Rebecca**

## Having another baby

Understandably, after a traumatic birth with so many concerns and question marks over the baby's survival and health, you may be scared when thinking about having another child. As Freya says:

*This birth has had a big impact on my feelings about another child. I always wanted three children but am petrified of having any more after the experience my baby and I had and continue to have.* **Freya**

Both Kathryn and Rebecca have faced similar feelings, and each found that another pregnancy brought new issues and fears to the surface. They both attended Birthtalk during their subsequent pregnancies; Kathryn had Deb from Birthtalk as her doula while a couple of years later, Rebecca had Kathryn as her doula. Both had amazing, empowering experiences, and gave birth to healthy babies at full-term without any of the issues of their previous births.

*My message to other women is you can birth again and it is okay to be afraid. Surround yourself with people who love and support you.* **Rebecca**

*You can birth again. It's hard and it takes courage but it's worth it if you want to have more children. One thing I'd say is that you need to have the next baby for the baby, and not to try and heal from the previous traumatic birth. It can't change what happened at the previous birth but, hopefully, it will bring healing and inner peace to you and your family. During pregnancy, it's okay to be scared and to worry about the same thing happening again – but surround yourself with positive people and support, be gentle with yourself, be honest about your fears, find a caregiver who is empathetic to your journey and who makes you feel safe, supported and respected. When I got pregnant with baby number two, the grief all came back again. What got me through was that I found a safe place (Birthtalk) to share all my fears about birthing for the second time and that helped to give me the courage and strength I needed to be able to welcome my little baby earthside with joy and love.*

*My second birth was the most amazing experience I have ever had – it was the birth that I'd always hoped for, but didn't know whether I'd ever be able to have. He arrived safely and gently and I met him just seconds after he was born, all gooey – the most life changing and incredibly healing moment. I shed quite a few tears at his birth. I was so overwhelmed that he was safe and healthy, that I was the first to hold him and welcome him into the world. Having another baby will never make up for your previous baby not being okay, but it can bring a great depth of healing. Be open to this new birth and do what is right for you.* **Kathryn**

We share more about birthing after a traumatic birth in *Birthing again* (p507). In that chapter we explore some of the information that supported Kathryn and Rebecca going into their second births.

## Taking your own journey

If you are in this position of having a baby who was very unwell at birth and beyond, or became unwell in the days after the birth, we recommend that you continue to explore the pages of this book and undertake a healing journey of your own.

If Kathryn, Rebecca or Freya's stories resonated with your experience, then perhaps your partner or other family need to read this section to know what you have been going through.

Go gently, take into account the good advice offered from women who have walked the same path, and know that you are, most definitely, not alone.

# I SUFFERED THE LOSS OF MY BABY

If you have lost your baby, we are so very, very sorry. And we welcome you as a mother on your healing journey as well. We do get women attending Birthtalk who have experienced the loss of a child. Mostly, they are attending to deal with the trauma of the birth – separately to the trauma of their baby dying. Some are also trying to gather the courage and information needed to birth again.

There are support groups designed specifically to deal with the many emotions that arise from losing a baby (see *Appendix A*), however, we find that, sometimes, there is trauma from the actual birth that needs to be processed, such as:

- how they were treated by health carers
- fear and confusion in a situation where they may not have been fully informed as to what was happening
- the intensity and swiftness of the unfolding events.

Whether the loss of a baby occurs during birth, or at a separate time (in the case where a baby's health issues become evident some time afterwards) a mother may not have had the time or space to process her experience of the birth. In fact, for many of these women it can feel hard or wrong to validate this need to themselves or others. They too, however, have a right to come to a place of peace with their birth (separate to how they feel about the loss of their baby) and importantly gain the strength that comes from healing.

We invite you to use this book to create a healing journey for yourself that caters for your specific situation. You will still find sections of the book relevant, and perhaps undertaking this process with the support of a counsellor or an understanding friend will help you feel safe as you walk this path.

Please know that we are holding you gently in our hearts, and are aware that it is an especially difficult path you are travelling. Thank you for considering taking this journey with us, and go gently.

# MY BABY WAS PREMATURE

*My standard response to the shock of having a prem was,
"We were really lucky – he was a healthy prem and we were out
of the hospital in less than ten weeks". It was true – our baby was
a healthier and a good-sized prem and I think, at times, I felt
guilty about how short the time was that we had in the nurseries
compared to some of the other babies. What I didn't allow myself
to acknowledge was we had a really shit time. It was really hard.
I didn't want to go to the hospital every day and I didn't want
to breastfeed to a pump. I resented not carrying to full term
and I blamed myself, which is ridiculous as no fault was ever
discovered. I just wanted to take my baby home and not be so
integrated into the health system. I didn't want to sound like I was
complaining and that I wasn't coping.* **Tina**

*It's a miracle my milk came in at all, twenty-four hours after
being delivered of my baby. Luckily for us, I had plenty of milk.
I stopped taking any pain medication that day, I wanted to feel
something – the numbness was horrible – and I guess looking
back now, I must have been trying to keep myself from going
under. I had no confidence with Maya at all, I was scared to touch
her, and I didn't do her cares until she was about five days old.
I was frightened I would break her and she didn't feel like she was
mine; in many ways I thought she belonged to the hospital as
they were keeping her alive. They were doing the job I couldn't do.
I would ask permission to touch her, in those early days.* **Leonie**

After a traumatic birth, a lot of women will hear, "At least you're fine and the baby's fine". However, after a baby is born prematurely, the woman might be considered to be fine, but often the baby is facing weeks of challenges before being able to go home with the family. Of course, the woman may not be fine at all, after the sometimes shocking experience of birthing early.

## Isn't prematurity trauma enough?

The shock of birthing early cannot be underestimated. However, it is usually not this shock alone that makes a premature birth traumatic. Even before the birth, there are often emotions of bristling fear and worry, if labour is threatening early. Feelings of being out-of-control in a situation where a woman feels unable to protect herself or her baby are common and understandable.

There are often feelings of confusion that can arise from lack of adequate communication from caregivers, especially in an emergency situation. Or a health situation such as pre-eclampsia in which, due to elevated blood pressure, a woman can be experiencing "mental confusion, a heightened sense of anxiety, and a sense of impending doom",[213] which can be very frightening, especially when unsupported.

The actual birth is often a result of a life-threatening situation where a woman fears for her life, or her child's. There is the possibility of experiencing symptoms of Post-Traumatic Stress Disorder (PTSD), which "can occur following the experience or witnessing of life-threatening events."[214] There is usually a roller coaster of emotions and ongoing anxiety and desperation, with the parents not knowing if their baby will survive.

There can be feelings of failure – a woman might feel like she 'failed' to grow her baby to full term and somehow has let her child down. There is often separation, both physical and emotional, that can occur with a premature birth, which can hinder bonding, breastfeeding and all-round confidence with a newborn.

It is about so much more than just being born early.

## The voice of experience

Both Tina and Leonie experienced premature births – Leonie at twenty-nine weeks and Tina at twenty-seven weeks. Their stories are very different, yet they express similar emotions about their experiences. We want to share aspects of their births and their responses with you, as hearing other women's stories can be so important in knowing you are not alone, and that how you are feeling is normal. We also present their stories here to illustrate to someone who has not had a premature birth, just what emotions a woman is dealing with.

## Initial shock and worry

A premature birth can be pre-empted by a series of events that take a woman and her partner through a series of emotions: from happy parents-to-be, to slightly concerned, to deeply worried, to the shock early arrival of their child. There are often feelings of helplessness and confusion at what is happening, while learning new medical terms, likely prognoses and procedures and, sometimes, dealing with periods of just waiting, willing a baby to be okay.

213   The Preeclampsia Foundation. (2010). *Signs & Symptoms.*
      Retrieved from *www.preeclampsia.org/health-information/signs-and-symptoms#pulse* accessed January 2014.

214   Birth Trauma Association, UK. *What is Birth Trauma?*
      Retrieved from *www.birthtraumaassociation.org.uk/what_is_trauma.htm* accessed January 2014.

*It was at the scan that everything flipped on its head. My twenty-eight week baby was measuring twenty-three weeks. Everything else seemed okay, but my baby was hardly any bigger than the last time I was scanned. I fell into despair, thoughts about me not being able to even grow a baby properly turned around and around in my head, and I was very worried about her wellbeing. A week later I had an obstetrical scan done by the head obstetrician. The results were devastating; she had not grown at all from the last scan. I had spent almost every day and night since the initial scan in a trance repeating this affirmation, 'Please Maya grow; please Maya grow'. I can't even begin to tell you how shattered I was. There was something very wrong with my baby, but they couldn't find out what. All my hopes and dreams of the peaceful homebirth were flying out the window and I was overwhelmed by this immense sense of failure. I couldn't even grow a baby properly.* **Leonie**

*When I reached twenty-six-and-a-half weeks, our lives changed dramatically. I had been having cramps on and off for about a month and dismissed them as Braxton Hicks. I wasn't feeling 'right' one night and spoke to a friend of mine. She suggested we go up to the hospital and get checked out. The worst-case scenario was that they would send us home. We packed a toothbrush and naively went to the hospital thinking we would be home in a few hours. How wrong we were. I was one centimetre dilated and was immediately confined to my bed except for loo visits. I was given pethidine, steroids and the little pink pill to relax the muscles. Work was over – it was unlikely I would be returning home until after the baby was born. We lasted three days. At twenty-seven weeks I went into spontaneous labour.* **Tina**

This period can involve a realisation that the birth a woman had planned for her child may not unfold and, instead, an unknown situation is arising, one for which she could not possibly prepare.

## There is going to be a baby

The moment when a woman realises that birth is imminent with her baby a long way from being at term can be overwhelming and filled with panic. Sometimes this moment is at the end of a discussion with health carers regarding the 'best way forward'. Sometimes it is accompanied by serious and frightening physical symptoms such as a massive haemorrhage or loss of consciousness. Many times, it is a moment of sheer terror with the woman and her partner not knowing what will result from the current series of events that they are unable to control.

> And so six days after that scan, I woke early to see Adrian off to work, went to the toilet still half-asleep and, as I sat down, noticed that I was covered in blood. I will never forget the feeling of absolute dread and my gut knotting. I can remember the shrill scream I let out (which according to Adrian was silent) and told him he needed to take me to the hospital. I became numb on the drive, almost not in my body. We called my best friend to meet us there as Adrian had to drive all the tools to Brisbane for the day's work and, just now as I write this, I realise how painful that was, how abandoned I felt. **Leonie**

> The cramping became more intense and I started to bleed. It was suggested that I have a shower (which I desperately wanted) and that was when things really started to move. I collapsed in the shower and lost all feeling in my hands and feet. On reflection I was probably transitioning at this point. I started to hyperventilate as I was panicking and did not know what was going on. I was put on a stretcher and rushed to the delivery ward with my mother and husband following. The pain was incredible and I kept passing out. Although I understand I was only blinking – I thought I was escaping! **Tina**

## Dealing with health carers

Being in a situation where a woman is at her most vulnerable, relying on others for her own safety and that of her child can be made even more challenging if she is not feeling well-supported by the medical staff. It can be hard to accept what is happening, and deal with the change in direction her pregnancy has taken. She may have been given drugs, or have physiological events (such as pre-eclampsia) that make it difficult to concentrate or to 'take things in'.

Meanwhile, the staff may be doing their best to work fast to keep her and her child alive, sometimes in an emergency situation, and may not realise that the woman is not understanding the specifics of her situation.

> I began to become my super-friendly self. I smiled a lot, I was quiet and meek and I felt quite dissociated. I was taken straight upstairs and put on continuous monitoring (one of the things I didn't ever want to experience). A very tired staff member came

*and tried to cannulate me. He tried five times. I sat there joking with him as my veins began to crawl away, my friend became enraged and started yelling at him to, "Hurry up and get the f---ing vein how hard can it be?" The midwife and the registrar had a discussion over the top of me about which hospital they would try to get me into; I felt confused and had to ask why I was going to transfer. They talked to me as if I was an idiot for not knowing they couldn't deal with babies that early at that hospital. I hadn't really thought that I was likely to be having my baby ([I'm]not sure what I thought was happening). I became really frightened. I was given the steroid injection and started to hope and pray that I would be able to hold her in so I could have the second one [injection] twenty-four hours later. The next thing I really remember was being packed into an ambulance on my own and lying there bumping around like I was in the back of a ute on a corrugated dirt road. The midwife didn't talk to me; she read a book and looked at me every now and then asked me how my pain was.* **Leonie**

*My husband and I had the sensation that the midwives thought I was being melodramatic and really only did my observations and were not very reassuring.* **Tina**

Note: Leonie's account of smiling a lot, being her 'super-friendly self' and joking with a staff member, despite being in an incredibly stressful situation, is something we hear a lot from women attending Birthtalk. It is possible that she was exhibiting a uniquely female stress response called 'tend and befriend'. It can be a huge relief to understand your behaviour may have been physiologically-based, particularly if it was out of character or felt all wrong. To read more about this see *I kept trying to befriend all the staff. Why did I do that?* (p214).

## Anticipation of a premature baby

The emotional intensity can increase when the enormity of parenting a premature baby begins to sink in even before the baby arrives. There can be more grief, more of a sense of loss, and more feelings of being overwhelmed by the magnitude of the situation.

*The next day, we went on a tour of the neonatal intensive care unit (NICU) and we looked at a babe about the same size as Maya was. I remember holding onto Adrian and looking around at all the lights and machines and hearing the alarms and looking and staring at this poor little babe. I felt numb with the knowledge that soon this would be my babe and I would be spending all of my time in the bright buzzing room with the alarms going off all the time. I was given the normal, non-informative information about caesarean. I signed the consent form. I have never felt emptier than in that moment. I was frightened and overwhelmed, sorely disappointed and angry: so angry that my body had let me down, angry that my baby was going to be taken from my body and terrified of the surgery ahead.* **Leonie**

## A tumultuous arrival

A premature birth can result in a 'handing over' of responsibility for the survival of mother and child to the health carers, an extremely vulnerable situation even if the woman is grateful for the intervention. There are also the physical sensations, and emotions and difficult things to face, perhaps even during the birth, which can make the event very challenging to deal with.

*I can't even remember if Adrian was with me during the spinal. I remember feeling sick and worrying what would happen if I vomited while lying like that. I remember feeling so vulnerable, so paralysed, so passive, but I was doing the friendly thing and talking to the obstetrician like he was an old school friend. And then he said it, the sentence that would change my life forever, "I've had to give you a classical incision; you'll always have to have caesareans now". I remember my body having an intense reaction to that statement and then before I knew, it the 'washing up' in my tummy had begun. I think I dissociated at this point, all that I could think about was how my mother had told me about how it felt like someone doing a load of vigorous washing up in your tummy.* **Leonie**

For mothers whose babies arrive early, they have often not yet attended antenatal sessions, planning these for the last weeks of the full-term pregnancy they were expecting. This can intensify feelings of being out-of-control as they may not have essential information about how childbirth 'works'. They may not have the benefit of insights into what happens during any kind of birth – vaginal or caesarean – nor considered how they might handle this emotionally, thinking they had months to go.

*Eventually the obstetrician turned up and announced that I was fully dilated and was about to give birth. I have never seen a midwife move so fast. All of a sudden there were people everywhere. My membranes were burst (and the pain stopped immediately) and I was being told to push. You need to keep in mind that I had not attended any antenatal classes and this was my first child so I had no idea what to do. At the third push I was threatened with an episiotomy and I tried my damndest to get that baby out.* **Tina**

## What just happened?

Those first moments of meeting a new baby are often lost in the case of a premature birth. There is urgency, with many faceless, though necessary, staff members on hand and often the baby is rushed to Neonatal intensive care unit (NICU). These moments can be desperate, and fraught with intensity.

*And then Maya appeared above the blue screen, bloody and crinkled and tiny. She was almost lost in the doctor's hands, 884 grams at 2.41 pm. Adrian tried to go over to the resus [resuscitation] table but they told him to wait, they were waiting to see if she would breathe well. She didn't and they took her to NICU to ventilate her. I don't remember much from here, it becomes very fuzzy, but I remember in recovery the midwife looking after me telling me she had five boys all growth restricted (not retarded – she hated that word). They were all fine now, big strapping lads and that boys don't do as well as girls. I wanted to cling to her, but I couldn't move. I became insanely itchy from the morphine and she gave me a lot of alcohol swabs to wipe on my face. I was very stoned. I can't remember if Adrian was with me or not – I think he was with Maya.* **Leonie**

*In a little under two hours from the time I collapsed in the shower, our son gave a little squeal. My husband cut the cord and our baby was rushed into intensive care. It would be a couple of hours until I saw him. Once he was delivered, I immediately threw up and then had to start to process in my mind what had just happened.* **Tina**

## The aftermath

It can take a while to comprehend what has just occurred when the situation has escalated, resulting in an early birth. There can be surgery recovery to deal with, tests and assessments of the new baby to try and understand, coping with fall out due to separation from the baby (who likely is in special care or NICU), or just a struggle to put together the events that have just unfolded.

> *When I went back to the antenatal ward, Adrian came back and showed me photos of my baby. I can't describe what that is like to meet your baby through some photos. I was (still am) resentful of Adrian that he was able to touch her, meet her, talk to her before me. I don't remember meeting Maya the first time; apparently the midwife got me up at ten o'clock that night and wheel-chaired me down to NICU, but I don't remember it at all. Later that night, I went into mild respiratory distress – a delayed reaction to the morphine. I remember not sleeping all night because I knew if I did I would stop breathing and die; I had to work on every single shallow breath I took. It was really frightening and I felt really alone.* **Leonie**

> *The first couple of days were filled with information from the hospital, questions from the staff, tests that had to be performed and a surreal sense of being hit by a truck. I stayed in the hospital for five more days and barely visited the nursery. I couldn't comprehend what had happened. There were lots of tears and staring out the window. I even had the head of the neonatal unit come and visit me. I suspect that they were concerned I wasn't in the nursery enough.* **Tina**

## Going home alone

Leaving hospital without your baby can be a devastating experience, going against everything a woman had ever imagined she would experience as a new mother. There might not even have been a chance to hold the baby yet, and it can feel physically painful to be apart. While this all makes sense hormonally, it can be the start of another challenging step.

> *I was discharged in the morning on day four. I will never forget how my heart broke that day, walking away from my baby and looking at the other mothers with their bundles walking out those doors. Adrian took me to dinner and his cousins met us there. I sat there completely shattered, internally broken but smiling on*

*the outside, listening to them talking about boyfriends and work.
I was sore, I still couldn't stand up straight and a bladder infection
from the catheter was beginning to raise its ugly head. As we got
into the car, I asked Adrian to take me back to the hospital so
I could see Maya. He made a comment about wanting to get back
to his dad's place where we were to stay for a few weeks. I lost it
and started to hysterically scream and rant – he drove me back.
It wasn't until day six that I held my baby for the first time. She
had dropped down to 730 grams by then and she looked very
frail. It was an amazing moment and from that day on I could feel
my milk letting down. I felt more confident with her cares and
felt less frightened of her.* **Leonie**

*Going home without your child is such an empty feeling however,
the minute I was home something inside clicked. The realisation
of the responsibilities placed on us occurred and from that day
onwards, I was beside my son twice a day – just about every day
for the next nine weeks and one day. My world involved monitors,
learning medical lingo, adjusting to different methods of nursing,
discovering how many doctors are involved with the care of
prems, pumping milk electronically, monitoring weight loss/gain,
care sessions and feed times. My first cuddle was when he was
four days old, first skin-to-skin at two weeks (magic!). Two weeks
after my baby was born I started to lose a lot of blood and I had
a curette as there was a fair amount of product left behind. The
hospital, staff and my baby became my life. I had mum as support
so I did nothing other than go to the hospital.* **Tina**

## Bringing baby home

Breastfeeding issues when feeding a premature baby, responsibilities for a
baby with compromised health, and the additional health risks created by the
prematurity are all part of the realities faced in the weeks after the birth of a
premature baby. These issues can escalate once the new family is home. This
is the next phase in an ongoing struggle to acclimatise to the new 'normal', to
process the events of the past few weeks and to begin life as a new family, at last.

*It was a long postnatal period. Maya was in hospital for nine
weeks. She didn't take the breast. We sat for four weeks everyday
with the most wonderful lactation consultant but, alas, she
would simply reject it. If she did latch well, it was because I was
wearing a nipple shield, but then she wouldn't suckle. I had no*

*confidence at all and I felt so anxious about her getting enough [milk] that in the end I resorted to bottle-feeding her my milk. This was almost as heartbreaking as walking away from her. I had this overwhelming sense of failure. I expressed milk for her for twenty weeks, it was an exhausting journey but I clung to it. We roomed in for four days and nights – they were worried about her dropping weight without the NG (nasogastric) [feeding] tube because I had refused to fortify my milk. She weighed a hefty 2015 grams when we took her home.* **Leonie**

*The day we took our baby home was a mix of excitement and relief, as well as fear. I lived in a bubble for two months, which involved monitoring and recording everything he did. Suddenly, we were on our own. Very quickly life revolved around milestones and doctors appointments. There were the issues with the eyes, the ears, a paediatrician was necessary and the growth and development checkups were necessary. It wasn't long before we were visiting Accident and Emergency [Departments] regularly as my son kept picking up everything that was going around. I coped because I had to. I had tasks to ensure the wellbeing of my baby was maintained and that kept me sane.* **Tina**

## Ongoing effects

The weeks, months and years after a premature arrival can be so difficult. The impact of experiencing or witnessing threatened death or serious injury to the mother and/or child can mean, for some parents, a diagnosis of Post-Traumatic Stress Disorder (PTSD) or at least experiencing of some of the symptoms, including flashbacks, panic attacks and hypervigilance. (You can read more about this in *Can you get PTSD after birth?*)

*I started to have panic attacks the week after she came home. I have only in the last year discovered that this is what those 'turns' are.* **Leonie**

*By the time my baby was four months old, I had my first panic attack, although I didn't know that's what it was.* **Tina**

When experienced in isolation, without an awareness of the possibility that some support might be needed to recover emotionally, these ongoing effects can add further to a woman's distress. Additionally, due to being in 'survival mode' for the first year or so, it might only be once the child is older that there is space for the mother to reflect, meaning that the isolation and painful emotions and difficult responses continue for a long time before being addressed. As the focus is (understandably) directed towards the baby's wellbeing and overcoming health challenges, there is usually little space for the mother to consider her own feelings separate to this situation, at least until things stabilise.

Other longer-term issues facing parents after a premature birth can be any ongoing health problems that the baby may have as a result of being born so early. When the baby requires therapy or extra care in the longer term, it can serve as a constant reminder of the tumultuous birth, which can make it challenging to move on. (You can read more about women's experiences with compromised babies, including the longer- term effects, in *My baby was very unwell* (p321).)

## How did they heal?

Leonie and Tina share aspects of their own healing journeys as they moved through their experiences:

The validation I received at my first Birthtalk *'Healing From Birth'* meeting was huge for me as it helped cement that, "Yes, I did have valid reasons for my feelings," and that my feelings were normal, as associated with birth trauma.

> *Birthtalk's tools have really helped me in bonding with my kids, and going to Birthtalk has helped me understand the issues we have had as a couple and is giving me tools to work on the problems that have come about because of our experiences. Just the simple validation that, "Yes", we have been through a traumatic experience with our children, the loss of dreams and all the fall out, was huge for us. We have been able to take it easier on our relationship because of this. We are currently going through an 'aha moment' regarding abandonment and Birthtalk has been extremely helpful in providing tools to help with being constructive with the emotional fall out of it. [Ed. See our Shifting from anger exercise (p433)]*

> *I have learned that, while the stuff that happens in birth is important, it's really the 'how I felt' that has made the biggest impact. It's been a long journey so far and I believe I still have a way to go, but Birthtalk has helped me to not be afraid of the healing. It still stings, but the intensity does lessen with time. And the bonding with my children is priceless.* **Leonie**

*I went home (after my first Birthtalk 'Healing From Birth' meeting) and couldn't sleep. I then spent the next couple of days crying. It was very, very cleansing. My journey had begun.*

*The next major progression was going through both me and my baby's medical notes to gain an understanding of what was happening to both of us, particularly in the first week from arriving in hospital. I have an analytical/factual mind and by having the notes explained it added another perspective to the hospital experience. Spending time with Deb (from Birthtalk) [and] breaking it down helped sort out in my mind what actually happened for the first couple of days I/we were in hospital. I felt emotionally drained, but reassured about what actually happened. Another layer of the onion had come off!*

*One of the greatest moments was being able to share my experience with peers at work on a conference and then raising over $2,000 for the neonatal nurseries.*

*Part of the healing process for me has been working out why my periods hadn't recommenced. I was convinced it was either a mental or hormonal problem. I was gob smacked when it was decided that I needed surgery and I had adhesions all over my cervix. However, after the surgery I started to feel aligned again physically. I used to joke about how I had the shortest pregnancy with the longest healing time.*

*I think, emotionally, I became more stable. The panic attacks reduced (they did turn up from time to time; however, my reaction to them was better). I was balancing work, kindy and a sick baby a bit better and we were becoming a lot wiser to the medical system and all it had to offer. It's not that we didn't have any scares, they were there. My son did end up ICU after another round of grommets were inserted and tonsils removed. That was a horrific time. However experience helped us cope with the situation.*

*A very important time for me was when my mum moved away. It opened the door for my son and I to bond. The problem was I didn't know how to [bond with him]. Birthtalk provided a few ideas. I sat down with him one day [Ed. See more about this process in Saying the words you couldn't say at the birth: a reconnection tool (p421)]. He was still in his cot from a sleep and I sat on the floor so I was down at his level. I discussed his birth and explained the circumstances and how much I loved him. I wasn't even sure he could hear me as his ears were playing up again. However, he looked me straight in the eye and gave me the hugest smile as if to say, "I love you too mummy". It was the best feeling and a connection definitely occurred. From that day forward our relationship has strengthened and, now approaching five years of age, he is my little buddy!* **Tina**

## Your own way forward

Leonie and Tina had different stories, yet you can see they share similar responses to their experiences. They both attended Birthtalk's *'Healing From Birth'* meetings as part of their recovery. More of their stories are peppered throughout this book in different sections, which illustrates the healing journey they took.

Leonie and Tina both have suggestions for a woman in a similar situation to themselves:

*My story is valid; the pain I feel is real and I'm not being self-indulgent or weak or silly for not being able to move on without help, so this is [also] true for you. Birth really does matter and I'm one of the lucky ones and, yes, I do mean lucky, who really gets just how important it is. Yes, it is for the wrong reasons, but I continue to heal and grow. This can be you. I survived the births of my children, I am strong and I have a lot to offer other women. This too could be you. Do the work – it's worth it.* **Leonie**

*I think we all need some form of debrief session from any traumatic experience. I don't think you can put a timeframe on it. It's when you find the right environment at the right time. It took me 18 months, as I couldn't find the right environment and I was too busy caring for my son and juggling work. Once my son's health started to settle, it allowed me [more time] to concentrate on me and how my actions were affecting others. Validation that what you went through was crap is the most uplifting experience. Once we acknowledge to ourselves that we had it tough, it allows us to then get on with the process of healing.* **Tina**

## If you have had a premature baby

The information we share in this book is very similar to what we shared with Leonie and Tina in person. To kickstart the process, we recommend reading the following sections: *What makes a birth good or bad?* (p37), *Why does it matter? And isn't a live birth a good birth?* (p40), and *What is a traumatic or bad birth anyway?* (p42).

Then we suggest reading about our tool for understanding your birth in *Birthtalk Breakdown – a new tool* (p47), doing a *Birthtalk Breakdown* of your birth, and reading *How do I heal?* (p61).

Then, as Leonie and Tina have done, explore the issues that resonate most for you at a particular time. You can do this with the book by reading the chapters and tools for healing that feel most applicable at different points of your journey.

Go gently, and take as much time as you need to move through this. We honour your strength to get through this experience, and we are with you as you take steps to heal.

## Footnote: Birthing again?

Both Leonie and Tina have since gone on to have empowering births of full-term healthy babies. Both of them came to Birthtalk as part of their preparation for their positive experiences. You can read more about birthing again after a traumatic birth in *How to have a better birth next time* (p507), and get more ideas about birth in sections such as *Why wouldn't my body work in labour?* (p230).

# I HAD ONGOING PHYSICAL SYMPTOMS AFTER THE BIRTH

*Many of my friends are aware I had a long physical recovery and complications after my birth, but very few are aware of the ongoing issues, as I found most people assumed I got better.* **Rachael**

*Constant pain is mentally draining. Everything I did was with effort because I was in constant pain. I was on the maximum dose of ibuprofen until I had surgery six months after the birth.* **Naomi**

*I have suffered Post-Traumatic Stress Disorder (PTSD) from the trauma of my baby's birth and the physical symptoms have certainly not helped. They are a constant reminder of the birth, and the physical changes in me feel like they reflect the emotional changes from the birth. I am definitely not the same person, physically or emotionally.* **Freya**

A birth that leaves you emotionally shattered can be incredibly difficult to deal with. If you add to that some physical symptoms that provide ongoing distress and pain, even months and years after the birth, it can take the impact of that birth to a new level. For women who have had a traumatic birth, these physical symptoms or injuries are a constant, tangible reminder of what they went through.

Many women find that even with significant physical trauma, the impact of their experience is unacknowledged and they are usually encouraged to 'be grateful' for their live baby, and perhaps to 'be glad it wasn't worse'.

## Not healthy, and still not supported

Commonly, those who express their confusion or grief over a traumatic birth are told, "Healthy mother, healthy baby – that's all that matters". This section aims to address some of the issues that affect those who are definitely not in the 'healthy mother' category. Unfortunately, they can still encounter a lack of understanding or awareness from others about how their injuries could affect their emotional health and ability to function as a mother.

Rachael, Freya and Naomi all had very different births, with different outcomes. All, however, have ongoing physical injuries and issues resulting from their births.

*My baby was born with her arm up above her head, which resulted in significant tearing to the skin and muscle of my right vaginal wall. My right labia was also torn completely in two. I have undergone three surgeries to attempt to repair my labia, however, all three surgeries failed and my right labia now remains in two separate parts. I also have symptoms of vaginal prolapse (heaviness, bulging and difficulty emptying my bowel) due to the significant damage to my right pelvic floor muscle, which was torn from the pelvic bone during the birth.* **Rachael**

*My baby suffered shoulder dystocia during his birth. He was eleven pounds and I am a Type 1 diabetic. I was taken into theatre when fully dilated because I couldn't push my baby out. I had an episiotomy, and a ventouse was used and his head was born. Shortly thereafter, there was utter panic in the room when they realised his shoulders were stuck and they had a limited amount of time to get the baby out. There were a lot of people there, all screaming at me to push. I knew if I didn't get him out then he was going to die and I was afraid he might already be dead. The whole room screamed at me to push and eventually (over five and a half minutes later) he was finally born. In the weeks following, my episiotomy became infected, I had no bowel control and my baby was very unwell.* **Freya**

*The damage to my pelvis was caused by excessive pressure to the right side of my pelvis by my husband (the leg pushed towards my shoulder). The midwife (pushing on my left side) was an average size lady of an average weight, my husband, who is six feet, six-and-a-half inches and weighs almost that of two average people, was instructed to push on my right leg. They essentially twisted my pelvis and applied excessive force. Not only was this agony, but [it] also led to the injury. I had surgery six months post-birth for the hip injury.* **Naomi**

## Private pain

Injuries from birth can present a tricky situation, as the areas of the body that have been damaged are often private, and the issues that arise can be highly personal. With issues around genital discomfort and pain, incontinence (urinal and bowel), problems with sex, and more – it can be hard to talk about and, therefore hard for people to understand the struggles and challenges you are facing.

*The skin, nerve endings and scarring of my labia are often irritated or catch on my underwear and clothing when doing simple daily activities such as walking, sitting, standing, riding a bike, going to the toilet or sexual stimulation.* **Rachael**

*The physical symptoms had a huge impact on my daily life in the weeks post-birth. I had zero bowel control and sitting on anything was absolute agony. It took months for my infected episiotomy to heal. When it did finally 'heal' it remained very uncomfortable and sex was extremely painful, and all of this still impacts my sex life over two years later. I still have uncomfortable scar tissue, which often throbs. Although my bowel control is much better than it initially was, it can still be an issue in certain circumstances.* **Freya**

*I was limping post-birth, which improved with physio. The right half of my pelvis was twisted and out of alignment. I had deep groin pain on the front of my right hip. Bladder control was reduced and, although it slightly improved, I was still unable to tell how full my bladder was six months down the track.* **Naomi**

Talking about issues that are so personal and private can be difficult, so women often soldier on and struggle quietly, adding to their sense of isolation and distress.

## Disregard from health carers

The response of health carers to a woman presenting with these ongoing symptoms can range from wonderfully warm and supportive to cold and clinical, to downright negligent. It can be challenging to find understanding and appropriate medical help.

*A few doctors early on after my birth suggested that any repair surgery would be 'cosmetic only', which upset me as they were disregarding the pain and discomfort caused by the injury, scarring and misplaced skin/nerve endings.* **Rachael**

*At three months post-birth I broke down in tears at the physiotherapist's clinic because I wasn't improving. At this point I changed directions, found other specialists, had an MRI and finally a diagnosis that I had torn hip cartilage during birth, which led to surgery.* **Naomi**

*Probably the least helpful thing was when I went to see
a (apparently) well known urogynaecologist about eleven
months post-birth with my one-year-old baby and his almost
three-year-old brother. After waiting to see her for over two hours,
she was very unfeeling both when it came to the history of my
traumatic birth and when she made a comment about my eldest
being badly behaved, all the while telling me very coldly I'd need
perineal surgery.* **Freya**

*One particular male doctor once suggested (four months after
my birth) that my pain may have been simply anxiety related to
resuming sexual activity after birth and that all women experience
this to some degree. I found this comment to be very flippant,
unhelpful and completely disregarding of the specifics of my case
and my ongoing symptoms and injury.* **Rachael**

*Health professionals have mostly been good, with the exception
of those who were actually involved in the birth. They never
even followed up on my infected episiotomy once I left hospital
and I only found out when I got my notes that I should have
been seen in a specialist perineal clinic post-birth, but this never
happened.* **Freya**

Experiencing this sense of disregard from health professionals can mean a
woman might put off getting medical help for her situation, and be unclear as
to the proper process to obtain accurate and friendly medical support. This then
contributes to feelings of being overwhelmed, isolated and helpless.

## People don't understand

Unfortunately, it is not only the professionals that struggle to understand. Even
a woman's own family might play down or be unaware of the seriousness of the
issues, and how they are impacting on her life.

*I also found general comments from health professionals and
lay people, such as, "Most women have some tearing after a first
vaginal birth, it's normal," and "At least you have a healthy baby,"
were very unhelpful at times as I felt they were disregarding my
ongoing problems.* **Rachael**

*My mother was good and understanding in the early days but,
since then, has never asked how I am physically or how I ended
up healing.* **Freya**

Of course, this situation is not restricted to women with ongoing physical health issues from the birth. However, when the woman is attempting to deal with physical injuries on top of dealing with a baby, on top of struggling with the emotional trauma, it can be a lot to cope with at once.

## What do I do now?

We asked the women in this section what they found helpful in working through the challenges they faced, and we are grateful for their responses:

> *The most helpful thing in moving through this has probably been time. As time went, on the physical trauma did become better and, although it has left me with some lasting issues, it is not as debilitating as it was in the early days.* **Freya**

> *Take responsibility for your own physical and mental health. Seek many different professional opinions and find people you trust who have the expertise and understanding to help. Become the expert on your own case by reading – the internet is amazing! – speaking to others, getting various professional opinions and be creative in discovering ways to work around ongoing physical issues. It can be very stressful and emotionally draining, so make sure you look after yourself by having social support and making sure you have activities/hobbies you enjoy to take time out. If you can't do activities now that you enjoyed previously, then find new activities or adjust the old activities to your new restrictions. Don't let ongoing physical issues define you, redefine yourself and learn to love the 'new you'.* **Rachael**

> *Seek out support from others who have had a similar physical injury so you don't feel so alone.* **Freya**

> *Seek help from the right people. If it's not working, try an alternative – it may take a combination of things, but remember it won't just disappear. Go over your notes from the hospital to sort out what actually happened and to help you find closure. If you have any injuries from birth or are taking a long time to heal, get them looked at – you may need additional treatment. There isn't an 'on' or 'off' switch for these feelings, but with time you can find yourself again. Be good to yourself, you may need longer than others to heal from your birth (mentally and physically).* **Naomi**

*Naomi requested that we include a link to PIA Australia Inc. (formerly Pelvic Instability Association) as she found a lot of support from this organisation with her ongoing injury – see *Appendix A* for details

We agree with these ideas and suggest you seek support from birth support groups, especially birth advocacy and birth reform groups, (such as Maternity Coalition in Australia, or the International Caesarean Awareness Network (ICAN) in the US, or the Association for Improvements in the Maternity Services (AIMS) in the UK) as they may have access to channels of support and health carers that you have not yet discovered. Details for these organisations are in *Appendix A*.

Birthtalk has offered such support to various women over the years, and it is certainly of value to explore all pathways to finding help. Sharing your situation in these circumstances can also have the added benefit of receiving validation from people who understand the importance of birth, and who will not downplay how it has impacted on your life.

> *After attending Birthtalk, I also felt validated to know that others agreed after hearing my story, that the physical issues I had were not just 'cosmetic' and were worth seeking further medical advice and opinions [about]. I still don't have an outcome as yet but I know it's not just 'in my head' and it's worth pursuing bit by bit when I have the strength and time (especially with a busy toddler now!).* **Rachael**

> *Going over my notes (with Deb from Birthtalk) was helpful. To know that my birth was not 'normal' and review the decisions that were made was a step towards healing, and helped me to figure out why some things happened the way they did.* **Naomi**

## Physically healed, but ongoing pain

If a woman's physical injuries have healed, there can be an expectation that she is emotionally healed as well. Unfortunately, this is unlikely to happen unless the underlying emotional trauma associated with the birth (and its ongoing issues) are validated, acknowledged and worked through.

## You are not alone

It is important for a woman who has injuries from her birth to know that she not alone in experiencing ongoing emotional challenges in response to her birth. Others feel the same way, even though they may not have had the same physical impact from the birth. Many of the feelings of frustration, sadness and grief can be related less to the injuries and more to how she felt during birth and thereafter. This is not to downplay the injuries, but more to accentuate that there are many women suffering who share similar feelings and emotions, despite different birthing experiences.

> I think the most helpful thing I learned from coming to Birthtalk was that there are other women out there who, for so many different reasons, had experienced difficulties after their birth, both physically and emotionally. Although each story was very different, there were common themes of feeling a loss of control and not being understood. **Rachael**

> Talking to others with similar ongoing issues when birth turns from what should be one of the best days of your life to a nightmare that you would rather forget, to know that you are not the only one [was very helpful] . To be able to talk to others who understand was a very important part of the healing process. **Naomi**

## Birthing Again

**Just after completing this section, we received this email from Rachael:**

> I contacted Birthtalk following the traumatic vaginal delivery of my first daughter, which resulted in several failed repair surgeries and ongoing pain and discomfort for a long time after the birth. It made a remarkable difference for me in validating and clarifying my feelings about the birth, and to give me ideas on what I needed to do both practically and emotionally to move forward.

> It's going to be a long journey but I recently gave birth to my second daughter (on 25 July 2013) and the preparation and birth itself was so empowering and amazing! I'd love to share my positive birth story with you.

> I spent a lot of time finding a care provider who I felt listened [to] and understood me (one of the main factors missing from my first birth experience). I felt confident, informed, listened to and cared for throughout the antenatal care. I was really hoping to avoid a medical induction and my obstetrician understood this; he was reassuring me and encouraging me to peruse natural induction strategies throughout the last part of pregnancy and only first mentioned induction when I was eight days overdue. It was very

*funny, then, when I went into labour naturally that night. I woke up at 3.00 am with strong contractions but was coping with them well so pottered around home and tried to go back to sleep. By 5.30 am the contractions were getting stronger and closer together so I told my husband we should get ready to head to the hospital. After organising my two-year-old daughter to stay with my mum, having breakfast and sorting out my TENS machine, we headed to the hospital at 6.15 am. [I did] a lot of breathing in the car and [pressed] a lot of boost buttons on the TENS. We arrived at the birth suite at 6.50am. The midwife said she'd monitor me then call the obstetrician. I said I'd go to the toilet first and she said she'd come back soon. I went to the bathroom and my waters broke as I sat down. I was so elated that my body was doing everything itself and I wouldn't need the induction!*

*In my excitement I was quickly overcome with the urge to push. I waddled out of the toilet and my husband yelled for help as he could see (and I could feel) my daughters head. The four midwives on duty ran to assist me. I was scared of another bad tear given my previous experience and how quickly the labour was progressing. The midwives were amazing. They were calm and clear in their communication and helped me to calm down and gently birth my daughter. Best of all I avoided a tear!*

*My birth record shows my total delivery time was four minutes after I arrived at the hospital. I really feel like my body just released my baby when I knew I was in a safe place. It was such an empowering experience. I really feel that everything I went through physically and emotionally in my first birth contributed significantly to the empowering experience and strength I felt in my second birth. I am so glad I did not let my previous traumatic experience and injury put me off another pregnancy and vaginal birth as the two experiences were different in almost every way.*

*I would like to thank you both for the help and support you provided me [with] and, more generally, for the amazing work you do in educating and encouraging people to talk about traumatic birth. It is great that there's somewhere safe that women can speak about these issues and gain validation and practical tools to heal and move forward.* **Rachael**

## Further ideas for healing

- Just reading this section may be helpful in your healing journey, as it can be powerful to feel like you are not alone.
- Reading the following may assist you in the healing process:

  *Why does it matter? And isn't a live birth a good birth?* (p40)

  *When health professionals don't get it* (p148)

  *I'm so angry with my health carers* (p163)

  *I feel anger towards my child for 'causing' all this* (p172)

  *I feel like a failure* (p227)

  *I feel sad* (p245).

We also encourage you to return to other sections within Part Two of this book, *How do you feel right now?* (p121) and take yourself through the process of discovering just which direction your own journey to healing will take. Go gently.

# I HAD A CAESAREAN UNDER GENERAL ANAESTHETIC

*My third and final birth was a deeply traumatic caesarean under general anaesthetic. The next day I kept asking if he was really my baby. For the first few months I adored my baby but didn't really feel like he was mine. I have had breastfeeding troubles since day one and even eight months later, it is not comfortable. I couldn't believe the difference compared to my previous two (natural birth) experiences.* **Kate**

*I finally let it out one afternoon after we arrived home from hospital (after a caesarean under general anaesthetic); I looked at our baby sleeping and cried as I said to my husband, "He doesn't feel like mine; it doesn't feel like he came from me". When I reflect now on that time, it was like I was just going through the motions of being a mum – feeding, bathing, changing etc. I knew I loved my baby deep down, but felt so distant from him.* **Helen**

*To go under a general anaesthetic and to not hear my baby's first cry or even see her straight away, still even now, knocks the wind out of me. How must she have felt to not see me or hear my voice, to not be cuddled straight away or protected? I feel like I let my daughter down.* **Sharona**

*I just felt sometimes that I was sad that I didn't get to see our daughter come into the world, even if it was a caesarean.* **Andrew**

A caesarean birth can present specific challenges for women and their partners postnatally, commonly in the areas of breastfeeding, bonding, feelings of failure, physical recovery and emotional impact. However, having a caesarean under general anaesthetic (when you are 'knocked out') often carries with it a whole added host of responses, which is why we have written a special section just for this experience.

## Critical situations, unexpected decisions and emotional fall out

Why are there often extra challenges for a woman who has been unconscious during her baby's arrival in the world? For starters, if a decision has been made to perform a caesarean under a general anaesthetic (GA), often there was an emergency situation occurring that made a it the best option for safety and speed. Or if a woman's body's was not responding to epidural anaesthesia, or some other situation was occurring that was outside the 'norm' of a regular caesarean where an epidural or spinal anaesthesia might be used. If the decision is made in a hurry, sometimes a woman is not given adequate information to process what is happening. This situation alone can be enough to create a traumatic event.

> When the decision was made that 'this baby needs to come out now', I had specifically asked would I be having an epidural/spinal and the answer was a definite "Yes"; and "please sign here". My next memory of my nightmare was being strapped to the operating table. I was never told that I was having a GA and [I] remember thinking, "But why is this happening? Won't I need to be on my side to be given an epidural?" Then the mask was put on and I was told to breathe deep. I had absolutely no idea what was happening. I was confused, lost, completely alone and downright scared. It was like I never existed. **Helen**

> When I was told that I was going to have to have a GA, because they could not get my epidural block up high enough, I was relieved at first. I was so petrified of having a caesarean, being awake while they cut me open. I had no idea that having this procedure under GA meant that my husband could not be present at the birth – I believed that he would be there; I don't remember them telling me otherwise. "I'm going to die," went through my mind just before they put me under. **Sharona**

When we describe the feelings common in a bad birth, we talk about feeling out of control, fearful, unable to ask questions, like we are not included in the process or treated like a 'piece of meat'. All of these feelings can be a common occurrence in the lead up to a general anaesthetic, even before the operation has taken place. No wonder women are often left reeling after such an event.

# Birthing without your partner

Hospital policy for most caesareans under a general anaesthetic is that the partner is refused admittance to the operating theatre. The reasons for this are purely practical – partners may understandably react emotionally to seeing the person they love 'put under' and being operated on, or may pass out, or may get in the way of a safe surgical situation. They are basically considered an unpredictable factor in the operating room. So, usually, the result is that partners are not permitted to enter theatre. This can create more opportunity for a traumatic situation to arise, for both partners.

> *At 9.56 am, our baby boy was born – or so they tell us. Being a GA, my husband was not allowed in the operating theatre and was left standing 'gowned up' waiting to see our baby enter the world. That never happened. The first he knew of the delivery was when they passed with our son to go to the special care nursery and someone yelled out "What about the father?" At that point Craig thought that something had happened to me. There was no explanation, only shock. Why wasn't he in the room?* **Helen**

> *At this point I started to panic; my husband was not in the room with me. I felt scared, alone, disoriented and in la la land. I think I even at one stage asked the nurse to not take my baby. At no point did I feel supported or informed.* **Sharona**

> *My first child was born under a GA emergency caesarean, which was very hard as we had gone through sixteen hours of labour and being monitored, then being told that the baby's heart rate was very high. In the end, I wanted the best thing for my wife and baby. I felt upset that I wasn't in the room to meet our daughter and keep an eye on my wife.* **Andrew**

# Effects of anaesthesia

Another reason a caesarean under general anaesthetic can be hard to process is due to the disorienting side-effects that can result. It is common after any general anaesthetic to experience nausea or vomiting, dizziness, blurred vision, a state of confusion or memory loss,[215] which can make the first meeting with your baby, and then the ongoing care over the first few days, more challenging.

---

215    The Royal College of Anaesthetists and The Association of Anaesthetists of
       Great Britain and Ireland. (2014) *You and Your Anaesthetic: an information booklet.*
       Retrieved from *www.rcoa.ac.uk/document-store/you-and-your-anaesthetic*, accessed November 2014.

> *I came out of the GA disoriented and panicked. I could not feel my legs (because of the epidural) and I don't think, at this stage, that I realised that I had just had a baby. I had no idea what was going on. No one was there to support me.* **Sharona**

It can be incredibly disorienting to emerge from a general anaesthetic, especially if the situation before to being anaesthetised was urgent. If a woman went 'under' in the midst of a critical situation regarding herself or her baby and then, when she awoke post-surgery, was in a confused state (due to the medications in the anaesthetic), it can be extremely challenging for her to ascertain the current situation ("Is my baby okay? Am I okay?"). Often she may be too disoriented to ask any questions, or there is no one there who can answer them.

> *The next few days were strange. There was still no explanation of what happened and I was still in a confused state about the whole ordeal, hitting my husband with a constant barrage of questions about what he was told, what he knew – which was nothing!* **Helen**

Many women find this situation causes them grief and guilt later, when they are trying to reflect on the birth and recall certain aspects. This can be exacerbated by well-meaning comments from friends and family.

> *I put on a brave face and listened to all the comments like, "Oh well, at least you have a healthy baby," and "Don't worry about not seeing him born; you missed all the gory bits".* **Helen**

## Women's recovery from anaesthesia

> *I have no recollection of our baby being born, I don't remember the first time I looked at our baby, and I don't remember the first time I fed our baby or even held our baby. The whole lot had been taken from me in a drug-induced haze, from the GA and the pain relief. The only memories I had of the day my baby was born were created with a camera.* **Helen**

Another factor affecting recovery is that, according to Australian research,[216] women emerge more quickly from a general anaesthetic than men, but take 25 per cent longer to recover, despite the women opening their eyes and obeying commands more quickly.[217] Women were also found to be "more likely to

---

216    Myles, P.S., McLeod, A.D.M., Hunt, J.O., & Fletcher, H. (2001). Sex differences in speed of emergence and quality of recovery after anaesthesia: cohort study, *British Medical Journal, 322,* 710–711

217    BBC News. (2001). *Anaesthetic's Effect on Women.* Retrieved from *http://news.bbc.co.uk/2/hi/health/1236380.stm,* accessed July 2014

suffer from side-effects such as nausea, vomiting, headaches, backaches and sore throats".[218] Associate Professor Paul Myles, who led this research, says, "Women recover more slowly, suggesting they are more sensitive to the side effects of the drugs, or recover more slowly from the effects of surgery itself. We have known for some time that women have higher rates of nausea and vomiting after surgery; but [this] study has found they also have more headache, and backache. Importantly, their overall quality of recovery is worse."[219]

It is important that health carers recognise this possibility and convey this information to the woman and her partner, as then they can take steps to compensate.

In addition to the actual recovery, there is also often the expectation or desire from the woman to care for the baby as soon as possible, which can create issues for a woman who has not yet recovered fully.

If a woman knew that she was likely to take longer than imagined to recover enough to care for her child, she could be supported to find ways to greet and be near her baby until she is appropriately recovered. She could also understand the reasons why she might not feel up to connecting with her baby when first roused out of the anaesthetic, rather than blaming herself.

## Feelings of failure

It is very common for women after a general anaesthetic to experience feelings of failure – that they have failed to 'be a woman', due to not only needing a caesarean, but missing their child's arrival into the world.

> *I cried a lot thinking about the way he entered the world. I felt like I failed, even more than most because I had to have a GA. I must be useless! I hated admitting that I was struggling with my feelings and thoughts because I had already failed miserably with our baby's birth.* **Helen**

> *Having our daughter under a GA has severely affected me emotionally. I felt like a failure; women every day give birth naturally and I feel like less of a woman and mother because I couldn't bring my baby into this world naturally. I feel like I have adversely affected my daughter's life because she didn't come into this world naturally.* **Sharona**

218    BBC News. (2001). *Anaesthetic's Effect on Women.*
       Retrieved from *http://news.bbc.co.uk/2/hi/health/1236380.stm*, accessed July 2014
219    Myles, P. in BBC News. (2001). *Anaesthetic's Effect on Women.*
       Retrieved from *http://news.bbc.co.uk/2/hi/health/1236380.stm* accessed July 2014

There is much that you can do to process these feelings and move on – see the tools for healing further in this section for ideas.

## Relationship with partner

A caesarean under general anaesthetic can bring up a lot of emotion between couples for a number of reasons. Firstly, they both had different experiences: usually the woman has put herself 'at the mercy' of hospital staff and feels extremely vulnerable. She is also recovering from the physical impact of major surgery under a general anaesthetic and is then struggling to deal with the fall out such as bonding issues, emotional trauma and feeding issues. For the partner, their situation is that they are usually left in the waiting room, unable to be there to keep their partner and child safe, unsure of whether they are both okay, and struggling to deal with the fears and worries that arise. They may then be left to support their partner through her recovery, while having no idea what to do, or how to help her. This situation can be very difficult to navigate as a couple.

> *Almost every time we left a Birthtalk meeting for the trip home, we both ended up crying. I never realised the impact it had on both of us. I just assumed because it didn't happen to him, he was fine. He had suffered as well, fearing something had happened to me and the baby.* **Helen**

> *My husband was very supportive, but I just didn't feel like he could say anything right to me. We just skirted the subject for a while. I think we both felt like we were walking on eggshells when it came to the birth.* **Sharona**

> *At times I felt resentment towards my husband because I wondered how he could have let it happen to me/us. Why didn't he ask more questions? Where was he in the room when things started going pear-shaped? (He was shoved in the corner by a room full of medical staff.)* **Helen**

## Bonding difficulties: is this my baby?

After a caesarean under general anaesthetic, women often comment that they feel distant from the baby, and they don't feel like the baby is theirs. This can be one of the most challenging aspects of recovery from a caesarean under general anaesthetic, and one of the least talked about. As a result, many women feel guilty, and worry that they must not love their baby. It is so important for women to know that feelings of distance, or that the baby is not theirs is *normal* and *reasonable* in this situation.

> I think I bonded more with our baby when my husband returned to work. I had to be the one to cuddle him and bath him and take care of him. I still had the feeling of distance with him for sometimes; I actually think they were still there until we attended Birthtalk meetings, until my husband and I really talked about how we both felt. **Helen**

To understand why these feelings are natural, normal and part of a physiological response (that is, your body has not received important things required to naturally bond and to feel instinctively that a baby is yours) see the tools for healing below.

## Feelings of grief and loss

It is common for women after a caesarean under general anaesthetic, to have feelings of grief about not only what happened, but also what didn't happen. Often they voice sadness about their babies not being able to enter the world in a gentle and peaceful way into their arms. Sometimes it is the 'not knowing' what happened at the time of birth that can really hurt emotionally. Many women in this situation do not remember when they first met their baby, which can bring up great sadness, and even guilt, as if it somehow signifies something about them as a mother.

A caesarean under general anaesthetic will always include an aspect of separation, and the impact of this cannot be underestimated. Being separated from your baby is *never* a small thing. Even if you were 'only' apart for an hour or less, it is still important. That is, it can be an important loss.

## Why does it hurt so much to be separated?

This is from our section, *I was separated from my baby* (p250):

> Even if you know your baby was being well looked after, even if your partner was with your baby, it is still significant that you were separated. The reason it is so painful is quite simple: mothers and babies are designed to be together.

Physiologically, women are being primed during a birth to become a mother. All the hormones are trying to set you up to mother your child when they are is born. This is not just an emotional thing – it is happening at a body level. So even if you know your baby needs to be separated from you for their best chance of survival, your body is waiting, wanting and looking for that baby that is supposed to be there.

It is important to know that if your baby is 'missing', even if you intellectually know where they are, your body and brain respond to that as a loss. You are physiologically primed to receive that baby, so to not get them is significant. It is the final step in the 'dance towards motherhood'.

We go into this in a lot more detail in the section *I was separated from my baby* (p250), where we look at more of an explanation of why it can feel so bad to be separated, and some ideas for reconnecting, healing and 'reclaiming' that lost time with your baby. This may provide you with more understanding about what was happening for you, and give you insights that lead to further healing, so we encourage you to explore that section as well.

## What if I need another general anaesthetic next time?

It can feel really important for a woman who has experienced a birth under a general anaesthetic to know what she could do next time should a similar situation arise. In the section *I was separated from my baby* (p250) we share a checklist of events that occur in a normal, undisturbed birth that we have found support women in the journey to motherhood. As we explain in that section, these events produce the optimum hormonal mix that stimulates bonding, promotes maternal instinct, initiates breastfeeding, supports the adaptation of your baby to the outside world, and more. Women who are separated from their babies often miss out on many of these steps.

When planning a future birth, if a woman is aware of the issues she may be able to plan to do as much as possible to complete this checklist of steps, which would obviously require some forethought.

We have seen this done by women who have access to this information and are able to prepare for this possibility prior to birth, often beautifully supported by their health carers.

Events that could be replicated after the birth include:

- holding her baby to her chest in a wet, gooey state
- the woman and her partner welcoming their baby into their family together if possible, before other family are invited in
- exploring her naked baby's body and determining its gender
- having her baby suckle or nuzzle to her breast for comfort and nourishment
- seeing her placenta.

Events that might need to be grieved and acknowledged as missing, which can really help with the healing include:

- seeing a baby coming out of her body
- being the first to see her baby
- witnessing their baby's first moments of life.
- You can read more about why these events are important in our section *I was separated from my baby* (p250).

## The healing journey

*The healing process started for us when we spoke openly about our experience and we received validation for the way we felt and the trauma we had been through.* **Helen**

*When I finally found Birthtalk and rang up Deb for the first time, I think that my partner and I found the strength to talk to each other about it comfortably.* **Sharona**

*Having the courage to get my birth notes and speak to health-care professionals also helped me realise that I had not failed, but that I had been failed in making decisions about me and my baby's physical and emotional health.* **Helen**

*Birthtalk was amazing. Finally I felt like it was okay to feel the way I felt. Learning about birth (through their Vaginal Birth After Caesarean [VBAC] course) was both hard and healing: hard because I longed to go back and re-do the birth with the knowledge that I now had, and healing because I realised that it wasn't my fault.* **Sharona**

## Here are some tools for healing the fall out from a caesarean under a general anaesthetic:

Firstly, just reading this section may be helpful, just so you know you are not alone and you are experiencing a normal response to an abnormal situation. This is important progress in the path to healing.

- To explore the situation that was unfolding before the caesarean, and immediately afterwards, it may be helpful to complete a *Birthtalk Breakdown* (p47). This may assist you to see exactly what was going on for you emotionally at the time, which can enrich the grieving process and help in explaining your situation to others.

- If your partner was not present, it might be helpful to journal about how you felt about that, and what it would have meant for you to have had them there. This exercise can be helpful in understanding the impact of their absence, which can then aid in the grieving process, as you know what you are sad about and how things could have been different. To support you as you grieve, go to *I feel sad* (p245).

- If you felt groggy and disoriented the first time you met your baby, or do not recall it at all, or you were separated from your baby, you may find it helpful to read the section *I was separated from my baby* (p250), and do the exercises there as a way of reclaiming that aspect of the birth. It might also be helpful to write your birth story, and then to rewrite the birth story – see *Writing your birth story – a healing step* (p445) and *The healing power of rewriting the birth story* (p451).

- If you are struggling with feelings of failure, you are not alone and it is possible to move through these feelings. In our experience, it is unlikely to be a case of the woman having failed, although we have seen many cases where the woman has been failed. Read *I feel like a failure* (p227) to find out more.

- If you are struggling with relationship issues, or anger with your partner, then we recommend reading our chapter *Issues with your partner* (p291) to get some insights on dealing with this. Many women have found an understanding of these issues to be extremely beneficial in supporting their relationship with their partner.

- If you are struggling to bond with your child, or have feelings that your baby is 'not your child', then you will likely benefit from a greater understanding of the physiological aspects of bonding; that is, the physical changes that are supposed to take place during birth to instinctively initiate and support bonding. See *I don't feel bonded to my child* (p218) for more information and for links to tools for healing. It can be really powerful to undertake the healing process of this aspect of a traumatic birth.

# I HAD A HOMEBIRTH TRANSFER

> *At first, I did not receive support from the hospital staff. The midwife on duty was rude and impatient with me.* **Catherine**

> *I entered into the birth process completely well read and confident I was going to be okay through it. I ended up doing every single thing I didn't want to happen. I felt like I had failed my child by having had so many drugs once I arrived at hospital. I then got a terrible infection from my cesarean scar.* **Kylie**

> *I really felt like I had failed where many others had succeeded. I experienced deep feelings of shame, especially as I had actually asked to go to the hospital. What a wimp!! I had a lot of feelings of failure surrounding the idea of birth, and I was envious of the women who had managed a successful homebirth.* **Catherine**

> *I was so cut up about the experience even straight after the birth. I felt ashamed of my failure and it would have been nice to be able to debrief but I was too ashamed to ask for help. I was devastated because I would never have the opportunity at this sacred first birth again and I felt I had failed my rite of passage into womanhood.* **Jessica**

## Homebirth transfer – why a separate topic?

Just as a hospital birth can be experienced as traumatic, so can a homebirth. It can be very challenging to work through the impact after any traumatic birth. However, when a transfer from home to a hospital is involved in a planned homebirth, it often adds a new level of emotions for a woman to deal with postnatally. These emotions are shared by many women who have transferred, and also by some women whose homebirths were traumatic, without transferring.

A recent study published in the Medical Journal of Australia looking at women who planned a homebirth, found that while 84% of the 1807 women studied did birth at home with both mother and baby well, 17% transferred to hospital during labour or within one week of giving birth.[220]

---

220  Catling-Paull, C., Coddington, R.L., Foureur, M.J., Homer CS; Birthplace in Australia Study, National Publicly-funded Homebirth Consortium. (2013). Publicly funded homebirth in Australia: a review of maternal and neonatal outcomes over 6 years. *Med J Aust., 198*(11):616-20.

These women can find themselves experiencing intense disappointment, grief and, in some cases, trauma. Unless they have good support and access to information, validation and understanding, these women can feel incredibly isolated in trying to make sense, make peace and move on. For this reason, we have opted to offer a separate section in this book to meet the specific needs of women in this situation.

We've asked four women who have planned a homebirth, transferred to hospital care, and found it to be a difficult or traumatic experience to share their stories, the impact of their births postnatally, and what they found helpful in healing. Similar themes are echoed throughout their stories and those of other women we have met who have debriefed with us following a homebirth transfer.

If you have experienced a traumatic homebirth transfer, you may find it helpful to learn how other women have felt during and afterwards, and see some of the most common responses to this situation. This may help to validate what you are experiencing, which can be the beginning of healing.

Your partner or other family members may also benefit from reading this section, to see that it's not 'just you', that your response is normal and healthy, and that it is possible to process these feelings and heal from such an experience.

## Our stories

Catherine's first birth was planned as a homebirth. However, after labouring at home for twenty-four hours without much progress and with excessive pain, she asked to be transferred to hospital for pain relief. After an epidural, and a rest, she proceeded to birth her baby vaginally.

When Kylie had her baby, the decision was made to transfer to hospital after thirty-six hours of labour, and becoming stuck at seven centimeters dilated. After a couple of hours with no further dilation, her waters were broken, with monitors attached internally to the baby's head. Four epidurals were administered, yet none worked. The baby's heart rate dropped, and an emergency caesarean was performed, under a general anaesthetic.

Jessica, a midwife herself, planned a homebirth with a registered midwife for her first child's birth. Towards the end of her pregnancy, she did not find her midwife to be encouraging or providing the guidance Jessica felt she needed when she expressed concerns about going post-term. She had a 'back labour', with lots of back pain., Jessica had a friend over, and found her friend's presence helped her relax, however, the midwife sent her friend home because she felt Jessica needed to rest. After twelve hours of labour, with two centimetres dilation, she recognised that the pain felt 'excruciating and wrong'. Sensing that her baby was malpositioned, Jessica tried doing lunges and squats to move the baby. Her midwife recommended transfer to hospital due to concerns about possible increased risks and did not offer suggestions or support when Jessica asked if there was anything more she could try at home. Jessica gave up, as she felt the midwife was not showing any confidence in her ability to manage without pain relief. Jessica feels the midwife had not contributed with warmth and compassion to any of her labour. After the transfer, an epidural, and having her waters broken, she birthed her baby vaginally. It was discovered just before the birth that her baby had a hand presentation.

Kirsten's labour at home went for thirty to forty hours. Although her cervix fully dilated, her posterior baby had not descended. After reaching a decision with her midwife and her partner, she transferred in an ambulance, and was put on Syntocinon and a baby heart monitor. After about forty-four hours total labour, the decision was made by the hospital health carers, her midwife, her husband and herself to proceed with a caesarean under general anaesthetic. The reason for caesarean was 'baby in distress, heart rate drop'.

## The fall out from a transfer

Catherine, Kylie, Jessica and Kirsten all experienced some intense emotional ramifications post-birth. Each woman shares the emotions that plagued her in the weeks after the birth:

> I felt terrible. I was utterly disappointed about what I saw as my failure to have a homebirth. Later, I had a lot of regrets and went through all those thoughts of, "If only…" and, "I should have…". And of course, I was completely exhausted. **Catherine**

> The impact was profound and it took me years to comprehend what happened. I had Postnatal Depression that went on undiagnosed. I started to suffer from anxiety and insomnia. I swore off having another child and after eighteen months my marriage broke down. **Kylie**

> I felt ashamed and like the biggest failure. Lots of people had advised me against home birth and not only had I transferred, I'd also had an epidural. I felt that I failed my baby. When she and my husband were asleep I often laid next to them and cried, every night for ages. **Jessica**

> I felt I'd failed. I did not consider myself a 'homebirther' because I hadn't birthed at home. **Kirsten**

All of these women initially had difficulty sharing with others how much their birth had affected them, and their sense of failure and shame was intense. This is partly due to the mentality of 'you should be grateful' that pervades our culture around birth.

It is important to look at why these feelings of shame and failure are so pervasive after a homebirth transfer… even one that ended in a vaginal birth with no further complications.

## Moving from homebirth to hospital

Having a homebirth transfer can feel like a heavy burden for women who experience it. There can be a feeling that to transfer is to fail. It can feel that the act of transfer is an indication of a woman's lack of birthing 'prowess' and, perhaps, that transferring is something to be ashamed of.

This perception is inaccurate and hurtful, and we explain more about this later when we look at what women healing emotionally from a homebirth transfer need to know. For now, we will look at Catherine, Kylie, Kirsten and Jessica's feelings, once a decision had been made to leave home during the birth:

> *At the actual moment, I felt relief because the thought of pain relief was uppermost in my mind. I also felt disappointment in myself that I hadn't dilated further or been able to 'be strong enough' for a homebirth. My dreams of a beautiful homebirth were broken.* **Catherine**

> *I felt like I had failed.* **Kylie**

> *I truly felt gutted, ashamed and a failure. The midwife told me that because I had laboured so long my risk for postpartum haemorrhage and foetal distress was greatly increased and she asked that we transfer to hospital. I asked if there was anything else we could try at home. She proceeded telling me that she thought that I needed Syntocinon. As a midwife, I was terrified of the extra pain and I said I might not be able to cope without an epidural. I wanted her to say that we could manage, but she just agreed with me and said she did not think I could do it. I gave up.* **Jessica**

> *I felt defeated. Defeated and disappointed. There was also a hint of relief that maybe soon I would get to meet my baby and all this waiting would be over. I think I remember a hint of concern about how I might be received by the hospital.* **Kirsten**

## Transfer plus caesarean

When the transfer also involves a caesarean, the feelings of failure can be even deeper. There may already be a sense of failure from not having a homebirth, and this can then be compounded by not birthing vaginally. If breastfeeding is difficult (common after a surgical birth due to anaesthetic effects, wound pain, limited movement and the hormones that promote breastfeeding being compromised), then that can be another area that adds to a woman's feeling of failure. It is a huge load for a woman to carry into motherhood, and can go largely unacknowledged by the people around these women in the weeks after the birth.

> I wondered what was wrong with me. I had done everything right and I still had a caesarean. I felt very fragile, like I might break apart or explode physically. **Kirsten**

These intense emotions, plus the compromised hormones, can play havoc with how a woman feels about her baby, how she feels about herself, and potentially may impact her relationship with her partner.

## Feelings towards the baby

The women we spoke with had differing experiences of their relationships with their new babies, largely due to their differing experiences of birth.

Catherine, who birthed vaginally with beautiful support from her midwife, hospital staff and husband, and had immediate skin-to-skin with her baby, comments,

> I felt very close to my baby. I felt we had been in it together and I was so happy when I saw and held him. The part of labour where I felt I had communicated with him and he had changed position was a very powerful moment – I felt we had already strongly communicated and bonded then. The hospital staff were fine with us waiting to cut the cord and also with skin-to-skin contact straight away, so everything went well for our bonding in that way. Breastfeeding went beautifully, which was a blessing. **Catherine**

However, Jessica, whose experience in the earlier part of labour was of feeling let down and unsupported by her midwife, shares,

*Seeing her come down the birth canal and catching her, I instantly fell in love. I loved her always, but I felt that I failed her. She was tiny and breastfeeding did not work too well in the first days.* **Jessica**

Kylie, whose birth ended in a caesarean under general anaesthetic, met her baby via a photograph, and had to advocate for herself even to meet her baby in person, shares,

*I felt completely disconnected at times and struggled to feel confident in what I was doing. My baby was pretty good in hindsight but I had an irrational fear he wasn't getting enough milk from me. I had no confidence. I opted to go back to work earlier and handed over the full-time parenting to my husband.* **Kylie**

Kirsten, who also experienced a caesarean under general anaesthetic, struggled with feelings of concern and protectiveness,

*I was worried about the impact on my baby of being separated from me after the birth and so many times again at hospital. I thought that he didn't smell like a baby. I felt very protective of him once I got home from hospital and didn't want anyone except myself or my husband to hold him.* **Kirsten**

## Feelings about partners

All the women we spoke with shared that they felt close with their partners after the birth, with Catherine telling us she felt "complete gratitude and love" for her partner. Even Kylie, whose marriage eventually broke down, said that the experience "actually brought us closer together directly after the birth". Jessica, too, says, "My husband was my rock. When our baby was born he stood next to me and he cried; we both did. I remember his face [that day] and I love him for the love he had in his eyes."

This may be due in part to the nature of homebirth preparation, which can require much more partner involvement than a hospital birth preparation. There are logistical factors that must be attended to, for the homebirth to be possible, for example filling bath pools and preparing birth spaces, and these jobs are generally undertaken by a partner. Through this process, the partner can be involved in decision making about a number of issues, and it may be that this prepares him for the decision making involved in transferring and choosing options once at the hospital. It is possible that this means that these women felt well-supported by their partners and thus felt close to them postnatally.

However, the emotional impact of a homebirth transfer can also take its toll on a relationship, especially if there is no outlet for the woman to debrief and process her experience outside of her partner's listening ear.

> *I felt love for him, but he was getting overwhelmed by my sadness and my need to constantly regurgitate the birth story. I needed to analyse and try and see at what point it all could have been different, and what I felt I should have done. After a few weeks he was getting impatient with me."* **Jessica**

Jessica's experience is a common outcome for many women after any traumatic birth, not just a homebirth transfer, although women in homebirth circles may feel even more isolated and find that they have fewer outlets for debriefing their birth.

## Will I be shunned by the homebirth community?

After a traumatic homebirth, especially after a hospital transfer, women may fear being shunned wherever they turn. Firstly, they may be concerned about receiving a cold reception from some in the community who had supported them towards their homebirth. Perhaps because those who choose homebirth are in such a minority, it can be hard for those within that community to hear 'less than great' homebirth stories. They may view homebirth as a potential 'saviour' from a 'dysfunctional hospital system', or as 'protection' against another traumatic birth.

It can be difficult for these women to hear stories about homebirth not going to plan, as they are desperately holding onto homebirth, perceiving it as their only hope for a positive experience.

However, as we know from our *Birthtalk Breakdown* (p47), a positive experience is dependent upon whether a number of the woman's emotional needs are met, regardless of the birth venue.

Some homebirth advocates may question the birthing woman's need to transfer, perhaps asking what she did or didn't do that could have led to the transfer. A lack of determination, commitment and 'positive outlook' may be (incorrectly) implied by others as possibly contributing to the transfer. These often-unintentionally unkind comments and incorrect assumptions can be very painful for the woman to deal with, as it can feel like a betrayal from the community she felt part of.

## Speaking out about their midwife

Some women find if they admit to having an issue with a homebirth midwife, that the ranks close around the midwife. This is sometimes the case in a smaller community where the midwife is well-known, and perhaps revered, by the other members.

Other women, who may have had positive experiences with that same midwife, will refuse to hear 'their' midwife being spoken about in negative terms due to the intimate connection that women can have with their midwife. They may even distance themselves or cut off communications with the birthing woman.

Different women can, however, have vastly different experiences with the same midwife. Their differing experiences depend on what each woman brings to the birth, on the relationship that midwife has with them, on the emotional 'space' she and the woman are in during the pregnancy and birth, on the birth itself and on whatever clinical factors may arise.

However for some homebirthing women who have dared to speak out about poor treatment or a difficult relationship with a midwife, they have feared being ostracised and losing their community.

## Birthworkers unsure how to support women

Courtney Jarecki* is a mum who experienced a homebirth transfer ending in caesarean, and Laurie Perron Mednick was her midwife during this experience. Courtney is now authoring a book, *Homebirth Cesarean*, with Laurie as a contributing author. *Homebirth Cesarean* is dedicated specifically to the issues that face women having a caesarean after transfer from a planned homebirth. Says Courtney, "Just as Homebirth Cesarean mothers often find themselves estranged from the homebirth community, many midwives and birth workers are at a loss as to how best support these women and their families."[221]

Confusion about the best ways to support women in this situation can lead to birth workers either offering unhelpful and incorrect advice, sadly avoiding the woman altogether due to a lack of information about her needs or not knowing if their support is welcomed. This can compound a woman's growing

---

* Courtney Jarecki and Ann Jamison, another Homebirth Caesarean mother, are the co-founders of a non-profit called Homebirth Cesarean International (HBCI). *http://homebirthcesarean.org/*. You can read more in *Appendix A*, and on their website.

---

221    Jarecki, C. (2013) *Home Birth Cesarean, Reframing the Story of Our Births*. Retrieved from
       *www.blogtalkradio.com/progressive-parenting/2013/07/10/home-birth-cesarean-reframing-the-story-of-our-births*,
       Accessed November 2014

sense of isolation and desperation, as she cannot find a suitable source of support, information, ideas for healing or, at the very least, validation for her swirling emotions.

## Shunned by the mainstream

We interviewed some women who were members of an online support group, who shared their experiences of dealing with the general community after their homebirth transfer.

> *One of the hard things about my failed (that's how it still feels) homebirth is explaining to all those people who throughout my pregnancy had asked what hospital I was birthing at, and then I had to explain about having a homebirth, and then say, after the birth, "Oh, I ended up needing to transfer." I could just feel them thinking, "… you should have just gone there to start with."* **Simone**

> *Basically the way it's panned out is, before I had the birth I was judged by the general community; "How could she be so selfish and risk her baby's life?" and after the birth I feel judged by the general community; "We told you homebirth was dangerous" and the natural community; "She obviously didn't trust birth enough". So again I am feeling quite alone.* **Caryn**

> *I did face a lot of judgement from extended family. The judgement increased when they found out I had a caesarean and I received the 'I told you so' attitude despite my transfer being due to placental abruption at 36 weeks. Even now the judgement has continued. I often get comments like, "It was just lucky you got to the hospital in time," and, "You both could have died." The silly thing is that regardless of where I had planned to birth my baby the outcome would have been the same – it's not as if at 36 weeks pregnant you set up camp outside the hospital doors waiting for something to go wrong!* **Samantha**

Regrettably, after a homebirth transfer some women also cannot find support within the wider community – largely due to the misconceptions and fear surrounding homebirth. Any attempt to share and debrief their experience may result in facing misinformed opinions like, "It's your own fault for making such a dangerous choice," or, "You should be grateful the doctors were there to save you and your baby," and even, "You made your own bed, now you need to lie in it."

These thoughts, which can magnify the extent to which these women feel isolated and alone, are sometimes already being presented to them from the moment they arrive in hospital after the transfer.

## Being handled by hospital staff

The reception by hospital staff can be a worrying factor over which a woman can feel she has little control. The fear of being treated poorly, purely as a result of your birthing choices, is a real one with many stories being told about unfair and inappropriate treatment of women transferring from a homebirth. This situation is slowly improving, with some efforts being made by staff and women to make this transition smoother.

The women we interviewed had varied experiences around this.

Jessica was concerned at the reception she would receive:

> When the decision was made to transfer, I was afraid of the judgement by some staff members who had already told me earlier (because I work at the same hospital) that they thought I had chosen an unsafe way to birth my baby. **Jessica**

Catherine felt unsupported when she first arrived at the hospital:

> At first, I did not receive support from the hospital staff. The midwife on duty was rude and impatient with me. The anaesthetist kept telling me to stay still even though I was right in the middle of a contraction. **Catherine**

She went on to receive a combination of great care that enabled her to feel supported and empowered, and less optimal care, that she found upsetting:

> Once the next shift of nurses and midwives came on, they were really great. They were kind and caring. One in particular had a real no-nonsense, encouraging 'coach' style, which I believe was exactly what I needed. As my labour was very long and not progressing, the doctor gave me an internal inspection which I found upsetting – I felt like a cow. He said it was taking too long and I would need a caesarean. At this news I burst into tears and begged for more time; he agreed to one more hour. I focused so intensely on communicating with my baby that he shifted into the right position and everything got started, finally! The midwives were so good to me – every time the doctor came in to

> *check, they would say things to him like, "Oh, she's doing so well,*
> *she's dilated to eight centimetres now and it's only been half an*
> *hour!" even though it had already been an hour.* **Catherine**

Kylie did not feel judged when she arrived, but found the following care to be
very disempowering:

> *The hospital staff were pretty good. They were surprised I had*
> *been in labour for so long, but I didn't feel any judgement. And*
> *I guess the situation wasn't critical when I arrived. But what*
> *happened while I was there was completely disempowering. I had*
> *four epidurals because they failed to work each time. I had asked*
> *the obstetrician to keep hold of the placenta and cord (which*
> *they didn't) and asked for my son to not be given the vitamin*
> *K injection but rather [receive it] orally, which they didn't. But*
> *the worst thing was probably the fact that when I came to (out of*
> *the anaesthesia) my husband showed me a photograph of my son*
> *and then had to go home to get some sleep as there was nowhere*
> *at the hospital for him. He'd been awake for days and was*
> *simply exhausted by the whole scenario. My private midwife had*
> *already left at some point. I was transferred to the ward and then*
> *eventually a nurse called and said my baby was hungry and asked*
> *if it was okay if they put him on a drip as they didn't have the*
> *staff to bring him to me from the nursery. I still had not even met*
> *my baby at this stage. My mum, who never left, eventually went*
> *down and got him against hospital rules, just so I could at least*
> *meet him. I also wanted to start breastfeeding and had read about*
> *the difficulties of nipple confusion if they go from drip/bottle etc.*
> *I wanted something to go my way at least! So my mum handed*
> *me my son and I just plonked him on the boob.* **Kylie**

Jessica feels that the fact that she is a midwife in the same hospital made a
difference in how she was treated, as well as having a support person there
to advocate:

I think I had a better reception than the average homebirth transfer because
I work at the hospital and staff respected me. Having my friend (another
midwife) there to be a mediator also helped. She knew all my wishes and I was
so surprised to get such a nice birth in the end. They turned the epidural
off and I squatted on the bed with a mirror and watched my baby descend
and birthed her in my hands. I actually held her first and kept her on me all
skin-to-skin for about six hours until we were discharged.

> *I did feel a little left alone when my husband went home after the birth to clean up and my friend left and the staff just left me pretty much alone. My catheter bag was full to bursting point and I was not comfortable to buzz for help.* **Jessica**

Kirsten found her experience to be varied, with some unwelcome and unnecessary comments and interventions from the staff:

> *For the most part of the birth, staff were very respectful; there weren't any comments about my choice to homebirth or the fact that I needed to transfer. I did object to the amount of internal examinations (four) as I thought they were unnecessary and the staff could have talked to each other about what they could feel during the examinations, rather than each professional thinking they would have a better assessment. One obstetrician called me 'girly' and said my uterus was 'fagged' and that's why the baby wasn't coming. This was unnecessary and unwelcome. One midwife kept poking me during contractions and I told her to go away, which she did. Once in theatre, my husband and midwife were not allowed to attend. I was scared of having the catheter put in and said so. One staff member assured me that they would put me under before inserting; however, before this preference was conveyed to the catheter inserter, the catheter was inserted. I felt quite a bit of resentment and anger towards some staff members of the hospital with regard to poking and prodding me during the birth, patronising me during my recovery about when I could see my baby, how I should feed or settle him, and what 'needed' to happen before they would 'let us' out of hospital.* **Kirsten**

## My midwife and I

During the transfer and subsequent hospital care, the women's homebirth midwives were present, although, due to regulations at the time, they were not allowed to offer clinical care to the women. Their presence meant different things for each woman, with her particular midwife, in that particular birth, on that particular day.

> *My own midwife was fully supportive and assertive. She stood up for me when the hospital staff were speaking rudely to me. She said, "Can't you see, she's in the middle of a contraction?" It was a real comfort to me to have her there.* **Catherine**

*My midwife was present the whole time, but I do recall at some point she really got pushed to the side.* **Kylie**

*After the epidural was in they told me they would break my waters and I broke down. I had forgotten that this was something we could have tried before they started me on Syntocinon and I would have liked to have tried this. I had never wanted an epidural and cried. My midwife just commented from the comfy lounge chair that I should stop crying, what was done was done, just rest. I did not feel validated at all. I felt that my midwife was happy to organise the epidural so she could sit back and not be a support person. She took the comfy chair that my husband should have gotten. She left very soon after the birth, big congrats and all, but too little too late for me. Her last words were, "Don't be bullied into staying the night". She was totally against this.* **Jessica**

*My midwife continued to support me well and explain things, choices, procedures. I think it was her gentle way that ensured staff entering the birth room were quite respectful.* **Kirsten**

## Long-term feelings towards midwife

How a woman feels about her midwife may change over time – the more the impact from the birth is felt, or the more opportunity the woman has to process and make sense of the experience. Catherine, Kylie, Jessica and Kirsten discovered this as they explored their birth in the months and years afterwards, and we asked them their feelings towards the midwife now.

*I am still very grateful towards my midwife, who stood by me all the way and had a very comforting presence. In hindsight, I feel that one of her initial suggestions for movement during contractions could be one of the contributing factors for things taking the course they did. I wonder if it just pushed my baby's head further the wrong way. I don't blame her for this but it has given me the wisdom to follow my own body more next time.* **Catherine**

*After seeing her a couple of times afterwards, I didn't really want anymore contact with her. I actually can't remember why I feel like this.* **Kylie**

*At first I felt ashamed as I let her down and had such a long labour and then the transfer. But soon I started to rethink and was getting angry 'cause I felt that she let me down in so many ways. To this day I cannot forgive her. I believe she did not have the experience as a midwife to help me cope with all the odds. I would never have laboured easy. I had a diastasis, that caused the malpresentation but she could have suggested trying things such as rebozo work (Ed. – a technique using a traditional sling to support movement and positioning in labour). She could have encouraged me more during the labour rather than making me go to bed and removing me from my birth room. She should not have belittled my wishes of being checked as unnecessary. Possibly, if we had transferred earlier, I would have been less tired and might have coped without an epidural. She did tell me afterwards that I shouldn't beat myself up. Whatever happened, happened (after all her birth was worse than mine). I was speechless. I will never recommend her and I am still angry at her behaviour.* **Jessica**

*I don't think my feelings changed towards my midwife. I felt very supported by her. She validated my experience and helped me be gentle with myself.* **Kirsten**

## What helped the healing process?

At the time of writing, Jessica's birth was four years ago, it has been seven years since both Catherine and Kylie's births, and Kirsten's baby was born nine years ago. Time does help, but unless some validation is received, and some processing undertaken, it can be difficult to move on. All four women share what they have found helpful in their healing journeys:

*I found coming to Birthtalk to be really helpful. When it got to my turn to share, I was ashamed to admit that I had asked to go to hospital and this made me cry in front of everyone, but the other women were so kind that it really did reassure me that what I had done and how I felt was okay, and that I was entitled to my feelings. The moment where I truthfully told what I was ashamed of, and everyone was so supportive, was a wonderful healing moment for me. Even being able to cry in front of others and show my true emotions was embarrassing at first, but a relief as well.* **Catherine**

*Out of desperation, my father and ex-husband begged me to
start seeing a counsellor. By this stage my son was about eighteen
months. She diagnosed the Postnatal Depression that I had been
in denial of for the longest time. I faked the tests and thought
I could fool the system. All because I didn't want to admit to
being susceptible to such a thing. She helped me deal with it and
put me in contact with the organisation Beyond Blue, who were
amazing.* **Kylie**

*At Birthtalk I finally felt validated, and that I was not just
an angry bitch, but that others also felt similar emotions.
Melissa's story resonated with me so much, and Deb gave me a
one-and-a-half hour phone conversation, with no judgement, just
love and validation. This changed me, and (in the emotional way)
saved my life.* **Jessica**

*What helped? Debriefing with my midwife straight after the
birth and in days/months afterwards, and being reassured that
I didn't do anything wrong, that sometimes things just happen
and that we all have our own journey with our own learning. Also,
breastfeeding my baby, co-sleeping, wearing my baby, massaging
my baby, having lots of skin-to-skin time and baths and showers
together to recreate moments that I felt I'd missed by not holding
him immediately after birth.*

*Going back to my homebirth support group and telling my
birth story was huge. I remember one of the facilitators asking if
I wanted to share my birth story and I was uncertain and I think
said as much, I may even have said, "Yes, but I didn't have a
homebirth." To which she replied, "You don't think you're worthy
to tell your birth story? Your experience isn't valid?" This really
challenged me to step up and claim my birth experience and tell
it as my own and part of my journey as a homebirther. I also
received a lot of support and validation from other women during
and after, when telling my story.*

*I read a book called Reclaiming your Goddess Sexuality. This
book was useful in challenging my ideas about sexuality, society's
ideas and how they did or did not influence me. I attended
Birthing Journeys with Deirdre Cullen (a local support group)
and retold and analysed my story, my experience and heard
similar journeys of other women. I had acupuncture on my scar.
This made it feel less creepy and I feel healed the 'cut in half'*

*feeling. I had cranio-sacral therapy and so did my baby. I attended two 'Caesarean Awareness' days that Birthtalk put on. I attended midwife Georgina Kelly's 'Art of Mindful Birthing Workshops'.*

*Each of these events presented opportunities for me to deepen my understanding of what happened during my pregnancy and birth and what my own learning and journey was regarding my son's birth.* **Kirsten**

## What any woman who has experienced a homebirth transfer needs to know

Beyond receiving validation, support, nurturing and an open ear from those around them, there are some important points that can be really helpful in promoting a path towards healing, for women who have experienced a homebirth transfer.

Even when a homebirth transfer goes smoothly, with good handover of care and continuous support, there are a multitude of emotions that can impact upon a woman in the weeks and months afterwards. It can be hard to know why there are such conflicting feelings, which go beyond the understandable disappointment of missing out on the more tangible, positive aspects of homebirth.

These aspects are often the initial drawcard for homebirth, and include: being in familiar surrounds, not needing to leave the home while in labour, having older children able to come and go within the birth area easily, and having one-to-one continuous care from a known midwife. Missing out on these aspects is worthy of acknowledgement, and there needs to be an honouring of the disappointment and grief that can arise. See *I feel sad* (p245) for ways to move through these feelings.

Often, however, the greater conflict lies beyond missing these tangible aspects.

## The homebirth quandary – knowing more about good birth

Most women planning a homebirth are exposed to a wealth of positive birth stories during their pregnancy. The stories they hear are often different to those in more mainstream settings. In homebirth circles, fewer horror stories are told about birth. More stories of empowerment and the many gifts for mother and baby that can result from an undisturbed birth are shared. Women planning a homebirth often have more of an awareness of the potential of birth's impact beyond the birth, and understand that a positive experience of birth can set up a positive postnatal experience. They know that birth matters.

The benefit of this sharing of information that occurs amongst homebirth mothers is that women develop a wider understanding of birth's potential gifts for motherhood. See *Why does it matter? And isn't a live birth a good birth?* (p40) to read more about these gifts. However, the difficulties that can result from these greater insights can be twofold. Firstly, a woman with this increased awareness about birth is also aware of more areas that she missed out on, raising more areas to grieve. This can be challenging in itself, although it is actually a positive thing, as other women without these insights feel the intense sadness yet are unaware of the reason for it.

Secondly, there is a misperception about the benefits of homebirth that can lead a woman to second-guess herself and feel intense confusion. To understand this misperception we have created the following table.

Women planning a homebirth often hear stories that share a number of aspects:

## One homebirth mum's path to birth:

| | |
|---|---|
| Goal for the birth | Healthy, emotionally intact mother and baby |
| Plan to achieve this | Undisturbed birth at home |
| What happened | Undisturbed birth at home |
| How I felt | Feel safe and supported because at home with midwife |
| Outcome | Positive feelings and hormonal gifts from the birth |

It could be easy to deduce from this that a 'good birth', that is, a birth with a positive emotional outcome, is one that is undisturbed and at home.

But at Birthtalk we have found that a good birth is one where the woman feels empowered, nurtured, central to the experience, able to ask questions and safe, regardless of the place of birth. See our definition of a good birth in *Why does it matter? And isn't a live birth a good birth?* (p40). If a woman does not know that, it can be easy to conclude that it is largely the 'undisturbed birth at home' that provides the positive emotional outcome. Of course, being at home CAN support positive emotional and health outcomes, but that is not a given.

It is understandable that homebirth might be seen as a solution to the stories of disempowerment and trauma prevalent around hospital birth. Homebirth often offers a higher chance of meeting the 'good birth' checklist due, at the very least, to having continuous care from the same midwife with whom there is usually an emotional connection, and being in familiar surrounds where the woman is on her own territory.

However, if homebirth is seen as the means to a positive experience, and the path described in the table above is not followed and a transfer occurs, it can be easy to view 'not having an undisturbed birth at home' as the reason for the bad feelings that may arise.

The following table looks at a homebirth transfer path.

## One homebirth transfer mum's path to birth:

| | |
|---|---|
| **Goal for the birth** | Healthy, emotionally intact mother and baby |
| **Plan to achieve this** | Undisturbed birth at home |
| **What happened** | 1. Labour at home<br>2. Transfer<br>3. Some poor treatment by staff, manipulation<br>4. Caesarean |
| **How I felt** | 1. Safe and supported at home with midwife<br>2. Sad, scared<br>3. Belittled, fearful, helpless<br>4. Terrified by the caesarean and recovery |
| **Outcome** | Feelings of failure, disappointment, grief, confusion, deep emotional pain and trauma |

## Where are the bad feelings coming from?

It is important to break down where the challenging feelings that can be an outcome of this path are coming from. In this case above, there are feelings of trauma, failure, and grief. The trauma feelings usually come from experiencing aspects of a bad birth. By our definition, that means feeling confused, out of control, unable to ask questions, horrified with what is happening, feeling unsafe and unsupported.

The simple truth is: these feelings can occur from a homebirth where the woman does not transfer, too. These feelings are actually separate to the grief or disappointment from not birthing at home. Jessica, for example, was feeling many of those feelings before even leaving home.

This is an important point, as it can offer more ideas about where you need to focus your healing. It can take the focus beyond grieving the tangible aspects that have been lost, and offer an opportunity to address the emotions that have arisen due to situations where you felt out of control, unacknowledged as an expert of your own body, confused, fearful, helpless and more (that is, the feelings of a bad birth).

The feelings of failure and grief are understandable and worthy of addressing, of course. Sometimes, however, these feelings come at least partly from believing that having a homebirth was possibly the only way to get the positive outcome the woman was working towards. Once women are aware that the positive outcome of a healthy, emotionally intact mother and baby is not entirely dependent on the baby being born at home, there can be a shifting of some of the guilt and feeling of failure. Catherine found this, once she was able to acknowledge she felt better about being in hospital rather than home, and says, "It was also a feeling of being forgiven that was nice. It was good to acknowledge that I actually felt safer in the hospital."

Of course there are other reasons for grief or failure feelings, with any number of situations occurring either at home or once arriving at hospital that a woman would wish had not occurred and that can incite these intense emotions. We address these in our other chapters *I feel sad* (p245) and *I feel like a failure* (p227).

## A homebirth transfer can still be a successful homebirth

This might seem outlandish, or even feel like a condescending comment, if you were passionate and committed about birthing your baby at home and ended up birthing in hospital – but it can help here to look at what defines success, and what a safe homebirth is.

For most women planning a homebirth, the underlying goal, as discussed above, is to emerge with themselves and baby healthy and emotionally intact and also then, of course, to experience the benefits and positive aspects of birthing at home.

So, if your baby was not born in your house, is that not still a continuation of the original goal? That is, if your goal was to birth your baby in the place that you felt was best able to provide support and safety for you and your baby, then moving to hospital as the situation changed to use the services available to meet your needs in that moment is still a success rather than a failure.

This does not, of course, take into account all the emotions that accompany the reasons for transferring, and any fears, concerns or situations that may have made the transfer experience traumatic. But it stands that a successful homebirth, when taken in the context of the original goals for a birth, does not need to end up at home.

When celebrity Dannii Minogue transferred during her planned homebirth in 2010, some media commentators described her birth as a 'failed homebirth'. However, others, generally within the homebirth community, put forward a different and more astute observation of the situation:

> *What this really is, is a successful home birthing story. Successful? How? She didn't birth at home?? Well, not knowing her actual history, we can only go on what we DO know from news reports… we can assume that she had some difficulties that required her to go to a hospital. So she went. That is what is supposed to HAPPEN. When you home birth and find you need or want to go to hospital, then you do! Quite simple actually.* [222]
> **DragonMumma**

> *To me a home birth transferred to a hospital is not a failure or a disaster. It's just that obviously for whatever reason, it couldn't happen at home, so the midwife has said, "Let's go to the hospital we've already booked into and get the medical help you require.* [223]
> **Donna Jones** (a homebirthing mother)

We just wanted to share this viewpoint, in case the overriding issue for you is the sense that you failed merely because you transferred. We, and many others, do not see this as being the case. Kirsten shares her feelings about her own experience,

222    DragonMumma. (2010). *Dannii Minogue's home birth.* Retrieved from
       *http://thejollydragons.blogspot.com.au/2010/07/dannii-minogues-home-birth.html* accessed August 2014

223    Jones, D. in Conroy, J. (2010). *Dannii Showed Homebirth Safe.* Retrieved from
       *www.bordermail.com.au/story/52032/dannii-showed-home-birth-safe/* accessed August 2014

*I didn't feel saved or rescued. I was glad that there were competent professionals to perform what was necessary and confident that they had done their best.* **Kirsten**

We are not, by any means, suggesting that this information will remove negative feelings about the birth – just that it might be a small step on the path to healing. As Ellie says about her own experience,

*I just wished everyone could see my homebirth then caesarean as what it was – a success in the sense that I had a fantastic midwife who got me to the hospital before things could have gone really wrong. That it was safe, it was right, I did my best but at the same time I hurt like hell both physically and emotionally for everything that happened.* **Ellie**

## Making the call to transfer is an appropriate decision

It is completely appropriate to transfer in the event that you no longer feel that home is the best environment for you or your baby's safety, even if you cannot express WHY you feel this to be the case. Catherine experienced a lot of guilt about her own decision to transfer, and found some peace from a discussion at a Birthtalk meeting she attended, where Deb shared the following with her:

*What is important for us to birth well is being in the place that we feel is the safest to birth. You chose homebirth as the best decision for you and your baby at that time, but things changed, and you then felt safer and more supported going to hospital. That was not a bad decision as we need to make the decisions that will enable us to birth most efficiently, and the place you felt safest changed. This was an understandable decision to make, especially adding in the fact that only YOU have certain instinctive insights about your baby, and it's important not to dismiss these. Basically, you were still doing exactly what you had planned, which was to make the best decisions you could for you and your baby at the time.*
**Debby Gould**

Catherine has since said that this information from Deb enabled her to honour her decision making at the time.

*It was also a feeling of being forgiven that was nice. It was good to acknowledge that I actually felt safer in the hospital. Weird, huh? I think at home it just felt a bit wild – all that pain and not knowing what was going to happen next. How long would it go*

*for? Was something wrong? I guess a little feeling of danger must have entered my mind; a feeling of having underestimated what I was in for.* **Catherine**

## A transfer does not mean anything was wrong with you

Even though something may have been amiss with the birthing process, this is no reflection on the woman. Interestingly, there seems to be some cultural differences in how a transfer to hospital is viewed, perhaps depending on the prevalence of homebirth within that culture. In the Netherlands, a third of the women having babies in 2004 had homebirths, compared to only 0.9% of Australian women birthing in 2010 choosing a homebirth.[224] Professor Hannah Dahlen, Professor of Midwifery at University of Western Sydney, notes that:

> *In the Netherlands, if you have a birth in hospital, the women ask each other 'What went wrong?' In Australia, for some reason, we ask 'What is wrong with you'?* **Professor Hannah Dahlen**[225]

For this reason alone, it would be worthwhile writing your birth story, perhaps including any notes from the birth written by the health carers, or your own notes, or both. (See *Writing your birth story – a healing step* (p445).) It might make exactly 'what happened' a bit clearer and allow you to examine this in relation to how you felt. It might enable you to see where there are gaps in your understanding of what occurred. This information could all lead to further understanding and healing.

You may wish to do a *Birthtalk Breakdown* (p47) to facilitate this process. You may perhaps find you need the support of a midwife to work through the details of the birth – perhaps even another homebirth midwife who was not involved with the birth. Getting clearer about the reasons for transfer and what happened at the hospital can be very helpful in working towards healing.

224    Creagh, S. (2013). *Study of Low Risk Women Reveals Good News on the Homebirth Front.* Retrieved from *http://theconversation.com/study-of-low-risk-women-reveals-good-news-on-the-home-birth-front-15236* accessed November 2013

225    Dahlen, H. in Creagh, S. (2013). *Study of Low Risk Women Reveals Good News on the Homebirth Front.* Retrieved from *http://theconversation.com/study-of-low-risk-women-reveals-good-news-on-the-home-birth-front-15236* accessed November 2013

## Releasing the myth of the birthing goddess

For some homebirthers, having the homebirth one desires is a sign of one's 'goddess' stature. Homebirthers can be inundated with images of a birthing goddess, often represented squatting as she births her child vaginally. Paintings, sculptures, and jewellery are all available depicting this 'mother earth' idol, or other pregnancy goddesses. What happens when you don't end up emulating this image? The loss of this anticipated goddess moment can be another insult to add to the feelings of failure and loss.

It can be a big step to reassess what 'being a birthing goddess' means, and to perhaps take the definition wider. It might be beneficial to actually write down what you believe it means to be a birthing goddess. This can help in the grieving process, as it can make it clear what you are grieving here. It may be that you believe a birth goddess is someone who births her own child, under her own steam, without intervention, in her own home. Well, that's one kind of birthing goddess – and if that's your definition that it would be easy to feel like a failure after a transfer, and especially after a transfer ending in caesarean. Yet does it need to be the only definition?

Is there a possibility that a birthing goddess is any woman who grows a baby and does what needs to be done, often at cost to herself, to see this child arrive earthside? By this definition, we have met many, many birthing goddesses. Some have birthed in hospital, some at home, some on the roadside, some have birthed shockingly fast, some have experienced lengthy labours, some with epidurals on board, some via caesarean, some via caesarean with general anaesthetic. These birthing goddesses are amazing. They make incredibly difficult decisions, they may labour long and hard, they go through immense pain (physical and emotional), they are required to make decisions while completely vulnerable. This, to us, is a birthing goddess.

We know, too, that most women who have experienced a homebirth transfer have only made the decision after much deliberation and after countless other avenues have been exhausted, with no other options available. What a goddess, to go through all that.

Erin, who experienced a homebirth transfer caesarean after four days, says,

> One thing I have realised, reading other homebirth caesarean stories…we are pretty epic birthers! Nowhere else have I read about labouring for days, pushing for hours, etc. Planned hospital births just wouldn't be allowed to continue … **Erin**

It's also nice to see how other birth workers can view women who transfer. This lovely comment comes from a homebirth midwife, speaking to other women on a homebirth caesarean transfer Facebook page (reproduced here with permission):

> Even though I haven't been through it personally, I feel like I do understand (to an extent) having travelled beside women over the past twelve years who have been in this very situation – some of whom feel that they will never get past it, others who have healed from the trauma through planning their next birth, others who have worked through it as much as they feel they can and have come to a place of peace with it. To have a three hour labour and spit out a baby in your lounge room is amazing and extraordinary in its ordinariness. The real warrior women and the heroines in my eyes are women like yourselves. Those who fight so hard for what they want and keep getting up and fighting against all odds and when they feel there's none left, they get up and fight some more. You are truly inspiring and without exception fabulous to work beside. **Jo Hunter**

So, we wonder if perhaps it might be helpful to think about what you could do to reclaim your birth goddess rights, and see yourself as an incredibly strong woman. A true birthing goddess. See our section *Redefining strength* (p488) for some ideas.

## Feelings of guilt if you had a caesarean or lots of intervention

Women from the online support group we interviewed shared their feelings:

> From the get-go, my biggest thing was to give my son the best possible start to life and the fact that we ended in an emergency c-section is where most of the guilt and shame stems from. **Rachel**

> I have only recently realised that I am healing from my own birth trauma. But when I think about the trauma that my babies must have felt, well it makes me cry and I think it always will. **Erin**

> Coping with the fact that my planned home waterbirth had instead turned into a caesarean section was hard enough without the added negativity about my choices from family members and the continued comments about how risky my decisions were. In those early days, when PND [Postnatal Depression] is so easy to fall into, I already felt like I had failed my daughter by having

*a birth so far from natural and each extra comment I received just made me remember that she wasn't born how I'd planned and made me feel like even more of a failure, not just for my daughter, but for my entire family.* **Samantha**

To go from a planned, undisturbed homebirth to a hospital birth that may have many interventions can be very difficult to process. It can feel like giving your child 'the opposite' of what you had planned, and result in much guilt and difficult feelings.

It is important to acknowledge the pain that can stem from this, and take steps to process and work through the emotions. We suggest reading *Reconnecting with your child* (p409), and especially look at the *Games for caesarean babies and mummies (and daddies too!)* within this section.

It is also important to release the guilt often associated with choosing interventions. See *Why did I agree to that epidural/episiotomy/caesarean etc.?* (p210) for ways to explore these feelings.

## Future births?

Having a hospital transfer can bring up a new set of fears and questions when birthing again. From making a decision about where to birth, to how to face the fears raised from last time, there is much to be acknowledged and addressed.

*My feelings about birth after experiencing it were varied. First up, nothing could possibly have prepared me for the pain! I had a lot of feelings of failure surrounding the idea of birth.* **Catherine**

*I swore off having another child.* **Kylie**

*I wondered if birth was elusive for me, if there was a secret I wasn't in on. I still believed that birth was meant to unfold naturally and that a natural birth at home was possible for me one day.* **Kirsten**

Interestingly, the effects of time, facing their fears and working on their healing, has taken these women on a path they might not have imagined following initially. Kylie says that now, if she had another child, she'd like to think she'd 'give VBAC a go'. She says, "Next time around I'd be way more relaxed. Things don't always go to plan – and it's actually okay."

Catherine and Jessica have both gone on to have subsequent homebirths, which were empowering experiences. These births came after processing the previous birth, and Jessica expresses that she took an intense healing journey to get into a space to meet her next child, which was a challenging, yet ultimately positive experience for her family.

Kirsten has gone on to be beautifully supported by the same midwife through a homebirth with her second child, then a miscarriage, and then another homebirth.

## What if I need to transfer next time?

It is important to know that if you decide to have another homebirth, but need to transfer again, that you can set certain things up to work towards an empowering experience, (that is, where you feel the 'good feelings' of birth we describe in our definition of a good birth in *Why does it matter? And isn't a live birth a good birth?* (p40)). Sarah, who had a caesarean with her first birth, ended up transferring with her second. However, she had attended Birthtalk's VBAC Course and gained many new insights, a lot of which we share in this book, that gave her and her partner some important skills and a new focus when their plans changed. She says:

> *Whilst it was not the birth I anticipated it was the perfect birth for me. One of the main things I got from Birthtalk was idea of having an 'empowering' birth whatever the circumstances, and that is exactly what I got. Yes, it had some drama and tears, and a reluctant and scary ambulance rush to the hospital. But I felt loved, supported and advocated for the whole time. And in the end… I had a drug-free, vaginal birth and it felt amazing when a bloody-gooey baby girl was lifted onto my chest. Thank you both for your support, wisdom and commitment to Birthtalk. It wasn't until the birth was over that I understood the power of what I gained from the Birthtalk VBAC course.* **Sarah**

The sections in this book about planning future births may be helpful in addressing this issue as well, so see our chapter *Birthing again* (p507).

## Where to from here?

Although this chapter has been dedicated to the specific issues facing women after a homebirth transfer, other parts of the book provide a much wider vision for healing and moving on. We suggest using the book the way we have suggested to other women – to read the opening chapters and then choose which areas you need to explore and process as you go. There is no 'right' way to heal, and your path will likely be just your own.

We encourage you to keep 'going there', as there are many gifts waiting for you in the healing journey. We will leave you here with two comments, one from Kirsten about her subsequent experiences, and a comment from Jessica, written recently:

> *These days, I feel good about my first birth. I did the best I could with the knowledge and awareness that I had. I also went on to have two homebirths (one in a birth pool and one on all fours with my husband doing the catching!), which went a long way towards my healing as well.* **Kirsten**

> *I was not sure I could ever work as a midwife again at first. I wanted to rescue all the women that had similar births to me, and I was happy, but jealous, of anyone with a nice birth. It nearly killed me to have such terrible thoughts. Had I not attended Birthtalk, I might never have overcome these feelings and [I may have] given up my beautiful profession. I am now a very empathetic midwife – I can see all sides, and I will inform women, not rescue them, and I will stand by them all the way. Today I teach antenatal classes and I rock.* **Jessica**

# PART THREE: TOOLS FOR YOUR HEALING JOURNEY

# POEM: HAPPY BIRTHDAY

three tomorrow
three

an age has passed since we first met
I have fought and screamed for the right to love you
to call you my own

tonight I have reclaimed a part of what was mine
all along
by rewriting the story of our first meeting

so that it was gentle
and empowering
and surrounded by love

I had no rite of passage
on the day of your birth

I have passed through the same tunnel as other mothers
but it has taken longer than any natural birth
for me to emerge victorious
certain of my strength
certain of my courage
certain of my body's celebration of womanliness
and you have emerged too

were you unborn for those first desperate months?

were you, too, weeping for your lost initiation?
we've done it together, you and I
symbolically reborn
both of us

showers and baths where we are slippery bodies entwined
a sling to carry you so you can be near my heartbeat
massages that mimic the pressure of birth
games where you push your feet against my hand
and find success, this time
whisperings of the lost words I was never able to utter
as you were taken from me in those early hours
spoken now in the half-light you smile in your sleep as I tell you
those sweet welcomes
that I was never able to say in my drugged state
and I feel us healing

my baby
we were robbed of our birthright
and I ache for the lost chance

and now you are three
three
not a baby anymore
but always my treasured child

your lessons have made me
reach within
and find the woman who would be
your mother

*©Melissa Bruijn 2002*

# HOW TO USE THIS PART OF THE BOOK

This part of our book is designed to take you further down the path to healing. We can't tell you what your path will look like, which way it will twist and turn, or what you might uncover along the way. However, we can provide signposts for every crossroad you approach in your journey and invite you to choose the direction that is calling for your attention. We believe women often know what they need to heal if they are informed about traumatic birth and have the beginnings of an understanding of what happened to them and are supported along the way. The earlier chapters of this book *The foundations of your healing journey* (p37), *Healing – the big questions* (p61) and *Do I need a diagnosis?* (p81) were created to give you the foundations on which your healing journey can begin.

By now, through reading these chapters, you have likely expanded your understanding of what a bad birth is, and have perhaps completed a *Birthtalk Breakdown* (p47) to unpack the aspects of your birth that need processing. You may be beginning to put the puzzle pieces into place, and finding some explanations of why you might be feeling so bad. You may also have read *How do you feel right now?* (p121), which offers insights and knowledge that can build on this new information and address common issues that women present at Birthtalk.

It can feel so powerful to be aware of how you feel, and to understand why you feel that way. But you also might need to know what you can do about it – which is where this part of the book comes in. These *Tools for your healing journey* are designed to be used in conjunction with Part Two, *How do you feel right now?*, or just on their own.

Some women like to work on these exercises and tools alone. Some women find it beneficial to work through these tools with support from another person. You might find it helpful to have someone to turn to, to share your journey with, whether it is your partner, a good friend, a family member or a support group. Ideally, you need someone who understands traumatic birth, or is willing to learn about it, and who might be able to offer a listening space as you travel and discover your way on this path. Depending on their situation some women find (depending on their situation) that this is too intense a role for their partner. By seeking a level of support elsewhere before sharing their new understandings with their partner, they can reduce pressure on their relationship.

If you are feeling vulnerable we do encourage you, to consider working through these tools with a trained counsellor or midwife, or another health carer who has the skills to support you in unravelling these, often intense, emotions. However, you need to choose someone who will honour this journey you are undertaking.

When you feel you are ready to explore the *Tools for your healing journey,* find a quiet space, grab your journal or pen and paper, and know that we are sitting with you in spirit, honouring your courage and strength as you work through the exercises that resonate with you on your path to healing. Continue going gently with yourself. You are unfolding and expanding and opening up your heart to new possibilities. You are taking the healing journey.

Acknowledgement: Most of the tools we share in this part of the book were initially used by Melissa from Birthtalk while undertaking her own healing more than twelve years ago, and were gleaned from various sources. Many wise women on the ICAN (International Caesarean Awareness Network) and HBAC (Homebirth After Caesarean) chatlists gave Melissa their experiences and ideas for healing as she struggled to work through her birth, and we want to acknowledge the support and input from these women towards Melissa's recovery. Some of these women were influenced by a book by Dr Lynn Madsen, titled "Rebounding From Childbirth: toward emotional recovery". Although Melissa did not read this book at the time, she has since learned that some of the ideas she was given, may have been derived from this source. We would therefore like to acknowledge the indirect influence of Dr Madsen's work on our own work. Accordingly, we would also like to acknowledge the work of Pamela Vireday, childbirth educator and author of the website, 'Plus-size Pregnancy' *www.plus-size-pregnancy.org*, particularly her article, 'Emotional Recovery from a Caesarean', where she outlines Dr Madsen's key ideas. This article was also used by women on the chatlists, and recommended to Melissa. After Melissa had completed her healing journey, she brought the tools she had found most helpful to Birthtalk, to share with other women in a similar situation. These tools have since been adapted and combined with Deb's knowledge and experiences, and with the work of other authors to create our own exercises and activities designed to promote understanding, processing and healing. Our heartfelt thanks and acknowledgement go to all these women who offered their professional or personal insights and stories so that others might learn and heal.

# *Supporting your relationship with your child*

## RECONNECTING WITH YOUR CHILD

Sometimes after a traumatic birth, our relationship with our babies and children needs to be rebuilt. It doesn't matter if quite a bit of time has passed, there is still much that can be done to reconnect. Before you try these methods or activities we encourage you to work on your 'stuff' first, perhaps looking at areas such as:

- Exploring and releasing any self-blame you might have for what happened in your birth. We suggest you explore sections such as *Why wouldn't my body work in labour?* (p230) and *Why doesn't anyone get it?* (p129) as well as *I don't feel bonded to my child* (p218).

- Making more sense of what actually happened in your birth – perhaps by doing a *Birthtalk Breakdown* (p47).

- Exploring any issues of sadness surrounding your child, for example, being separated after the birth, or feeling you have failed your child, through *I was separated from my baby* (p250) and *I feel like a failure* (p227).

- Exploring any issues of anger and guilt through the sections *I feel angry at my child for 'causing' all this (and then feel terrible for feeling that way.)* and *Why did I agree to that epidural/episiotomy/caesarean etc.?* (p210).

This can then clear a space to begin to reform a bond with your child.

## Connection reclaimed via contact

Skin-to-skin contact at birth has many benefits for the mother–baby bond. According to Dr Sarah Buckley, "Skin to skin contact … benefits the mother, who releases high levels of oxytocin, the hormone of love, when skin to skin with her newborn".[226] Dr Buckley explains that oxytocin also called the hormone of calm and connection, switches on the mother's instinctive mothering behaviours. She says, "It actually alters our brain – probably permanently actually – to switch on those areas that we need for mothering".[227]

Although it is optimal to receive these benefits from skin-to-skin contact (and oxytocin) at birth, it is not always possible. Thankfully, as noted by Linda F. Palmer, author of *The Baby Bond*, "A lifetime opportunity for bonding and love is not lost if this initial window is missed".[228] We have also found with Birthtalk mums that skin-to-skin contact with your child can have a beneficial effect, even if you don't intentionally have that skin-to-skin contact until months or years after the birth, and it can significantly impact on your feelings of closeness with your child.

## Restimulating the oxytocin

So, how can we kickstart the hormones and improve connection between mother and child – particularly when that child is no longer a baby? Linda Palmer says, "Beyond birth, [the] mother continues to produce elevated levels of oxytocin as a consequence of nursing and holding her infant, and the levels are based on the amount of such contact".[229] So, just the simple act of holding your child can positively affect your oxytocin levels and its ongoing role in your body. Dr Buckley puts it beautifully, saying, "Mother Nature realises sometimes birth

---

226    Buckley, S. *What are the benefits of skin-to-skin contact upon birth?* Retrieved from *http://canaustralia.net. s150349.gridserver.com/%E2%80%A8what-are-the-benefits-of-skin-to-skin-contact-upon-birth%E2%80%A8- %E2%80%A8/*, accessed November 2013.

227    Your Baby Booty. *Interview with Dr Sarah Buckley: The Silent (but insanely powerful) Impact Hormones During Pregnancy Have On Helping You & Your Baby at Birth.* Retrieved from *http://yourbabybooty.com/interviews/ hormones-baby-body-birth-interview-with-dr-sarah-buckley/*, accessed November 2013.

228    Palmer, L.E. (2002). Bonding Matters…The Chemistry of Attachment. Reprinted from the Attachment *Parenting International News*, 5, 2. *http://babyreference.com/bonding-matters-the-chemistry-of-attachment/* accessed November 2013.

229    ibid.

doesn't go according to plan, but this is her back-up system: your skin-to-skin contact with your baby and early and continuous breastfeeding as much as possible".[230]

Why does breastfeeding help? Dr Buckley explains, "[Oxytocin is] a hormone of breastfeeding. So all the time that we're breastfeeding our babies, we're getting a hit of this hormone … which rewards us, which makes us calm and connected, which increases our bond with our baby, and makes us feel good".[231]

## When breastfeeding is not an option

However, at Birthtalk we are aware that often part of the fall out from a traumatic birth is that breastfeeding doesn't work out, usually for a wide variety of reasons. Sometimes it might be due to the hormonal interplay being compromised, either from feelings of fear and feeling unsafe, which inhibits oxytocin during labour and birth. Or it might be due to being separated from your baby, or not receiving skin-to-skin after birth, or simply not being supported by your caregivers in your breastfeeding – or a combination of all of these things. Either way, there are still methods of increasing your bond with your baby that do not involve breastfeeding.

## Carrying and 'wearing' your baby

The simple act of holding your baby, even without skin-to-skin contact, has benefits that can include reduced crying and more secure attachment.[232] One way to facilitate holding your baby and to receive those benefits is by wearing a soft baby carrier. Some people refer to using a carrier as 'babywearing'. Dr Maria Blois, author of *Babywearing: The Benefits and Beauty of This Ancient Tradition,* quotes a study where mothers of newborns were assigned either a soft baby carrier or a plastic infant seat, and asked to use their product daily. The result? The mothers who were given soft carriers at birth were more responsive to their babies and the babies were more securely attached.[233]

---

230 Your Baby Booty. *Interview with Dr Sarah Buckley: The Silent (but insanely powerful) Impact Hormones During Pregnancy Have On Helping You & Your Baby at Birth.* op. cit.

231 ibid.

232 Blois, Maria MD, *"Hold me close: encouraging essential mother/baby physical contact"* excerpt from Blois, Maria. *Birth: Care of Infant and Mother: Time Sensitive Issues. Best Practices in the Behavioral Management of Health from Preconception to Adolescence,* edited by William Gordon and Jodie Trafton. Los Altos: Institute for Disease Management. 2007–8. pp. 108–132, accessed at *http://babywearinginternational.org/wp-content/uploads/2014/07/Blois_research_summary.pdf* in November 2013

233 Anisfeld, E., Casper, V., Nozyce, M., & Cunningham N. (1990). Does infant carrying promote attachment? An experimental study of the effects of increased physical contact on the development of attachment. Child Developement 61:1617–1627. in Blois, Maria MD, *"Hold me close: encouraging essential mother/baby physical contact"* (as above)

*I did not know about babywearing with my first child, whose birth was traumatic. When it was introduced to me, my child was two years old, and we had not yet begun the healing journey after his birth. Although he was an older child, I popped him in an appropriate sling (a Babasling) and 'wore' him when we went to the shops, or if I felt he needed me in close proximity. My husband wore him for long beach walks, and the sling became a part of our parenting paraphernalia. The sling gave us opportunities for so many more cuddles, and conversations and closeness. I am sure it contributed to the rebonding process we underwent. With my subsequent babies, whose births were not traumatic, we wore them from the newborn stage onwards in a variety of slings and carriers. I so wish I had known about this when my eldest was tiny.* **Melissa**

*My first baby was very small and spent his first 10 days in NICU (Neonatal Intensive Care Unit) and for the first six weeks our house was filled with NICU staff doing home visits and weighing him and attempting to get us to bottle feed and so on. I struggled immensely with a lot of this, not only as the pressure on a new first time mother, but also because this is very close to my profession (I am a Paediatric Intensive Care Clinical Nurse Specialist). I didn't really know a lot about baby wearing, but a friend offered me a Peanut Shell sling. When I had him in that I felt like I was able to protect him and, for a little while, it was just him and me. We moved onto an Ergo [carrier] once he was a bit bigger. With our second child we used a Hugabub [carrier] for the newborn phase, which both my husband and I preferred. I do think that the wearing was an important part of my ability to bond to my baby allowing the closeness and constant touch that we missed out on in his early days.* **Kate**

*I began wearing my son as soon as we left the hospital. I wore him everywhere because it felt like I could protect him by keeping him so close to me. I wore him without my shirt at home for some much needed skin-on-skin [contact] too. He was so peaceful and happy when being worn. We tried a variety of carries: Ergo, Manduca, ring sling, Hugabub and a woven wrap. Our favourite was the Hugabub when he was small and then the woven wrap as he got too heavy. I wore him right up to two-years-old on occasion. Wearing my baby gave me a sense of finally being able to do something for him – something that I knew he liked and that soothed him. Plus, I felt like I was able to protect him while he was so close to me. It also helped us get a better breastfeeding relationship happening. Baby-wearing was an important part of my healing. It gave me the chance to really 'be there' for him in a way I had felt unable to in his birth.* **Katie**

*I had always planned to baby-wear, but having a traumatic birth made me feel a deep need to connect and keep my baby close and safe. I wore her nearly all the time. I also used to rock her at night in the Ergo [carrier]. Putting her into a pram felt like abandoning her. I used a Storchenwiege wrap. As a newborn, the wrap felt more snug with closer body contact and almost like she was still in my belly. I continued to carry her till she was two-years- old. Then, I wore my son (whose birth was not traumatic). My daughter loved being carried. She still loves the close snuggle now. My son never seemed to need to be held as much. So I guess it felt like both my daughter and I had that need for being held close.* **Mia**

*I carried my son because I didn't want anyone else to hold him. Wearing my baby made me feel in control and [gave] the sense of still carrying my baby. To feel his warmth and [see] my son looking up to me made me feel needed and loved by him. I was very fortunate that my mum went all out and bought me an Ergo baby performance carrier because I was unable to use the sling after my caesarean section. I still carry my almost three- year- old in it to this day. Wearing my baby made me feel like a mum. To be able to look down at my son and build our bond with eye contact and cuddles. Baby-wearing to me was essential so that I could feel closer to my baby and feel more love towards my son as I feel I missed out on knowing that my baby definitely came out of me.* **Kristina**

For babywearing safety information, see:
*http://babywearinginternational.org/pages/safety.php.*

For information about the best carrier for healthy hip development see:
*http://hipdysplasia.org/developmental-dysplasia-of-the-hip/prevention/baby-carriers-seats-and-other-equipment/.*

## Baths and showers

A delightful and simple way of re-stimulating those hormones can be bathing with your child. Two slippery bodies together, similar to how they were designed to be at birth, skin-to-skin, snuggling, playing or even feeding can ignite the oxytocin production, bringing with it the benefits of this wonderful birthing and mothering hormone, replicating some of the hormones produced during birth. Many of the benefits of skin-to-skin contact we have mentioned can be experienced through this simple process of bathing. So many Birthtalk mums have told us how these intentional baths with their child have enhanced their feelings of closeness and bonding.

> *We certainly have had that bath and while awkward at first, it is now our Sunday routine. My husband even tried it a couple of times and today told me he felt closer to our baby because of it. Who would've thought something so simple could have such massive effects!* **Virginia**

Kate shares the process she went through, using baths for bonding after her traumatic vaginal birth:

> *Jaxon was six-months-old when we first had a bonding bath. I turned the lights off and lit candles to make the room as dim as it was when he was born. I had my husband hand me him once I was in the bath, and shut my eyes and imagined it was him handing me my fresh, wet, newborn baby, just as we had hoped it would be. I lay him on my chest and we enjoyed warm, wet cuddles. He lay really contentedly and just stared at me. Soon he started moving his head looking for a feed, so I moved him on his side and fed him in the bath.*
>
> *The feeling was incredible; I had a rush of joy – a hit of love. Having his little, wet body skin on skin with me, feeding so contentedly, staring up at me – it was all just how I had imagined it would be after the birth. He was so quiet and so relaxed through the whole experience. As I began shedding tears, he stopped feeding to smile at me. It felt like for the first time he and I were really aware of each other.*
>
> *It was definitely the beginning of truly bonding with my son for the first time I felt like we really were connected, our lives intertwined, like no matter what happened we would love each other. After six months of feeling virtually no bond other than a hypervigilant need to 'protect' him after our traumatic experience,*

*it was honestly the first bonding moment we had. We went on
to have more bonding baths, and lots and lots of skin on skin
snuggles whenever I could.* **Kate**

## Games for reconnecting

While most of these games are designed to be used with toddlers, you can adjust
them for older children too.

### Surprise package

Often with a traumatic birth, you and your child miss out on that joy-filled
moment of the first greeting. Melissa tells how she used this game with her son
to try to reclaim some of that special moment:

I would wrap my son in his towel after his bath, and then we'd go to the living
room couch. I'd stand him in front of me, between my knees, and feign surprise
and say, "What's this? The postman has brought me a package! What could
it be? I'm so excited! I'd better unwrap it!" The whole time he'd be standing
there giggling, his face shining, while he kept the towel firmly wrapped close
around him. Then I'd open up the towel and say, "It's a Harry! I got a Harry!
Oh wow, I've always wanted a Harry! I am the luckiest mummy in the world!"
And I'd hold his little body close to mine, and snuggle him up, and kiss all over
his face and he'd laugh and laugh. Then he'd ask to do it again. We began this
when he was very young – maybe just three years old. It really restored a sense
of 'rightness' in our relationship – he knew he was very much wanted and
welcomed, and I got to experience those feelings of joy and immersed myself in
his gorgeousness. It was healing and affirming for us both.

### Mummy turtle

This is one that Melissa played with her kids, even as they grew quite a bit older.
It is adapted from a similar activity in a book by Steve and Shaaron Biddulph
called *Raising a Happy Child*.[234] It is a great one for re-enacting the birth, except
with a happy ending, of course!

*We play this game on the big bed. I am the mummy turtle and
I 'dig a hole in the sand' with my 'flippers' and talk about it like
a story, "Once there was a mummy turtle. One day, she climbed
s-l-o-w-l-y up onto the beach, and began to dig a hole. She used
her flippers to scoop, scoop, scoop out the sand. She worked very*

---

234   'The Mother Turtle game' in Biddulph, Steve and Shaaron. (2010). *Raising a Happy Child in the precious years
from birth to six*, Dorling Kindersley Limited, London. P 156.

*hard. When she had finished, she laid her eggs!" At this, both kids jump into the 'hole' I have made (just a cleared spot on the bed), and curl up into little balls. I make sprinkling movements on their backs with my fingers and continue the story. "The mummy turtle covers the eggs with sand to keep them safe. She pats the sand down carefully (I pat their backs all over) then goes back into the ocean. It is very quiet until, suddenly, the eggs begin to move... and crack!" The kids are imitating baby turtles, moving their 'flippers' and breaking open their 'shells'. Now, here we digress from what actually happens in nature. Rather than the baby turtles being left to fend for themselves, the mummy turtle returns to see her babies. So I say, "Oh, my babies! Oh, you are so beautiful! Come here and let me love you! Oh, a girl baby turtle and a boy baby turtle!" And they make 'baby turtle noises' and flipper their way to me, and we have a big cuddle on the bed while I kiss them.*

*Then they usually ask to play it again! Sometimes, for variation, they are baby crocodiles, or birds, and once they were even Pokémon! Regardless, this is such a reconnecting, nurturing game that we all love, and we all walk away with feelings of being welcomed and loved and wanted.* **Melissa**

## Games for caesarean babies and mummies (and daddies too!)

When Melissa was working through her own experience, she found a website called Cesarean Voices,[235] which is put together by adults who were born via caesarean. The website invites the reader to consider the possible psycho-social implications for the child being born in a caesarean delivery. It is suggested that caesarean-born babies (especially those where there was labour prior to the caesarean) don't get to achieve their 'goal' of being born, or to experience the feeling of success from doing so. These missed birth rites are thought to be of emotional benefit to the development of aspects of a child's personality, confidence and attitude. Exercises are suggested to replicate and allow the child's body to experience similar sensations and outcomes to what was missed, to reclaim some of the benefits of the birthing process.

Dr William Emerson is the President Emeritus of the Association for Prenatal and Perinatal Psychology and Health in the US. He wrote an article on the Cesarean Voices website titled, *Treating Cesarean Birth Trauma During Infancy and Childhood.*

---

235    *www.eheart.com/cesarean* accessed November 2013

Part of Dr Emerson's treatment model for caesarean birth trauma in babies is the use of 'empowerment' exercises where "infants and children are guided and supported in finding consistent success, engaging in exercises and games that return them to the potency that was denied them during their births".[236] He writes, "In order to heal birth traumas, babies need to undergo corrective experiences which allow them to use their bodies in confident ways. This process is called empowerment. Empowerment first involves the identification of specific movement patterns that were impotent or ineffectual during birth. Parents and practitioners next help infants and children articulate powerful movement patterns".[237]

Dr Emerson suggests a range of exercises and activities designed to support a caesarean-born baby in their own healing process. Melissa adapted some of the suggested activities with her toddler, and found it really did make a difference to him. Other Birthtalk mums have since found they worked for them too. Melissa explains how she and her husband adapted this idea of empowerment and achieving goals in an activity with their son:

When a woman is in labour, her baby is actively working too, pushing with their feet, inching themselves down towards the birth canal. But with a caesarean, they are extracted before they can finish the task, and sometimes before they even begin, if the caesarean happens before labour.

> We would put our son at the end of the big bed, right down near the foot. We'd pop him on his back, his head pointing towards the bedhead, and bend his knees like a frog, and place both of his feet in my hand, or my husband's hand. Then we'd show him how to p-u-s-h his feet against my hand so his body slid up further towards the bedhead. We then showed him to tuck his knees up again, and I'd move my hand further up, and we would encourage him to keep pushing, showing him that the idea of the game was to make his head touch the bedhead. He loved it. Every time he'd push we'd say, "Yay!" and barrack for him, "Come on, you can do it! Come on, that's it! Not much further, nearly there! Go baby, go baby!" And then, when his head would gently touch the top of the bed, we'd erupt into cheers: "Yay! You did it! You did it! Hurray!" And he'd be so excited and laugh and bounce on the bed. And then want to do it again. He really did seem to 'walk taller' afterwards. I can't explain it, but it just seemed to answer some deep need within himself, and the explanation from Dr Emerson's

---

236    Emerson, W. (2001). Treating Cesarean Birth Trauma During Infancy and Childhood. *Journal of Prenatal and Perinatal Psychology and Health, 15*(3), 177- 192.

237    ibid.

> *article did make sense to us. The poor lad had being trying and trying for thirty hours to be born so, for us, doing this exercise was a way of letting him feel the satisfaction of success.* **Melissa**

Dr Emerson states that when babies face their traumas, and there is a response of empathy, compassion and understanding from parents and therapists, then lifelong bonds occur. The babies "internalise the bonding and attachment process, and exhibit it throughout their lives". He believes the purpose of treatment is to free babies and children from the impact of birth trauma so that they are able to "experience and express the love, the joy, the compassion, and the uniqueness that are their birthrights."[238] And from our experience, these exercises and activities can do just as much for the mother in reconnecting with her child.

You can explore much more of Dr Emerson's work in his published research article (linked in the references) about the idea of supporting your child to release the trauma of their birth, especially if it was an emergency caesarean. The article also outlines ways to make the experience empowering, gentle, respectful and supportive for the child. However, please read our note titled *'A Word of Warning'* at the end of this section first.

> *I have also played the birthing game with both my caesarean-born kids. The game involves them pushing off with their feet on the end of the bed and they birth their heads through something like hands to enact the work that babies miss out on when they are born via caesarean. Every time I pull a shirt down over their heads [and] I make birthy noises and say, for example, "Here she comes, yipppeee! It's a Maya, just what I've always wanted!" I do the same thing if I pick them up from the floor – I bring them to my chest like you would with a just-born.* **Leonie**

## Birth-like massage

As the baby passes through the birth canal, it is squeezed all over with rhythmic compressions and releases; this stimulates the nervous system, stimulates hormone production, clears the lungs and prepares the baby beautifully for its upcoming transition to the outside world. The baby's skull bones 'mould' (shift over each other allowing the head to become smaller), reflexes are activated and the nerve pathways are released at the base of the skull by the skull bones springing back open with the release of the birth.

---

238   Emerson, W. (2001). Treating Cesarean Birth Trauma During Infancy and Childhood. *Journal of Prenatal and Perinatal Psychology and Health, 15*(3), 177- 192.

These processes allow the baby to smoothly adapt to its extra-uterine world and have the appropriate reflexes and systems functioning well to support it to do the jobs it needs to do from this point on. When this process doesn't occur, a baby's external adaptation is not optimal and various body systems are commonly affected, especially the respiratory, nervous and digestive systems.

When Melissa's firstborn was young, she learned about birth-like massage for babies, where a caring adult aims to gently mimic the pressure of the birth canal, in an effort to replicate the sensations of a vaginal birth. She felt this might be beneficial for her caesarean-born son, from a physiological point of view, to possibly provide some stimulation of his nervous system, and also as a healing, connecting exercise for them both.

She says, "We would give him massages where I would put both my hands on the top of his head, forming a small circle shape. Gradually, I would bring my hands down, gently, over his face, shoulders, torso, keeping a gentle pressure on, right down to his toes, then off the end. We would say, "Ahhhhhhhhh!" in a downward sounding way, like going down a slippery slide, and our son found it very relaxing and smiled the whole time. It felt great to be proactive in hopefully triggering some parts of his systems that might have been 'missed' due to being born by caesarean. And it really connected us as there was lots of skin-to-skin, and oxytocin, and smiling, and positive energy surrounding the experience".

Note: Some mothers have found it beneficial to consult with qualified health carers, such as cranial osteopaths, who use gentle modalities to support babies who may have missed out on the benefits of this initial stimulation of birth.

## Birth-mimicking massage combined with a bath

This lovely story, told from a birth worker's point of view, shows how one couple and their midwife used massage and a bath as part of their healing process after an unplanned caesarean after a transfer from a planned homebirth:

> *Cat undressed (just wearing post-birth knickers!) and Jules donned his swimming trunks. The rest of us remained dressed and little Freddie was naked. Cat sat next to the pool, and Jules knelt at her feet, placing Freddie in the 'optimal position' for birth. Cat placed her hands low against her pelvis, making a small 'circle' for Freddie to pass through (this represented the birth canal). Hemi and I eased Freddie down through Cat's loving circle of hands, all the while massaging Freddie along his body in a rhythmically, squeezing embrace (this represented the uterine contractions and the squeezing of the birth canal), and Jules*

*'welcomed' Freddie into his waiting arms once he had been moved down and through the circle of hands. Freddie remained awake and alert, but never cried throughout.*

*Immediately following Freddie's 'birth' into his father's arms, Cat, Jules and Freddie climbed into the pool together and welcomed their beautiful baby boy into their family, as they would have done if he had been born in that pool. It was absolutely beautiful and I was amazed and surprised by how emotional I found the experience myself! I am often known to cry at births, and this felt like a really special birth. Cat's face was jubilant – and as she climbed out of the pool a little later, she looked into my eyes and said to me, "He's mine now. I feel that I have birthed him and I feel healed from his caesarean". Freddie was passed into his waiting Grandmother's arms, and there were tears and smiles from everyone present. It was a very powerful experience.*

*Cat and Jules gave me the honour of dressing Freddie, who was soft and relaxed. Up until that point, he has always laid with his legs straight out, but we all noticed how he tucked his knees in and had returned to the foetal position. Freddie slept deeply for many hours, and we all felt we had been part of something very special.[239]*

**A word of warning:** It can seem pretty depressing to look at the negative impacts of caesarean birth for the baby that Dr Emerson lists. However, it is important to know that the 'possible' flow-on effects of a caesarean birth are not set in stone. The mothers of these babies are unlikely to have been receiving any support or information that would enable them to heal from the experience. And many Birthtalk women find that changing and healing themselves changes how they relate to their children, which can in turn change how their children respond and behave.

It is also important to note that Dr Emerson follows the wider cultural belief that all emergency caesareans were due to an actual medical emergency and were unavoidable. It is important to remember that, sometime, this is not the case and the reasons for some caesareans are due more to limitations in a woman's support, care, labour management and the institutional requirements of the hospital.

239    North Surrey Midwifery Practice. (2010). *Freddie's Birth Story.* (Appeared in Juno Magazine, Summer 2010). Retrieved from *www.northsurreymidwives.co.uk/freddie*. Shared with kind permission from North Surrey Midwifery Practice and Cat and Jules, who run the Barron Chiropractic Clinic *www.barronclinic.co.uk*

# SAYING THE WORDS YOU COULDN'T SAY AT THE BIRTH: A RECONNECTION TOOL

*I have also talked to her about her birth and told her the things
I would have loved to have said and done if her birth had gone
the way I had planned. She sat with me and listened quietly
(not usually possible for her) and then gave me a kiss and
got up.* **Leonie**

*The problem was I didn't know how to bond. Birthtalk provided
a few ideas. I sat down with my son one day. He was still in
his cot from a sleep and I sat on the floor so I was down at his
level. I discussed his birth and explained the circumstances and
how much I loved him. I wasn't even sure he could hear me as
his ears were playing up again. However, he looked me straight
in the eye and gave me the hugest smile as if to say, "I love
you too mummy". It was the best feeling and a connection
definitely occurred. From that day forward our relationship has
strengthened and now, approaching five years of age, he is my
little buddy!* **Tina**

This exercise may be helpful if you were separated after the birth, whether
for half an hour or for weeks, or if you were too 'out of it' from surgery or a
traumatic birth to recall the first few hours with your baby.

We have heard testimonials from countless women attending our *'Healing
From Birth'* sessions over the years who have used this activity with their child.
They have shared how it has somehow, even subtly, shifted relationships.
We have heard on many occasions how it has lifted a lot of guilt and allowed
for reconnection with children of many different ages, from tiny babies to
big kids too.

The idea for this exercise originated from a story shared by Nancy Wainer in
her book, *Open Season: Survival Guide for Natural Childbirth and VBAC in the
90s.* She describes a series of sessions she undertook with a childbirth therapist
in order to further heal from her caesarean. One particular session involved an
exercise that was then followed up further at home with her caesarean-born son.
It is this follow-up aspect of the exercise that we have found to be very profound
for women in their journey; however, we will share the entire exercise to give
you a clearer picture.

Nancy was instructed by her therapist to imagine she was reliving the caesarean again, beginning with when her baby was born; however, this time she was to imagine insisting on receiving her baby. In her birth, her son had been removed from her to the special nursery, purely for routine hospital procedure reasons. She was told to close her eyes and imagine it was a gentle birth, where her needs were being respected and met. A doll was placed in her arms by the therapist, wrapped in a blanket. The therapist said, "Here is your child, Nancy."

Nancy writes, "I hugged him to me. Oh how I cried!" The therapist told Nancy that now she had an opportunity to tell her son all the things she wished she had a chance to tell him when he was firstborn, before he was taken from her. Nancy continues, "I began talking to him, and brought him close to my face. A while later, I opened my eyes… I felt so peaceful, so happy, so filled-up".

Her therapist suggested taking the process one step further and going home and doing this with her son.

Nancy goes on to share how she bribed her son with the latest Lego set (he was about eight years old) if he would just sit in her lap while she told him some things she never got to tell him after he was born. After negotiation, he agreed and came to sit in her lap. She began telling him all the things she didn't get a chance to tell him, and he eventually relaxed in her arms, getting "kind of newborn floppy". Nancy acknowledged that "something subtle occurred when I held him that day. A wound that had been opened eight years earlier was closing".[240]

**Melissa from Birthtalk shares how she adapted this beautiful idea for her own healing:**

> After my caesarean, I was separated from my son for around an hour – he was whisked away from me after being placed on my chest wrapped tightly in a blanket. I just got to stroke his little hand before they took him away. (He was completely healthy – just hospital policy). When I did get to see him, I was so 'out of it' from the long labour and the drugs of surgery that I have only a hazy memory of those first hours. It wasn't until much later (a year or so) that I realised that I'd missed out on precious moments that I could never get back. Then I read a book called Open Season by Nancy Wainer, who also wrote Silent Knife. Nancy talked about reclaiming those lost hours with her firstborn, also born via caesarean.

---

240    Adapted and excerpted from Wainer Cohen, N. (1991). *Open Season: Survival Guide for Natural Childbirth and VBAC in the 90s*. New York: Bergin and Garvey: pp228 – 229.

> *I wanted to try this with my son, so, when he was almost*
> *three-years-old, I crept into his room when he was just waking*
> *from an afternoon nap, when he was all dozy and cozy. The late*
> *afternoon sunlight was making the room hazy, and I just stroked*
> *him and started telling him softly, "When you were born, there*
> *were lots of things I couldn't say because I was very sick, so I want*
> *to tell you now". I just told him all those things we think we are*
> *going to say to welcome our child, "We are so happy to meet*
> *you. You are so loved and welcomed. You are so beautiful, we are*
> *so happy to have you in our lives. We love you so much, and we*
> *have been waiting to meet you". It was just magical – he went*
> *into a foetal position and just listened, and looked up at me*
> *with this radiant face – it was such a healing moment. And then*
> *he just matter-of-factly jumped off the bed and ran off to play.*
> *But I noticed a real lifting of heaviness and just a lighter mood*
> *between us after that.*

Melissa also notes that, while she did not enact the earlier part of the exercise Nancy Wainer undertook with the therapist, she did also take care to release these intense emotions before trying this exercise with her son. She says:

> *I must reiterate that it was very important for me to not take*
> *any of the intensity and anger I had felt about his birth into*
> *this moment. I did not want to 'dump' all of that onto him.*
> *Before I had this moment with him, I had been working on*
> *understanding exactly what happened, and had written letters*
> *to my son (that he would never receive) telling him how sorry*
> *I was and how sad I was for everything that happened. I had*
> *begun to understand how I had been failed by the system I was in.*
> *Of course, I had great sadness. And I was a bit weepy while telling*
> *my beautiful boy these lovely things I'd had inside me (without*
> *knowing it) for nearly three years. And when he trotted out of*
> *the room I had a big (quiet) cry on his bed. But it was extremely*
> *important that the only thing he took from the experience was*
> *the love I had and, yes, the sadness I felt. But I was sad because*
> *I loved him so much. This one experience was so healing. I did*
> *not feel such a gaping hole in the birth anymore. I felt closer*
> *to my son. It seemed as though a weight was lifted from his*
> *shoulders too. It was one of those special moments.*

Other women who have been separated from their babies for a myriad of reasons have also found their own versions of this exercise to be healing and to support them in moving forwards. Deb from Birthtalk shares how she adapted the exercise with her own daughter, who was born vaginally in an empowering birth, yet with a very challenging postnatal period:

> *I tried this experience with my daughter too. Although her birth was an empowering one, I was re-hospitalised at two weeks with retained placenta and then at four weeks with a uterine infection. On the first admission she came with me, but on the second one, I was forced (by the situation) to leave her at home with my husband and my mother-in-law.*

> *I thought I'd just try this exercise, because, as a very small toddler, she often seemed to be pushing me to see 'how much I loved her'. Her behaviour seemed to be trying to figure out just 'how far' I would love her.*

> *I put her on my lap quietly one day after naptime, and told her how when she was just a new baby, "Mummy had to go to the hospital because she was very sick". I told her, "Mummy didn't want to leave you, and it made me very sad not to be with you, but I was happy because I knew that Daddy and Grandma were looking after you very well, but I missed you".*

> *My daughter seemed to take this all in, and hopped down and toddled off and we got on with our day. But that evening, I put her to bed and as I was leaving her room I said, "I love you". She asked, "Mummy, how can you love me when you're not with me?"*

> *I said to her that I always love her, and when I go out into the lounge room I am loving her, because my love for her is always in my heart. Whether we are together or not, I'm always loving her. And she said, "Like when you were in hospital?" And I said, "Yes, I was loving you then too".*

> *She just thought about this for a moment, and said, "Oh!" And that was that. But I too noticed a shift. She seemed happily accepting of my explanation, her behaviour settled, and she did not try to test me so much anymore. She seemed more content, somehow. And I'm so glad that I 'went there', as it was like an invisible barrier had lifted.* **Deb**

It is important to be at a certain stage of your healing journey before undertaking this exercise. We suggest making sure you have explored your own experience to a level where you feel the intensity dropping. You might find it helpful to use other Tools for the Healing Journey first, such as *The unsent letter* (p468), *Writing your birth story* (p445), and *How do I tell my child about the day they were born? (below)*, alongside exploring any sadness, guilt or anger that has arisen. When an opportunity arises you will then be more prepared, and more able to say what couldn't be said.

# HOW DO I TELL MY CHILD ABOUT THE DAY THEY WERE BORN?

At first, it can seem impossible to imagine a way to talk about your birth to your child that does not involve you breaking down or falling apart. We want you to know that it is not only possible, but it can become a positive step in your healing journey.

The most important thing is for you to be able to make sense of your birth and to have processed it to be able to get to a place of greater peace. Many women have done this by:

- completing a *Birthtalk Breakdown* (p47)
- writing their birth story (see *Writing your birth story – a healing step* (p445))
- getting their birth records (see *Retrieving your birth records: how and to get them and what to do with them* (p437).)
- exploring and processing any feelings of failure or grief (see *I feel like a failure* (p227) or *I feel sad* (p245))
- Using tools such as *The unsent letter* (p468), *Using art as a healing tool* (p461), and the *Shifting from anger exercise* (p433)

These exercises can be healing in themselves, and also help to reduce the intensity when talking about the birth to your child, and give you a new perspective from which to approach the birth story. The following is Melissa's account of her own experience, illustrating the journey and processing that she undertook.

> It took quite a while to make peace with my experience, and to feel that I could talk to my son about his birth. When he was little, I dreaded the time I knew would come when he would ask me how he was born. I found it so difficult to talk about his birth without being upset, and I did not want him to think that I was upset about him being born. I just couldn't imagine being able to talk to him about it without an extreme level of intensity, and I did not want him to take on that intensity.
>
> But when the time came, I had actually worked through it to such a degree that I was able to talk to him in more of a matter-of-fact way. I had thought *at length* about how I would explain it to him, and it became part of my journey to healing.

*Some of the processing had to do with recognising a separation between my grief at how he was born, and my joy at the fact that he was born. I now realise they are two different things – that how I felt about the birth was no reflection on my love for him. In doing that, I released a lot of the guilt I had felt for feeling so bad about what was supposed to be the best day of my life.*

*He and I have had some amazing talks, starting when I became pregnant with my daughter, when he was three-and-a-half years old. They have often been difficult talks for me, but I have kept them matter-of-fact (or tried to) and answered the questions he asked, "Why couldn't I come out between your legs?" "Why didn't the midwives help me be born?" "Why didn't they know what our new midwife [for the upcoming birth] knows?" "Did it hurt to be cut open?"*

*I would often have big cries after the conversations (maybe in the shower by myself or in bed) and I am sure he was aware that there was a lot of emotion there. But I made it clear that although I was very sad about the midwife not helping me to get him down, I was absolutely so happy when he was handed to me.*

*I have told him lots of stories about how wonderful it was to touch his little hand when he first came out, and to hold him, and give him 'booby' for the first time, and how gorgeous he was, and how I was the happiest mummy in the world that he came to me. And that I was very sick after he came out, so he had to have cuddles with Daddy, and that I was sad because I had wanted to hold him and be with him, but that I was so glad Daddy got to spend some special time with him. Even though so much of it was traumatic, after working through it a lot I was able to remember the good bits.*

*I think the key for me was doing the work, a lot of work, so that I could talk to him without him shouldering the intensity of the experience, as I felt that was my responsibility to clear, not his.* **Melissa**

**Some things Melissa did to help heal, reconnect and process include:**

- Reading a book called *Birthing from within* by Pam England and doing lots of drawings. (See our section *Using art as a healing tool* (p461))

- I found it really helpful to write letters to my child (not to be read by him), about how I had wanted the birth to be, and how sorry I was that it was so different, and how sad I was that I could not give him what I had wanted to. This really helped me discover more about what I was grieving for. It also really reduced the intensity when I actually was speaking with him. (See *The unsent letter* (p468))

- When my son was five he was very ill for a whole year with severe eczema. When he was trying not to itch at 3 am, I would tell him about 'when he was born', and just tell him about the amazing feeling when they held him over the sheet (after the caesarean) and I saw him for the first time. I showed him how we would cuddle him and stroke him, and again whispered all the things I wished we could have said, and I told him how we would just look and look at him because he was so beautiful. It took me quite a while for me to get to a place when I could talk about these things. (See *Saying the words you couldn't say at the birth: a reconnection tool* (p421))

- 'Reclaiming' the birth by accessing my birth records and going over them with Deb also helped. (See *Retrieving your birth records: how and to get them and what to do with them* (p437).)

- Rewriting my son's birth story with this new perspective helped to make it more 'my' birth. (See *The healing power of rewriting the birth story* (p451))

**Conversations at appropriate times with my child, once I had a better understanding of my experience:**

> I remember, the year he turned seven, two days before his birthday I told him, "This is when the plug came out, and we called Daddy and Grandma, and we were very excited because it meant you were on your way." And on the night before his birthday, he was having a shower and I told him, "This is exactly what I was doing this time seven years ago – I was in the shower at the hospital and swaying and moving you down".

> This led to an interesting discussion where he said he was glad he was a boy because he didn't want to be cut open. We talked about the reasons I had the caesarean ("The midwife didn't know how to help me or give my body the time it needed, and I didn't have enough information to trust in my body"). Then he said he didn't want the pain of having a baby, so we talked about how the pain is different to normal pain and that it is good pain because

*it tells you how to move your body to get the baby out (if you are well-supported of course), and that it comes with some amazing chemicals that actually make you feel good at the same time, so our bodies are pretty amazing.*

*Then on his actual birthday, I said, "In one hour seven years ago, you were born!" and he said, "I wasn't born, Mummy, I was cut out." So we had another discussion about what being born means –that you arrive in the world –and again I sensed a lifting of his mood.*

*I guess what it came down to, for me, was to be able to have some real clarity about the reasons for his birth going as pear shaped as it did. I was able to get clear on all of this from a lot of debriefing, and learning more about how birth works best, and release myself from the guilt. And that came about from using all the healing tools I have mentioned, as well as having lengthy chats with Deb, who now runs Birthtalk with me, about what happened. There were so many steps. But each one gave me more understanding, and brought me closer to healing.* **Melissa**

For more about your child's birthday, see *How do I deal with my child's birthday?* (p261).

Melissa's story illustrates how many possible paths can be followed on the healing journey, and how they all have the potential to bring you closer to your child as the intensity reduces and the clarity increases. Melissa's story is not unique – many women have discovered that through focusing on their own healing, they create a new space where their child's birth story takes on a new light. This can create a fresh way of looking at the birth for themselves, and the possibility of a different way of sharing it with the very person who the story is about.

**At the time of writing this, Melissa's son was thirteen-years-old. This is her comment:**

*I feel totally comfortable talking to my son about his birth these days. This has been something that has developed over the years and began with my own healing journey, which led to a new understanding about birth, which was instrumental in my new 'take' on his birth story. He knows so much about birth now, and has a real understanding of why the circumstances surrounding his arrival were so different to that of his younger sister and brother, which were both empowering vaginal births after caesareans.*

*He has taken on no negative emotions, that I can detect, from his birth apart from wishing that his dad and I knew then what we know now, with which I heartily agree!*

*I had a chat with him while writing this book and asked him if he felt comfortable talking about the birth, and he was very okay with it, and happily sat with me to answer some questions. I asked him if he knew what happened at his birth. We haven't talked about it for quite a few years now, as it just hasn't been necessary. This is his response, given in a very matter-of-fact, thirteen-year-old manner:*

*"Basically, it was going to be a normal birth, but it had to be a caesarean for a reason I can't remember. And you weren't treated very well by the people at the hospital and I wasn't allowed to see you for a while. And they washed me, which meant that it didn't activate the hormones (for bonding and breastfeeding), and I went straight to Dad, I think, afterwards and I didn't get to see you straight away, but eventually you did see me."*

*I asked him if there was anything he wishes was different about his birth, and he replied,*

*"I wish that I didn't have to be washed and I didn't have to be born by a caesarean and that you were allowed to see me as soon as I was born, although I can understand why you weren't able to 'cos you'd had a caesarean and they needed to patch you up."*

*I shared with him that for some women who were at the beginning of their healing journey, hearing that he wished these things hadn't happened might be very hard for them, especially if they were still blaming themselves. I wondered if he could share, for their sake, whether he felt sad or mad, or something else, about it all. He replied,*

*"I wish these things hadn't happened but I don't feel sad about it. I'm not mad with you at all; it was obviously what you thought was the best thing to do at the time, and it's not your fault."*

*He mentioned that if he and a future partner were having a child, he'd probably want her to have a homebirth, but, "If it was a hospital birth, I'd make sure they didn't wash the baby afterwards so the mum could still bond with the baby properly".*

*Finally, I asked him if he felt his birth affected his life now. His response? "Nah."*

*My son has just left my office after sitting with me to answer these questions. I have tears in my eyes as I am flooded with emotion. I have a moment of tugging at the heartstrings, feeling the tiniest remainder of the massive agony I felt when he was tiny: the incredible guilt, the enormous grief, the question mark over his future relationship with birth due to this experience and, of course, his future relationship with me. I am consumed again by my love for this person I helped create, for whom I would do anything. I love hearing how his knowledge of birth in many ways goes beyond what my own was prior to healing. And I am reminded, again, of the powerful healing journey, which has given me this gift – to be able to sit here and have this conversation with my son. **Melissa***

# Shifting from anger exercise

*If feeling angry signals a problem, venting anger does not solve it.*[241]
**Dr Harriet Lerner**

Anger needs an outlet. Yet venting it towards someone can work in the opposite way to which we want. The following exercise can be so helpful in getting to the bottom of angry feelings in a safe way that does not require any input from the other party. It is based on the 'love letter' technique outlined in John Gray's book *Men are from Mars, Women are from Venus.*[242]

This original exercise was designed to move towards being able to access loving feelings about your partner. This goal holds true if you are working towards healing aspects of your relationship with your partner after a traumatic birth (for example, if you are feeling angry with them because you feel they should have rescued you in some way). The exercise can also be modified to use in situations involving relationships with others, perhaps a health carer.

John Gray identifies four levels of feelings to move from anger through to love (or peace in some situations following traumatic birth). He believes that, to find the loving feelings, we need to feel and express anger, then sadness, fear and regret.

We have adapted this technique to be used to shift anger in a variety of scenarios surrounding your birth, involving other people, perhaps including your partner. So we have called it a 'Shifting from anger exercise' as the end goal of accessing loving feelings may not be applicable when using this tool to deal with anger towards a health carer, where the desired outcome may simply be more peaceful feelings.

---

241   Lerner, H. (1985). *The Dance of Anger*, New York, US: Harper and Row Publishers. p4.
242   Gray, J. (1993). *Men are from Mars, Women are from Venus*. New York: HarperCollins Publishers, pp209 – 211

You may want to release anger towards any party involved in the birth, maybe a midwife or a doctor or even the hospital. Then, rather than moving towards feeling love, the goal would be, perhaps, moving towards feeling a release from the iron grip of anger, and gaining clarity and peace. The beauty of this exercise is that you can reap many rewards from the process, without requiring any action being taken by the other person. This process can take the power away from that person and be quite freeing for you, and can really support the healing journey. The process can also enable you to understand all of your feelings, resulting in being able to communicate with your partner (or health carer) in a calm and centred way.

Amid the confusion of emotions following a traumatic birth, it can be difficult to pinpoint our feelings. We can feel angry with the hospital, grateful for our baby's health, sad we missed out on so much, or regret certain decisions and all these feelings can be all jumbled up together. So this exercise is an opportunity for you to pull apart your experience a bit, and make sense of the swirling emotions. The ensuing clarity can be so helpful in many areas, such as explaining your situation to others and in understanding more about what you need to heal.

We do not generally recommend that these letters be written with the intention of being sent to the person in question. The process is often more effective if you know they aren't going to be read! So, write with abandon as the more you can get on paper, the less will be stuck in your head. Some people have chosen to share their letters with partners, but we would only recommend it if they have read this section of our book, and understand the purpose of the letter, and if you feel that your relationship is in the right space.

> *I usually did not give the letters to those they were written to, except a couple of times with my hubby. Mostly I used them to get the feelings out and get clearer, so I could then talk with my husband with clarity, or understand my feelings better. I also sometimes did this with the support of a wonderful counsellor.* **Melissa**

We have created a template (adapted from John Gray[243]) that may help you undertake this exercise:

> *Dear (husband/partner/health professional/child/support person/ institution or other), I would like to share with you some feelings about aspects of my birth.*
>
> *I am so angry that... (complete at least five sentences that talk about what you are frustrated about, annoyed with, angry over)*
>
> *I am sad that... (complete at least five sentences that talk about anything you feel disappointment over, hurt about, or grief)*
>
> *I am afraid... (complete at least five sentences that talk about what you are worried about, what you do not want, what scares you.)*
>
> *I regret that... (complete at least five sentences that talk about what you regret, or feel embarrassed about, or feel sorry about, or mention what you didn't want.)*
>
> *I am grateful/thankful that... (complete at least five sentences that talk about what you want, what you understand, what you appreciate, what you forgive, what you love, what you are thankful for.)*

John Gray suggests adding a postscript, letting the person know the response you wish you could hear from them. While it might sound a little silly, we have seen this section be highly successful. Melissa from Birthtalk shares her experience:

> *One time in particular, I was reading my letter aloud to my husband (while crying) and got to the bit at the end letting him know what I'd like to hear from him. He gently took the letter from me, and read that bit out himself. It was just so powerful and meaningful to hear him say – with intent – the very things I so needed to hear. He just hadn't known they had mattered. It was such a huge moment, and further cemented our love and our commitment to my healing.* **Melissa**

---

243    Gray, J. (1993). *Men are from Mars, Women are from Venus.* New York: HarperCollins Publishers, p.211

When writing to someone other than your partner, for example, you may find that writing 'What I'd like to hear is…takes the intensity out of needing a direct response from that person. It can feel almost as if they have said it – which can be very helpful when you are planning on communicating with that person again, for example writing a formal complaint. It can remove the feeling of desperation before you communicate with them formally.

John Gray's book, *Men are from Mars, Women are from Venus*, offers other tools and exercises that can be extremely helpful to couples at any stage of their relationship, and particularly in the crisis time after a traumatic birth. Indeed, the introduction to the book is a story about the week after one of John's children was born, detailing how he was trying to deal with the high emotions and intensity after his wife tore during the delivery and the substantial pain she was in once she returned home. He shares his resulting life-changing epiphany, which led to the research that ended up being his abovementioned book. You will find more about the love letters exercise in this book.

# Know your story

## RETRIEVING YOUR BIRTH RECORDS: HOW TO GET THEM AND WHAT TO DO WITH THEM

Many women who have had a difficult or traumatic birth retrieve their birth notes to help in the healing process, and in preparation for a subsequent birth. Going over your notes, especially with a midwife who understands that birth matters, can be very powerful in helping you move to a new level of healing and knowledge. At Birthtalk, we often support women in the process of retrieving and reviewing their birth records, and using the information to move further along the path in their healing journey.

> Birthtalk helped me ask the tough questions and to face the elephant in the room. I remember when it was suggested to us that getting the birth notes might help us in the healing process. I remember when we got them, and feeling like I had a live grenade in my hands (What if the birth was different to how I remembered? What if I feel it all again?). But when we had gone through them with Deb (from Birthtalk), it all made sense and, although it hurt, it helped us move on. **Sharona**

## How do I get my notes?

The following steps can help you get access to your birth notes.

- Begin by contacting the medical records department (or equivalent) of the hospital where your baby was born to find out their particular process for retrieving your records.

- You can try explaining to the staff that your reason for wanting access to your records is to be able to make sense of your birth emotionally. This might evoke a more helpful response from staff and allay their fears of litigation somewhat.

- Keep in mind that you have the legal right to access your records, but you do not own them. Your request for access to your records can be denied in certain circumstances. The healthcare provider can also determine what parts, and in what format, they will allow you to access them. So, during the retrieval process it is important to present yourself as being reasonable and calm, enabling the person you are interacting with to feel empathy for your situation to increase the likelihood of getting the best outcome for your request.

- Be aware that in many hospitals an administrative fee is applied. It is not uncommon for some private hospitals to charge a large fee and to suggest that for you to avoid this cost and to speed up the process, you request to have your notes sent to your family doctor. However, we have found that once this occurs, your records are considered the doctor's property and generally remain at their office. You may only be able to discuss it briefly with the doctor, rather than explore them privately, or with the health carer of your choice. If this option is suggested, you may prefer instead to thank the hospital, but let them know that you would rather go ahead with the initial request for all your records.

- Most women find it is worth paying the fee to be able to have the opportunity to move their healing process forward, and also to gain insights about their birth that could be useful if planning future births.

## What should I ask for?

When asking for your notes, you will need to request certain information, otherwise a brief outline may be all that is offered. To gain as much information as possible, ask for your full notes including:

- Progress notes
- Partogram (labour record)
- Theatre notes and anaesthetic record if you went to theatre
- Medication chart, which may be helpful if you received significant medication, or if the circumstances surrounding the administration of the medication or the effects of the medication is relevant to your experience
- Antenatal notes if there were any problems in your pregnancy or if they induced you for some reason
- Baby Notes if there were any concerns about your baby like a special care nursery or neonatal intensive care unit admission

## Now what do I do?

> *When my birth records arrived in the mail, I felt sick. I couldn't bear to look at them at first, shoving them in a drawer. I was afraid of finding out that I'd imagined it all, that there would be nothing in there that would illustrate what a horrific experience it was. And worse, I was worried that it would show that I was somehow responsible for things going so wrong. After a few weeks, I took a deep breath, brought the notes out, and began to read. And thank goodness I did. Going over my notes with Deb beside me interpreting and explaining, was a major turning point in my healing journey.* **Melissa**

Going over your notes with a midwife who understands that birth matters can be very powerful in moving a woman (and her partner) to a new level of healing and knowledge. It can also help with the interpretation of your hospital notes, which can be difficult to understand if you are not familiar with the environment of a maternity unit or the terminology, abbreviations and shorthand used in note taking.

For these reasons, we strongly encourage you to make contact with a trained midwife who understands birth trauma and can support you in this aspect of your healing. See *Appendix A* for suggestions on where to find independent midwives who may be able to help you with this.

Going through your notes with a midwife who 'gets it' can lead to meaningful education to further your understanding of your birth and to empower you for possible future births (yours or someone you care about). You might gain insights about the reasons things occurred. For example, you might learn why things might have been happening a particular way in your body. Or, you might discover what was happening around you, and realise some of these things might have been happening purely for institutional reasons. You may also discover options for future birthing: perhaps options you may not have been made aware of previously and, therefore, could consider if similar things occur in a future birth.

> *The greatest 'a-ha moment' for me was acquiring a copy of the medical notes for myself and my baby, and then spending time with Deb (from Birthtalk) breaking down what actually happened. It helped sort out in my mind what actually went on for the first couple of days we were in hospital. I felt emotionally drained, but reassured about what actually happened. Another layer of the onion had come off!* **Tina**

## Moving on

Once you understand your notes, you may have all this new information available to support you in other healing exercises. Using your birth records as a guide can be a great help when writing your birth story. See *Writing your birth story – a healing step* (p445). Or, if you have already written your birth story, the process of adding this new information from the birth notes can be another cathartic tool. It can enable you to really grasp exactly what happened, and feel very certain about aspects of the birth that may have had question marks over them. Some women find that this process of writing their birth story, especially with information from their birth notes enables them to reclaim the birth experience as their own, which can be an important step towards healing.

## Guess what I found out?

When one woman went over her birth notes from her traumatic caesarean birth, translated and explained by Deb from Birthtalk, she made an interesting discovery.

> *The notes said that I had dilated two centimetres more than I had remembered! My emotions moved from initial anger that my body had been working so well yet still I was sectioned, to*

*excitement to see that my body had not failed me quite as I had been led to believe. The courage and confidence boost this information gave me was palpable, and really paved the way for my journey towards my empowering VBAC (vaginal birth after caesarean).* **Olivia**

Birth notes can provide highly valuable information for planning and preparing for another birth, supporting you as you make your way towards an empowering experience.

## Now I know what to grieve

Seeing the progress of a traumatic experience in black and white can be a difficult thing. It may, however, allow you to pinpoint areas that you need to grieve and process to truly heal. One woman found just seeing her signature consenting to a caesarean was an extremely emotive moment. She felt it signified, 'the end of my innocence' and finally allowed herself to grieve for the trauma and pain that followed the birth. She said, "Every new aspect that I allowed myself to acknowledge and grieve led me closer to healing, and making peace with the experience".

## A note of caution

Sadly, some women find that their notes do not accurately reflect their experience (beyond mild discrepancies such as the order of events, timings, and who was present). Sometimes, there are large variances between what a woman or support people recall from the birth, and what the birth notes reflect. Unfortunately, this is a more common occurrence than most people expect. It can be a real blow to discover, and may lead to feelings of betrayal, hurt and self-doubt, with the woman wondering, "Did it really happen or did I imagine it?"

With that in mind, we share what you can do if you do find discrepancies in your notes.

## When birth notes are inaccurate

Errors in birth records can range from minor details being left out, to blatant omissions of important events, or even statements that are untrue. Reasons for these discrepancies can range from lack of due care, for example, the health carer being rushed with too many patients, through to pure negligence or falsifying records. Perhaps the health carer was getting confused between patients, resulting in inaccuracies. Or a health carer may have written notes about your situation without having really investigated it, for example, not taking the time to see where you were 'at' emotionally, and therefore documenting with a standard line, 'coping well', despite you knowing that this was not the case.

## What can you do about this?

The first thing we recommend is to initially do nothing that involves the health carer or you may create a situation where you feel powerless and reliant on a particular response before you can move forward in your healing.

In the first instance, it is more powerful and helpful for you to be able to work on this for yourself. Try writing your story with what you know to be true, collating your information from what they have written, from your own memory, your partner's memory or with help from anyone else who was there. It can be difficult to refrain from doubting yourself, but we encourage you to hold on to what you know to be true.

To deal with the emotions that arise, we suggest reading the sections *Dealing with anger* (p161) and *I'm so angry with my health carers* (p163).

## Rectifying the situation

If the events of the birth that are missing from the records are more subjective and reliant on a health carer's memory, it will most likely be a disappointing process to try to get the records adjusted, because most of the carer's memory of a birth will actually come from reading the notes. It can feel very disheartening and you may feel a lack of acknowledgement when they can't recall your birth among the many they see. This situation has the potential to unnecessarily delay your healing process further. It may be better to focus on what you can control and change, which is your own response to your birth and your healing journey.

However, if there are events outside of your birth records, for example, a blood transfusion, an admission to intensive care, signing for drugs, or even physical evidence on you or your baby, you may be able to use this information as evidence to get the notes changed. Proceeding with this is your own decision and may depend on the level of incorrect information, and whether you see the correction of these oversights as being essential to your recovery, or as important for the future health records of you and your baby.

The most important aspect of this process is retaining power over your own experience and your own emotional clarity, so perhaps sitting on the decision for a while might give you some space to work on your healing, and get to a place where there is less intensity involved in getting answers and changes made. Either way, you are working towards reclaiming your birth for yourself and moving on.

## A worthwhile exercise

If you feel ready, we encourage you to consider taking the step of retrieving your notes. The process of exploring your notes can offer guidance in where you need to focus your healing, and help you work towards making peace and moving on from a traumatic birth.

> *About two months after Grace was born I requested a copy of all my pregnancy, birth and postnatal notes, along with a copy of Grace's full medical file for most of her time in the neonatal intensive care unit. Why? I needed to know more about Grace's birth and to fill in a lot of the gaps that I had around what happened and when. I had been in such a daze for those first few days that even though I had a recollection of what happened, I needed to read through it all again and try to make sense of the jumble in my head. It wasn't easy reading my or Grace's notes. To this day, reading them still makes me sad and on some days, very teary. But at the same time it has been incredibly healing to read through them and when Grace is older, I'll be glad that she can look at her notes and know what happened to her and what was done from a medical point of view.* **Kathryn**

## Some useful links:

**Can I access my records from a private hospital or practitioner in Australia?**

- *www.oaic.gov.au/privacy/privacy-topics/health-for-individuals/
  private-health-sector-access-to-health-information/
  can-i-get-access-to-my-medical-records*

**How can I get a copy of my medical records? Who owns them, what does it cost, can I challenge a refusal to grant access in Australia?**

- *www.findlaw.com.au/articles/1086/
  how-can-i-get-a-copy-of-my-medical-record.aspx*

## How long will my records be kept?

If the records are about your child, then they must be kept for a number of years after the child 'comes of age'. This is different across the world. Further information may be available at the below links:

AUSTRALIA: Australian Government Department of Health.
State/territory general medical record retention requirements
*www.ehealth.gov.au/internet/ehealth/publishing.nsf/Content/*
*pcehrlegals-document-toc~pcehrlegals-document-app04*

USA: The American Health Information Management Association
*http://library.ahima.org/xpedio/groups/public/documents/ahima/bok1_049252.*
*hcsp?dDocName=bok1_049252.*

UK: NHS Choices *www.nhs.uk/chq/Pages/1889.aspx?CategoryID=68*

## What is the rule for health privacy and freedom of information?

The rules for health privacy and freedom of information can differ from state to state in Australia. For example in New South Wales, "Many hospitals and even some private doctors keep copies of their records much longer than seven years. The rule for health privacy and freedom of information is that if the health care provider has a record, you are entitled to access a copy of that record if it is about you. The exception is that you have no right of access under the *Privacy Act 1988* (Cth) to health records made before 2001."

Mental Health Coordinating Council, Mental Health Rights Manual, Part 3 Section H: Access to health records *http://mhrm.mhcc.org.au/chapter-3/3h.aspx.* Accessed July 2015

## What if I am being refused access or find my records are incorrect?

If you are in Australia and want to complain about accessing or correcting personal health information or medical records held by a private healthcare provider, such as a general practitioner, specialist or private hospital, contact the Office of the Australian Information Commissioner (*www.oaic.gov.au/privacy/ privacy-topics/health-for-individuals*). This agency can assist with complaints about access to health information, charging for access to health information, correction of health information, and handling of personal health information.

# WRITING YOUR BIRTH STORY – A HEALING STEP

*Writing my birth story gave me my birth back. Somehow, knowing the order that things happened in, and what was going on beyond my own experience, and expressing fully what was going on for me, worked together to give me the feeling that, finally, it was 'my' birth. At last. Such a massive leap forward, without even knowing that I needed it!* **Melissa**

*I have been writing my birth story slowly but surely and it's really helping a lot; there are some emotions that I am discovering for the first time by writing it down.* **Jodie**

The act of writing down a birth story can initially seem like a daunting task, especially if you have had a traumatic birth. It can feel too hard to take yourself back into that scenario, to recall the happenings of that day, and as though it might make things worse to dredge up painful memories. We understand – yet we also know that this process has been a powerful healing step for many women.

## What am I grieving?

When women attend Birthtalk for the first time, they are often a swirling mass of emotion, struggling to figure out where to start with their healing, and trying to understand what has happened to them. Often the details and the order of events at their birth can feel hazy, with confusion about timings and when certain things occurred, even uncertainty about what was said and by whom. Before they can begin to pull apart the birth, and before they can undertake a *Birthtalk Breakdown* (p47) to separate the emotions and the events, they need to know more about what actually happened.

Unfortunately, it's hard to pull apart something that has not been 'put together'. So we often encourage women attending their first meeting to consider writing their birth story, as an important early step on the path to healing. The process of putting together the factors that make up their birth often provides a new clarity that can in itself ease some intensity. The exercise also means that the woman now has her own documentation of 'what happened', and this document can act as an important tool for further understanding her experience.

## How do I start?

In the first instance, many women just write the story as it happened for them. They might start their story from the moment when their labour started or when their waters broke, or when they were hospitalised for high blood pressure in the last weeks, or similar. This can present itself as a 'stream-of-consciousness' type of writing, where the woman just begins, and follows the story where it takes her, not worrying about punctuation or grammar, just allowing the story to unfold.

Sometimes, it can be tricky to know where to start, so below are some questions to kickstart the process:

## Questions to help you get started:

How did your labour start? Where were you? Who were you with? How did you feel? Did anyone say anything that stands out to you? What were your thoughts?

- Did your birth start with a complication that involved hospitalisation? Maybe you can begin by writing about the complication, the options suggested to you (if applicable), your thoughts as you negotiated this, and the events once you were admitted to the hospital.

- What was the series of events that led to your baby's arrival, once labour had started, or a decision had been made about how your baby would arrive? Who was there? What do you remember feeling about the people present? What stands out to you about that part of the birth?

- Even if you are not sure of the order of events, just write it as you remember, as those details can often be checked up later and the story amended. For now, it is just an opportunity to get it all out 'on paper'.

## I still can't start

If some aspects of your story feel to 'big' to tackle just yet, that's okay. Maybe beginning with another part of your story might be better for now, until you feel able to write about anything that was particularly traumatic or intense. You might find it helpful to seek the support of a friend, your partner, a birth worker or counsellor to be there for you as you recount difficult events.

If you are having trouble getting words down, maybe you could just write about the part of the birth that is playing on your mind right now. It may be that the act of writing down this part of the birth that is really troubling you may open the gates for the rest of the birth story to flow out once you've started. You can focus on the pertinent part of your story for the moment, and write the rest of your story around it, perhaps at a later time.

If you feel that writing anything is too difficult, you could consider perhaps using a voice-to-text tool, where you talk and the device translates it into the written word. There are apps that have this function, such as Dragon Dictation, a free voice recognition iTunes app available for iPod Touch, iPhone and iPad. It may be that when you are free of the writing process and can just talk, the words may flow more easily.

## I've written my story as I remember it

The written story of your memories of the birth is incredibly important, as it is a representation of your experience of your birth. It provides important information about how you have recalled the experience, and what stood out to you. It may reveal your interpretation of snatches of conversation or your understanding of reasons for decisions of health carers. It may include your emotional response to events happening to you, and events going on around you. This information can be a vital clue for you and those supporting you, in understanding more about your experience. This raw version of your story now is available to you for use in exercises to deepen your understanding and shift you to a new place of healing.

## Now what?

Writing the birth story in freeform is actually just the starting point to this exercise. Once you have a basic outline of the events that occurred, it's time to 'colour in' the rest of the story. This step involves getting very clear about the order of events, and finding out more about what was happening in the birth outside of your own experience.

## Reclaiming your birth

After a traumatic birth, many women express feelings that the birth was not 'their' birth – that it belonged to the doctor, or the hospital, or the midwife, but not to the woman herself. This can be hard to express, as it sounds strange, yet really, it makes a lot of sense. Writing your birth story can be an important part of 'returning the birth to its rightful owner' – you! We call it 'reclaiming your birth' and it's important to know why this step can be so helpful.

## My birth was 'done to me'

Often, women describe feeling that their birth was 'done to them', rather than it being a case of them 'doing it'. This is an important distinction, as we have found both of those feelings have outcomes postnatally.

Having things 'done to you' in birth is a disempowering experience. It does not instill confidence in your capabilities or in your body's capabilities. It also does not acknowledge that you are the mother – the most important stakeholder in this birth.

Compare having birth 'done to you' with 'doing the birth'. In this scenario, the woman is the key player in the team, she is making decisions, working with her health carers and support people, being involved and owning the birth. This is how nature designed birth to be.

## How nature meant birth to be

Birth was designed for us to be 'doing it' in order to gather the gifts that nature intended from birth. These gifts enhance the discovery of our strength (physical and mental), patience, the ability to be flexible and to surrender to the moment – all important skills to have with tiny babies and toddlers.

It is important to note that feeling like things were 'done to you', or feeling like you were 'doing it' are possible in any kind of birth: vaginal, caesarean, drug-free, birth with interventions, homebirth, hospital birth, fast birth, long labour, and so on.

Unfortunately, having a birth where things were 'done to you' – even if they were life-saving things – can result in a woman feeling out-of-control, confused, frightened or even just like she wasn't important in the process. However, a woman who feels she was a key player and was 'doing' the birth, often feels strong, in control, important and acknowledged, regardless of what path the birth took.

If you check back to our definition of a bad birth in *What is a traumatic or bad birth anyway?* (p42), you can see that these feelings during the birth will have repercussions postnatally.

# Returning the birth to the woman

If you felt that the birth wasn't yours, then you are certainly not alone, and it is completely normal to feel that way. Most importantly, *there is something you can do about it*. The process of reclaiming your birth really means returning the birth to the woman. This can occur when a woman understands:

- exactly *what* happened
- exactly *why* it happened
- exactly *when* it happened.

This process can have a powerful effect on your healing process; suddenly, the birth becomes yours and it often seems to somehow mend the broken timeline and restore the natural order of things.

**This is a path we suggest in reclaiming the birth. It is comprised of a number of individual steps:**

- Write the birth story from memory, as outlined above.
- If possible, ask your partner or others who were at the birth to tell you their version of events, in the order that they occurred. Either take notes as they talk, or ask them to jot down the events that they remember occurring. If they are open to it, perhaps ask them questions to try and fill in any gaps in your story's timeline, for example, ask them what the doctor said to them before a particular decision, or ask them if they know where your baby was when you awoke in recovery, or ask if they remember why you needed to have a certain procedure. If your partner struggles to understand why you want to 'go there', or feels too traumatised himself to be able to assist you, this may not be the right time to ask for their help here. You can read our chapter about *Issues with your partner* (p291) to gain more insights regarding how to work through these issues, so that there might be a time in the future where they are able to share their own memories from the birth.
- Retrieve the birth notes from the hospital, doctor or midwife. See *Retrieving your birth records: how and to get them and what to do with them* (p437).
- Review the notes with a midwife who 'gets it'. Finding this midwife may take some searching – see *When health professionals don't get it* (p148) to understand more and gain insights into how to know when a particular midwife is *not* the right person for this task. You can also see *Appendix A* for suggestions on where to find independent midwives who may be able to help you.
- Write the birth story again using the birth notes as a chronological guide, and the notes from your support person or partner as an extra tool to try and get the wider version of your story as accurate as possible.

## Steps towards healing

Each of these steps has its own healing aspects, and can bring new revelations, new areas to grieve and new understandings about the event. Combined, these steps have the potential to enable you to arrive at a new relationship with the birth. It can become 'your' birth at last.

> *I remember writing my story, again, when my son was around three-years-old. This was not the first time I'd sat down to write on this subject, but I'd learned so much between sittings. This time, I worked with papers all around me – it was like doing an assignment. I had my original story written at three-months post-partum, plus my support person's notes from the birth, as well as my hospital records and labour progress chart. And what a valuable and empowering process it turned out to be. Bit by bit, I pieced together the true story of my birth, the one I had not fully known until now. As it fell into place on the computer screen, it somehow fell into place in my mind. And it became mine. I was not a helpless victim who had things 'done to her' quite so much. I knew what happened, and that was very powerful.* **Melissa**

## Postscript – birthing again?

The good thing is you will likely find nuggets of information during the healing process that will help you know more about what you *do* and *don't* want for any future births. Some birthing situations can be extra challenging, for example those considered 'high risk', when unexpected issues arise, making informed decisions against your hospital's policy or experiencing an unsupportive caregiver. Without certain information, it can be difficult to be a key player in an empowering experience – especially in our current health system and culture. You will find some ways to support you in setting up an empowering scenario for future births in our chapter *Birthing again* (p507).

# THE HEALING POWER OF REWRITING THE BIRTH STORY

*I have also written [my children's] alternative birth stories, writing
how it would have been if my wishes had come true for them.
This was powerful for me and I feel like some of the time I am
able to be okay with how it turned out for us, after allowing
myself to really sit in the fantasy of how I would have wanted it to
be.* **Leonie**

Sometimes, after a traumatic birth there is much sadness and, often, much
confusion over the reason for this sadness. It's hard to grieve if you don't know
exactly what you are grieving about. Using the following tool can support
you to find the source of this pain, which then can enable you to grieve and
continue your healing.

In the earlier section, *Writing your birth story – a healing step* (p445), we discuss
how creating a written record of your child's birth can be a great way to begin
making sense of a traumatic birth, and one that we recommend highly. It can
go hand in hand with the process of getting your medical records from the birth
and, together, these exercises can create a powerful healing tool. See *Retrieving
your birth records: how and to get them and what to do with them* (p437).

However, there is a way of using the birth story in the healing process that goes
beyond just writing a chronological account of the event.

## Using your birth story to explore, discover and heal

Before working through this section, we suggest undertaking the process of
writing your birth story 'as it unfolded' by looking at *Writing your birth story – a
healing step* (p445) and *Retrieving your birth records: how to get them and what to
do with them*.

This initial birth story can then be used as a basis for the tool we look at below.

## Rewrite history

Find a quiet time, when you have space to think and reflect. Before beginning the exercise, you may find it helpful to try and recall your feelings, hopes and dreams just prior to the birth. What had you planned for the birth? How had you visualised the birth unfolding? Who had you imagined would be there? What had you visualised or assumed would occur in the hours after the birth?

We know this is not easy, so go gently and know that it is an opportunity to heal, not merely dredging up the past. You are just using your knowledge about yourself to move to a new stage of your healing.

Now, try writing your birth story again, but this time write it the way you wish it had unfolded. See Melissa's explanation below for what this meant for her:

> *I had written my birth story a few times already: once three months after the birth, and then again two years later using my birth records and my support person's notes to get everything in the right order. I'd also explored my birth notes – going over what was written in them with Deb – and I had many epiphanies and important healing moments from that exercise.*
>
> *But this time, I was doing something different.*
>
> *The process of rewriting my story as a healing tool had been suggested to me,\* and that getting clearer on the birth that I had imagined I was going to have might offer some important clues as to why I was so affected emotionally.*
>
> *It would have been tempting to write, "Went into labour. No pain. Opened legs, birthed baby, felt great." But, to be honest, that's not how I'd thought things would pan out, even in my wildest dreams! So I just wrote the story as it happened. up to a point. Oh, and I decided to give myself a vaginal birth instead of a caesarean this time!*
>
> *I wrote the beginning exactly as it occurred: going into labour at home, and then the miserable transfer to the hospital via peak hour on the Sydney Harbour Bridge, and then the wonderful feeling of warmth and welcome I felt in the birth centre. I wrote again about the great midwife I had on arrival, and how safe I felt. I even wrote about the unpleasant midwife who replaced her. I wrote about my baby turning posterior, and the feelings of despair and desperation that brought.*

*But then – I got to the point in my story when the midwife seemed to put me in the 'too hard' basket, and did not acknowledge my distress or attempt to connect with me. My request to have 'no drugs offered unless I ask' was ignored. This was the point where I could see my birth spiral further out of control. So instead, as I rewrote my story, I invented this 'angel midwife' who came in and began supporting me. I could not believe the words that were just flowing out of my fingers onto the keyboard. It was as though I was telling a story that already existed. I described this angel midwife, and the words she spoke gently to me and the encouragement she offered, and her acknowledgement of my situation.*

*I wrote about how I relaxed, and found new strength, and felt encouraged to try different positions, and my support team felt renewed energy. Then I began to describe pushing my baby down, and out. I was astonished at the level of detail that was appearing on the screen – had I really envisioned it down to such fine details? I wrote about every push and every nuance of feelings within my body, and my emotional experience as well. I made note of what this fictional midwife said to me, of looking into her eyes and gathering strength, and pushing my baby out, inch by inch. And then, I wrote about that wonderful moment when I reached down and gathered my baby into my arms, and drew him to my chest.*

*As I wrote, I was sobbing great gasping tears onto the computer keyboard. I struggled to see through my tears, and wrote about those moments of holding my wet, gooey baby to my chest, and whispering to him all those things I'd not been able to say when he'd been whisked away after the caesarean. I wrote about the feelings of relief, exhilaration, exhaustion and contentment. Then I stopped typing.*

*And there on the page I saw so many lessons and messages for my healing journey.*

*I finally could see what I was grieving – not just a gentle, vaginal birth, but a birth where I was special, important, acknowledged, nurtured and encouraged. I had been given those things by my support people in real life, but never by the person from whom I most needed to receive them – my midwife in whom I had placed the responsibility of my life and my baby's life.*

*I could see where the gaps were in my care during my real birth.
I could see what to grieve – and that gave me direction. I also
received some wonderful insights into what I would need for my
next birth; I needed someone who would care for me like my
angel midwife did. This information proved invaluable when
preparing for my daughter's birth four years later.*

*Most importantly, this process of rewriting the birth story enabled
me to see that it was not me who was wrong – it was my care.
It became another opportunity to let myself off the hook and
forgive myself a bit more for something that was never my fault in
the first place.*

*Note: Melissa would like to acknowledge the origins of this exercise came from suggestions from
women on the International Caesarean Awareness Network chatlist, as well as Pamela Vireday,
who discusses this exercise as a tool in her article, 'Emotional Recovery From a Caesarean'.

*www.plus-size-pregnancy.org/CSANDVBAC/csemotionalrecov.htm.*

## Using the information

After writing this new version of your birth story, you may, as Melissa did,
discover new areas that need exploration.

Perhaps you might realise that you are very sad about what you and your baby
missed out on as a result of the care you received that separated you from your
baby, regardless of whether that separation was necessary or not. If so, you could
check out *I feel sad* (p245), and in particular the section titled *I was separated
from my baby* (p250), and then look in the *Tools for your healing journey,* to find:
*Saying the words you couldn't say at the birth: a reconnection tool* (p421) and begin
to work through this.

You might unearth some anger about what actually occurred in your birth
and need to express this appropriately, whether you are angry generally, or
specifically direct your anger towards your health carer or partner. You could
check out *I feel angry* (p161) for ideas on how to explore this aspect of your
healing, with sections including *I'm so angry with my health carers* (p163) and
*Anger about 'what happened' or 'what should have happened, but didn't'.* You can
see the chapter called *Issues with your partner* (p291) for ideas on dealing with
anger towards your partner.

You might gather ideas from this process about your needs for an upcoming birth, and begin to list your new understanding of what is important for you. This exercise can be most helpful in assessing the appropriateness of choosing a particular health carer, or in expressing to your partner what you will need this time around.

There might be other gifts from this exercise, too. Whatever they are, it can certainly be an eye-opening experience and one many Birthtalk mums have found useful as they work through and process their births.

# Self-discovery

## WHAT'S REALLY GOING ON FOR ME?

### Tools for gaining insights

Sometimes, it can be tricky trying to figure out why we are upset, or angry, or distressed or sad. It can be helpful to find ways to access what's really going on, to give you more opportunities to make sense of your situation.

Many Birthtalk mums have used the following tool as a way to tap into hidden emotions and beliefs, and awakened new understandings about themselves and their journey as a result.

### The art of self-discovery

Much of the following information is drawn from a book titled, *The Art of Self-Discovery* by Nathaniel Branden, one of the pioneering figures in the field of self-esteem. This book was written to show you "how to become an active participant in your journey to self-discovery,"[244] and we have found the exercises within the book are valuable as a tool for healing from a traumatic birth.

---

244   Branden, N. (1985). *The Art of Self-discovery*. New York: Bantam Books. (back sleeve)

The basic process of the exercises in *The Art of Self-Discovery* involves writing a minimum of twelve 'endings' to a particular sentence, designed to enable you to pick up on beliefs and emotions you carry within you. You can use these endings as insights to guide you towards where you need to focus your energy, or to help you understand why you are feeling a particular way.

As an example, let's say you just want to explore your feelings about your child's birth, because it's all a bit muddled in your head and confused in your heart. You might start with a sentence like this: "When I think about the birth I feel…"

Dr Branden recommends working as rapidly as you can and suggests that it helps to repeat the sentence in your mind each time before you write a new ending. He urges you to be completely honest, reminding you that you are doing this for yourself, so writing honestly will benefit you. He cautions that not being honest results in a lost opportunity. We would agree, as hard as it is to sometimes face the truth of a situation. He advises, "Don't give up and stop"[245] and suggests moving quickly to "outpace your internal censor and tap into your raw, unguarded, true feelings".[246]

Dr Branden believes that this process facilitates self-understanding and also self-disclosure, and we have certainly found this to be true. It can be quite surprising what unfolds and the great relief it can offer.

So, to continue with our example, it might look something like this:

When I think about my birth I feel:

> *Lost.*
>
> *A mess.*
>
> *Confused.*
>
> *Devastated.*
>
> *Shaky.*
>
> *Like I want to block it out.*
>
> *Upset that I couldn't do it.*
>
> *Annoyed that I didn't try harder.*
>
> *Worried that it means something about me as a person.*
>
> *Worried that it means I let my child down.*
>
> *Like I want to hold my baby and bawl for hours.*
>
> *Like I want to put up a wall and pretend it didn't happen.*

---

245    Branden, N. (1985). *The Art of Self-discovery*. New York: Bantam Books, p.63
246    ibid. p.61

Dr Branden suggests this process is followed with a period of reflection, which involves reviewing your endings and noting any patterns or developments you may detect. He suggests that you may wish to discuss how it feels to let go and reveal your emotions. He also puts forward that you may wish to continue an idea or describe a memory that has surfaced.

One Birthtalk mum shares below an excerpt from her private journal written in the months following her traumatic birth (a long labour followed by an emergency caesarean). She says, "I wrote this when I had little understanding of birth trauma, and no inkling of how to heal, as I didn't even know what was wrong".

The truth I have to face is:

> *I can't be a good mum.*
>
> *I failed from the moment of my son's birth.*
>
> *I can't be anyone to be envied or admired.*
>
> *I can't retrace my steps and change what happened.*
>
> *I privately jeered at other girls for doing exactly what ended up happening to me. I couldn't 'hack it' either.*
>
> *Not a good mum.*
>
> *Not even a good birther. I deserved a rough time, as I failed.*
>
> *I am a complete failure in my parent's eyes … in everyone's eyes.*
>
> *Nothing will ever be the same again.*
>
> *I am at the point of no return.*
>
> *No one can take me there. I have to go through alone.*

What was distressing for her about this journal entry is that she could not find validation for her emotions or her experience, so she truly believed that she had failed. In fact, she did not admit she felt this way to anyone. If she had access to this book, we would have recommended that she pick out the comments she had written that felt the most 'pressing' to address, and either (a) find sections in our book that relate to them and explore them further or (b) repeat this 'art of self-discovery' process to learn more about her feelings.

For example, to deal with her comment that, "I can't retrace my steps and change what happened," she could look at our section, *Why take the healing journey?* (p76).

To explore her comment, "Not even a good birther. I deserved a rough time, as I failed," we would suggest looking at *I feel like a failure* (p227) and *Why wouldn't my body work in labour?* (p230).

When she says, "I failed from the moment of my son's birth," we'd suggest completing another 'art of self-discovery' activity with this as the topic. For example, "I failed from the moment of my son's birth because…" This might reveal more about how she feels she is letting herself and her son down, and give her more directions to explore via this book, which would help to enable her to see herself as without blame, and that her response is a normal one in this situation.

## Processing with support

You may find it useful to undertake this activity with the support of a health carer, especially if you are nervous about the depth of emotions you may uncover. A counsellor or psychologist may be able to provide a safe space in which to go there, or to just bounce ideas off in the discovery process. Even if you work on the activity at home, and then present your findings at a support session, it can be helpful to know you have someone to share this part of the journey with. Just a warning – it takes a special health carer to be able to support you in this work. Many do not have an understanding of birth trauma, or even birth, so if you already have an established relationship with a counsellor, we recommend inviting them to read aspects of our book. At the very least, it could be helpful for them to read *The foundations of your healing journey* (p37), and then to read *What's really going on for me?* (p457) so they can offer appropriate support.

## Acknowledgement without judgement

It is important to point out that you may be surprised, or even shocked, at your thoughts and emotions during this exercise. Keep in mind that the feelings you see on the page are not necessarily an indication of 'who you are' as a person. They are there to give you guidance in where you need to direct your healing journey. They might give you insight about some myths you are hanging onto about birth, or some aspects of your birth that you have misinterpreted. You can acknowledge the darker side of your emotions, without having to see them as representing you as a whole. They might be representative of how you felt for one moment in time. Or they might be a signpost for where you need further information. Acknowledge them, even thank them, and know that they are merely insights that can lead you to say, "No wonder I feel so bad", and take steps to address and process whatever you find.

*Note: The book* The Art of Self-discovery *is now out of print, but is available as a free PDF here* http://happinesscounseling.com/The_Art_Of_Self_Discovery.pdf. *More of Dr Branden's updated work is here:* www.nathanielbranden.com.

# USING ART AS A HEALING TOOL

*Art washes from the soul the dust of everyday life.*
**attributed to Pablo Picasso, artist, 1881–1973**

*Art is a wound turned into light.*
**attributed to Georges Braque, artist, 1882–1963.**

One of the most powerful tools a woman can use in her healing journey is art. You don't need to be 'artistic' to use this tool. It doesn't matter if you can only draw stick figures and your pictures are wonky. What matters is that you are getting a visual representation of what's going on in your head and your heart. Many women have found that through this process they have discovered a wealth of information that has enabled them to know what to grieve, to know what to be angry about, to know why they are hurting – and more.

The powerful book, *Birthing from Within*, presents the idea of using 'birth art' as part of the preparation for an empowered birth, and offers examples of women's stories and their artwork. For some of the women mentioned in the book, birth art was also a way to explore their previous birth as a significant part of the preparation for their next birth.

At Birthtalk, we often recommend using birth art as a tool for women in their healing journey, whether they are planning subsequent births or not. We sometimes refer to it as 'healing art' instead, as sometimes it might not be about birth at all, yet still related to the fall out that can occur as a result of a traumatic experience, for example, impacts on relationships, feelings about self, or the upheaval of becoming a family.

## How can art help with my healing?

Pam England, author of *Birthing from Within* writes, "In making birth art or journaling, just bringing an image to light can be surprisingly revealing (and sometimes healing)… Dreams, reverie and art all carry messages from the unconscious".[247] She believes that the use of art can release us from the limitations of language, enabling us to express "details, affect and symbols that might never be expressed in conversation".[248]

---

247    England, P., & Horowitz, R. (1998). *Birthing from Within*. New Mexico: Partera Press. p. 32
248    ibid.

Maybe you are stuck in a certain part of your healing process. You might be angry although not sure at whom your anger is directed. You might feel sad about a certain part of your birth, yet not be clear on why it hurts so much. Some healing art might give you vital clues as to where to direct your energies, and provide some clarity about why a certain situation has impacted on you. There are endless opportunities within healing art for exploring an aspect of your birth or the postnatal period from a different angle, and further processing your experience.

## But I'm not creative

In *Birthing from Within*, Pam England reiterates that the drawings you create are not meant as 'artworks' as such. Instead, "Birth art doesn't have to be pretty, colorful or carefully planned. It is as raw, honest and spontaneous as birth itself".[249] This is a freeing idea – and perhaps different to how we usually travel through our everyday lives. Part of the healing process from a traumatic birth can be letting go of some long-held beliefs and developing new understandings, which can mean a new version of you may evolve as you heal.

## How do I start?

So – how do you go about creating a drawing? And what do you do with it once you have finished?

We suggest finding a quiet space, with few distractions, maybe when the kids are in bed at night, or if your baby is sleeping during the day.

- Invest in a few tools to enhance the healing art experience. This is not essential, just nice. You can do your drawings as rough sketches with biro on a lined notepad. Or you can pinch the kids' crayons and scrapbooks. Or, you can purchase your own pastels and a good sketchpad and hide them so they are just for you!

- Pam England suggests "entering a meditative, receptive sta te rather than a goal-oriented one"[250] to heighten creativity, and that "images which speak to us truthfully and eloquently surface when we are not trying to make them happen".[251] She cautions that "bringing an intention to create something fantastic or original, or trying to impress someone, does not enhance the process".[252]

---

249    England, P., & Horowitz, R. (1998). *Birthing from Within.* New Mexico: Partera Press.

250    ibid. p.39

251    ibid.

252    ibid.

- We recommend undertaking this exercise with the support of a counsellor or a trusted friend, or perhaps investigating 'Birthing from Within' workshops in your area to create your art with a small group of women with similar goals. (see *Appendix A* for details)

## What do I draw?

- Sometimes you will know what you want to draw. Other times, you might sit there staring at a blank page for a bit. Both of these scenarios are okay.
- If you have not done healing art before, perhaps you might start by drawing your birth, or a certain part of your birth. Just draw what you remember, what stood out to you, what you recall seeing.
- You can use words to illustrate your art as well, for example words to describe your emotions pouring out of a caesarean scar, or floating around your head.
- Let your hand choose the colour you will use – don't think too much about it. You might find the colours you instinctively choose say a lot about the emotions you are bringing up.
- Use a gentle hand or rough stabbing strokes – whatever is required.

## One healing art journey

Melissa (from Birthtalk) shares her experience with using art as part of her healing journey:

> One day I drew my birth story and lashings of emotions poured out of me, emotions I did not even know were hidden inside. I created a timeline that wound across the page – all thirty hours of my birth represented by this winding line, big ticking clocks, people gathered around my bed, me stranded on the operating table, and all my thoughts dashing across the page, just as they had dashed through my head throughout the ordeal. It was just a sketch with blue biro onto an old lined journal. It allowed me to see that – yes – it was a traumatic experience, and it had affected me more than I thought. It was a real turning point.
>
> I noticed that for a lot of my drawings, I was angry and dug into the paper as I drew. All the drawings I created were in red at first. Another time, I drew a close-up of my face in profile. My hair was blue, my closed eyes and sad mouth were blue, my skin was pale and washed out. I looked morose and dejected. It was exactly how I was feeling. Seeing it so starkly represented on the page shocked

*me – was I really that sad? And if so, what was I going to do about it? It was like an acknowledgement of it being okay to reach out and gain support.*

*One of my first drawings was a figure of a woman with no breasts. She was crying and her face was hidden. I chose a blue pastel. On either side she was hemmed in by blue waves. She looked trapped to me. My periods hadn't returned two years after my traumatic caesarean. I drew a bright red picture of my bright red ovaries, with my uterus between them with a big ugly black scar on it. I drew a black cross under my cervix, with the words, "No access to the outside" and "Storing the pain". Above all this, in big swirling red, I wrote, "Anger, Hurting, Rage" with a black sketch of a very small person curled-up saying, "Mama, it hurts," with red tears falling down the page. It still makes me sad now to see how much pain I was in then. But getting it out onto paper allowed me to see what was going on for me, and that it warranted addressing so I could move forward.*

*As my healing progressed, the colours I chose changed from angry reds, to gentle greens. Rather than stabbing at the page I was using a soft stroke. I began to draw ripe, pregnant women with breasts weeping with milk. Then I conceived our second child.* **Melissa**

## Does it have to be a drawing?

You don't need to limit yourself to drawing if there are other forms of art that resonate with you more. Art mediums other women have used to create healing art have included painting, pottery, tapestry, quilting and more.

GeorGina Kelly is a midwife and mindfulness practitioner, who runs workshops titled 'The Art of Mindful Birthing', and Melissa Fox is a mother who is passionate about empowered birth, as well as quilt-making. They have combined their skills to run workshops called 'Sew… Birth'. They invite women to "awaken your creativity to mindfully create a small quilted wall hanging as an expression of your relationship to birth: what is birth to you? Connect with your inner resources to birth. Cultivate awareness and acceptance around feelings and needs from your previous births. Celebrate birth as a powerful rite of passage".[253]

---

253    The Art of Mindful Birthing. (2012). *Flyer for 'Sew…Birth'.*
        Retrieved from *http://mindful-birthing.blogspot.com.au*, accessed January 2014.

One Birthtalk mother, Stacey, who experienced a traumatic first birth, attended a 'Sew… Birth' workshop before becoming pregnant with her second child. She reports the benefits of the experience, which began with a "safe circle in which women can be present and open to their beliefs, emotions, experiences and memories around birth".

> *The overall feeling is to move from darkness into light. The stone at the bottom represents my past birth hurt (with the yellow flower representing my spirited, beloved child) while the tree represents my journey – moving from hurt, pain and the need for control to acceptance, understanding and empowerment with knowledge. At the top of the tree, mind, body and soul are shown as a reminder that all of these are of equal value and are core to birthing. The extra flowers at the bottom represent our hope of future children, while the blue flower space represents the community I have found that has embraced me and given me strength. Finally, [are] the words that I sewed onto the quilt: in the stone is "Pain" and "Control", a reminder of what I am leaving behind, while in the branches of the tree are "Safe" and "Belief", which is what I am moving towards. My quilt is a reflection of my current space while looking forward to where I want to be. The process was both liberating and daunting at first. Trying to put all my emotions into one piece was a challenge, but I am really happy with the way it was born.* **Stacey**

Melissa Fox, one of the facilitators of 'Sew… Birth', says, "It takes trust, courage and willingness to go deeply into places of light and dark, plus perseverance to lean into your creative challenges and openness to allow your piece to unfold. I love witnessing the pleasure evident in each of the attendees at having created a stunning work of art, which holds such personal meaning for them".

## How do I use my art piece in my healing journey?

Your healing art often is like a window into what is happening inside you and can offer clues for where to take your healing path next. Sometimes, you will look at something you have drawn and the pain and emotion will be so clear. Then you will have a lot of information to guide you in the next stage of your healing, and you can work through sections of this book to help you.

If you discover that you have a lot of hidden anger towards your health carer, then you can go to *I'm so angry with my health carers* (p163).

- Perhaps you realise you have some unresolved tension between you and your partner. You can go to our chapter *Issues with your partner* (p291) and begin exploring.
- If you find that your art brings up a lot of sadness and you need to grieve, go to *I feel sad* (p245).
- If you are drawing your birth story and notice huge gaps, it might be time to find out about *Retrieving your birth records: how and to get them and what to do with them* (p437).
- If something else comes up, it may be time to write. Write about what you drew/created, how it made you feel, the insights you gained, the steps you want to take next. All of this will support the healing process, as you reach further into the pain and confront what happened, while in a safe space.

Sometimes, you may not be sure of the meaning of your drawing or art piece, and that's okay, too. You may want to just sit with what you have created for a bit. Or maybe that art piece is just a lead-in for another piece of healing art that will reveal more insights. You can try writing about what you have drawn, and see where it takes you. Or maybe you just need to close your sketchpad and walk away for now.

For more ideas we highly recommend reading *Birthing from Within*. Regardless of whether you are planning more children or not, it has some wonderful insights and asks poignant questions that can assist with moving to a deeper level of healing.

# THE THING IS...

I am aching to be heard
but I won't listen
to your logic
justifications
frustration
fear and anger
as I present myself
raw to you

did I give birth?
does it matter?
Oh yes yes yes it does
the thing is

I ache now from not
expressing the pain
of before

how to express my pain?
dance it out?
sing it out?
scream it out?
paint it out?

either way it needs
to be heard
I need
to be heard

and I can let your protestations
go through me
I will tell
someone else

*by Melissa Bruijn©1999*

# THE UNSENT LETTER

*Oh, I have written so many letters in this healing journey. And not one of them has been sent! They have been such a huge part of this path to healing.* **Melissa**

## Why would you write a letter and not send it?

Well, for many reasons, all of them to do with healing. The process of putting pen to paper (or fingers to keyboard) and composing a letter to someone involved in your birth experience can be very powerful in unleashing hidden feelings, exploring unspoken needs, and getting thoughts and ideas out of your head. The process of letter-writing has the power to change your headspace, alter your emotional intensity, unearth your hopes and dreams, and carve a pathway for new relationships. We also suggest you check out the *Shifting from anger exercise* (p433) as it provides a format for working through the emotions that can arise when letter-writing from the heart.

Following is a list of ideas of who to write to, and some suggested topics based on real-life letters written by Birthtalk women.

## To your child

Tell them the birth you had planned for them and let the grief pour out about how different their arrival was.

- Tell them all the things you wished you could have said when they arrived.
- Tell them what you've learned from their birth and the early days, the lessons they've given you that you will take into mothering them.
- Tell them what you wished you'd known before their birth.

## To a particular midwife, doctor or other birth worker

- Sometimes different midwives or doctors in the same birth have a different impact, so you may need a few letters here!
- If you were unhappy with the care you received: write how you felt when they spoke to you, what you wished they had said, how their comments or actions affected you, what you wish they had done, what you wanted to tell them (or yell at them) but didn't, the impact of their actions on your family.
- If you were happy with the care you received, thank them for their involvement, tell them what a difference they made.

## To your partner

- Tell them your hopes and dreams for this birth. Tell them how you imagined it would be. Tell them how you thought you both, as a couple, would face things.
- Tell them where you feel let down by them (if applicable). Tell them how you thought they'd be have during the birth. Tell them how you imagined it would be for each of you in the birth.
- Tell them what you are finding out about now, that you needed then.
- Tell them what you wish could have happened after the birth.
- Consider what it might have been like for them during, and after, the birth. Write about your desire to make peace, to move on, and to become closer.
- Tell them what's happening for you. Tell them how it makes you feel when they roll their eyes and tell you to get over it. Tell them what you want for your future together.
- See *Issues with your partner* (p291) for more ideas, especially in terms of moving towards connection with your partner.

## To the mother in the next bed during your hospital stay

- Tell her how jealous you were when you heard her laughing and talking about her birth to friends on the phone.
- Tell her how you felt when she was able to get up to use the bathroom, as you were unable to do that yourself yet.
- Tell her how envious you felt when she told you about her straightforward birth.
- Tell her how grateful you were for her understanding and kindness as you struggled to feed your baby.
- Tell her how much you appreciated her presence in the loneliness of the night.

## To your mum or mother-in-law

- Tell her how you feel about the comments she's made.
- Tell her how grateful you are for the help she's offered.
- Tell her what you actually need from her.

## To yourself

- Let yourself know what an amazing job you did in the situation you were in.
- Tell yourself how courageous and strong you are just to get through that experience.
- Give yourself the same encouragement and support that you would give a friend in the same situation.
- See *How do I deal with my child's birthday?* (p261) for more ideas on letters to write to yourself.

Writing these unsent letters is a valuable tool that Birthtalk women have used to explore and release strong emotions. Following are a series of unsent letters written by Melissa from Birthtalk in her healing journey. These letters were written across a span of a few years, and demonstrate ways her understanding of her experience evolved. She moved from strong guilt while questioning and blaming herself (in the first year) to bitterness and grief as she gained insights about some aspects of her care during the birth that had been lacking and how this impacted on her (in the third year). She also began to explore where she had received good care during her birth and the difference it made.

Please note that some letters may sound bitter and accusing, and that the end of each letter might feel sad and heavy and somewhat unfinished. However, each letter gave Melissa a chance to air her emotions in a safe way. Each letter was an opportunity to get these tricky and poisonous emotions out of her head and body, and onto a page. The end of each letter really acted as a springboard to making sense and moving on. Each letter gave her many insights to where she needed to go next in her healing path. She gained information about what she needed to grieve, and then took steps along her healing. She got more ideas about what she would need for next time as well. Each letter (and she wrote lots!) guided her further down the path towards healing and, while she often sobbed while writing them, she felt cleansed and more connected to her experience and herself with each one, and more able to let go and move forward.

# To my son

Did I let you down by not being able to give you the birth experience I so wanted for you? And for me? I feel I did. I feel wretched that there was not something more I could do.

I feel your arrival was surrounded by pain, confusion, fear, drug-induced stupor, deep sadness, intense feelings of failure, inability to care for myself or you and frustration at my weakness mixed in with awe at your miniature perfection. At your likeness to your daddy. At the way the pain went when you were in my arms.

The pain went, when you were in my arms. I clung to you willing it to all be 'worth it'. I despaired as you struggled to feed. Was it because you were drugged too?

The guilt is searing. What more could I have done? What affirmation did I not say? What deep secret of my past did I not uncover that would have allowed me to birth you the way I wanted?

I had planned for a gentle birth, soft lights, soft music, and yes, pain, but healthy pain. Not the gut-exploding, brain-searing torture that happened.

I had planned to breastfeed you straight after you were born, and a relaxed loving introduction to life with you, me and your daddy together in the big bed.

Instead, I was getting stitched up under the brightest lights while you met the world without me.

I wanted to be there so you were always with me. It was too soon to be separated.

Daddy held you instead, close, with your bare skin to his bare chest. I am glad that was the case, but I wanted to be there.

Did I let you down?

All my pain disappeared when they held you over the sheet, my little friend.

I felt disengaged from what was going on. I wanted to hold you, whisper greetings, stroke your little cheek, hold you near my heart where you will always live. But you were plonked on my chest, too close to really see you. You squawked bravely. I could see your little face but I wanted to hold you close and welcome you into a world of joy, love, peace.

Why did it have to be pain, confusion, fear?

Why is it still?

A year has passed. The grief is stronger. The acknowledgement of what I missed and what I was unable to give you has brought new sadness.

When will I be able to just live? When will I be able to give you love *now*, peace *now*? How can I settle this in my head so I am not the bad guy?

Can I possibly let it go?

Maybe I can start again, with a new year, a new city, a new understanding of my strengths.

What can I give you *now*? Peace, quiet, love, joy in my own life. They can only extend to you when I feel them myself.

I can let what happened go.

There will always be pain surrounding my memories of your arrival, but that pain has made me strong and given me what I needed most.

You.

**by Melissa** (*written around the time of her son's first birthday*)

## To my midwife

I hesitate to call you 'my' midwife, as I hadn't met you before the labour, had no connection with you during the labour, and no acknowledgement from you after the birth. However, you were my carer. I want you to read the birth story that follows this letter, which I wrote after two years of pain, grief, confusion, invalidation from others. I also want the decision-makers to see it, to know how they do not meet the needs of the women they profess to support.

I felt shunned by the birth centre (in Sydney) after my baby was born by caesarean – why? Because no one helped me 'cross over' to the birthing suite and eventually the operating theatre, no one from the birth centre visited me in the ward afterwards, and no one made any acknowledgement that I might be traumatised in any way. I was abandoned as soon as my labour was proving to be less than text book, and put in the 'too hard' basket.

Please read this to know what I needed. It wasn't much. Just a commitment to the philosophy you promoted. I believed that *you* believed women are made to give birth. So I naively expected you to have skills to help you support this belief. But you did not put yourself in a position to support me as you spent no time observing me, listening to my sounds, watching my movements. I knew you were busy, and there were other women there too, but when my support people told me – two years later – that you were watching TV, I have never known such anger. It took a long time for me to channel that anger in a positive direction.

Do you see what I am saying? This has affected my relationship with my husband, my bonding with my precious child – whom I loved from the moment I saw him, but felt stymied in my expression of that love, as I was so traumatised. This has affected my social interactions – I felt flawed, guilty for feeling so terrible about 'the best day of my life' and unable to move beyond it, as no one would acknowledge it.

Please read this, and think very carefully about why you became a midwife. Was it to catch the baby? Because you did not get that rush with me. Or was it to support women as they make the transition to motherhood? For that is what labour and birth are.

I trusted you with my life and my baby's life. And now my life has to deal with the fall out. Birthing is not something that happens over *x* hours in the hospital, and then it's all over when you leave. It infiltrates your WHOLE life.

I am stronger, I have healed, but you can see the pain will always be there, somewhere below the surface.

## Here is my birth story:

### My birth story

This is the real story. Not my earlier recollections where I am
stuck on the pain of those terrible hours of transition, and
grateful for the intervention. Yet so damaged and confused and
convinced my body didn't work, and that I had been 'saved'.

No. I am wiser now.

My birth story begins not with what I did, but what
THEY didn't do.

They did not offer me continuous care by the same midwife
and let me develop a relationship with the woman who would
support me as I birthed my child. Instead, they gave me a stranger.
A blunt, uncaring stranger who watched the tennis as I broke
little by little. Starting with my heart and moving down, down,
through my alive and active uterus. It was working, but she
abandoned it. She abandoned me, and I felt myself splinter into a
thousand pieces as my dream for a gentle birth was shattered.

They did not tell me my baby was posterior. It was not an issue
for them. A long labour? Well, they had methods.

They did not tell me how easy it would be for them to abandon
their philosophy when faced with a situation for which they were
unprepared and in the process abandon me.

The midwife did not stay with me, address my pain, feel it with
me, acknowledge it, honour it.

She was watching the tennis on TV while around me women
birthed and I saw death.

She failed me.

What did I need? Reassurance, confidence in my birthing body,
eyes to connect with me, and to honour the pain and listen to
its message.

That's all I needed. Instead, her fear fuelled that of my support
people and we gave in. They still did not honour my body's skills.
Is 9 cm 'failure to progress'? More likely it was 'impossible to
progress', given the way I'd been set up from the start.

I am angry and sad.

*by Melissa (written when her son was three, after many other letters had been written. She had recently found out that her midwife was watching the Davis Cup tennis series on TV during her labour, and Melissa had retrieved her birth notes, discovering for the first time that she actually dilated to 9 cm before having a caesarean).*

## To midwife #4 (of the five midwives who cared for me over the thirty hours of my first child's birth)

You were not ever really 'my' midwife, you were just 'the' midwife, who happened to be lumped with me. You were so young, only just graduated. Was that why you were able to connect with me, to listen to me, and really hear the fear I was trying to express? Was it because you were not yet jaded by a system that makes women faceless numbers?

Whatever the reason, you were the only one who listened. You held my hand throughout the caesarean, when I was so terrified and trying desperately not to get overwhelmed by the horror of having someone cut me open *while I was awake*. I begged you to stay, I begged you not to let go of my hand – and you didn't.

Finally, after thirty hours, during which I felt abandoned, that my fears were misunderstood and their validity queried, where I was manipulated, misled and suffered countless other indignities, someone listened. Out of all of the midwives who attended me throughout that ordeal, you were the only one I thanked afterwards. Because you were the only one who really looked at me. And you were the only one who listened.

*by Melissa (written when her son was around four-years-old, after she had discovered more about what women need in order to feel supported during the birthing process.)*

# Reconnecting with your body

## WAYS TO RECONNECT

*I did not project any feelings of failure on my husband; I saved those feelings all for myself because it was my stupid body, right? I just hated my body and was angry at myself for not being able to birth my son or breastfeed him.* **Skye**

*When I booked into pregnancy yoga classes with my second pregnancy, I rang the yoga teacher prior to attending. I told her that I did not know how I was going to 'be' in her classes, as I'd shut myself off from my body since my first birth (a traumatic experience ending in caesarean) four years earlier. I hated my body for a long time after my first birth, and blamed it for doing a 'bad job'. I sobbed my way through every single yoga session as I reconnected with my body, and found new strength. I took this strength to my homebirth vaginal birth after caesarean a few months later.* **Melissa**

*I had trouble breastfeeding and bonding with my baby. I just felt like a failure. I also had this feeling that something wasn't quite right with my body. I kept getting infections and it felt like my body kept letting me down.* **Trudy**

> *My body just felt – jarred. Like I'd been shaken repeatedly and
> dropped to the floor. It's really hard to explain, but I felt like
> I hadn't been put back together properly after my caesarean. It just
> felt like my insides were all jumbled up and a bit in the 'wrong
> order'. It was a really uneasy feeling.* **Melissa**

Women often speak about their disconnection from their bodies in the weeks,
months and years after a traumatic birth. Many express their hatred for their
own body, calling it 'stupid', and blaming their body for letting them down.

Part of the healing journey can be reconnecting with your physicality.
We suggest two ways this is possible:

Read and process the various chapters in this book on your path to healing.
This process can release your body from blame as your understanding grows
and you learn more and explore what was at play in your experience. As you
process your birth, your stress levels may be reduced, meaning your body may
feel more relaxed for the first time in a long while. Even this feeling of relaxation
can be enough to allow reconnection with your body.

Undertake exercises specifically focused on reconnecting with your body to help
the healing process, which is where this section comes in.

## Get some answers

Do you know exactly what happened in your birth? Could you be blaming your
body for things that are quite possibly not its fault?

If you are directing high levels of blame towards your body, you may want
to read *Why wouldn't my body work in labour?* (p230) to get some more ideas
about what your body was coping with, and why it perhaps did not do as you
expected. Then come back to this section for ideas on reconnecting.

- Have a look at *Retrieving your birth records: how and to get them and what
  to do with them* (p437), as this process can give you many insights into the
  situation that your body and mind were challenged with while birthing, or
  even show you just how much work your body was actually doing.

## Get some nurturing

When your baby is hurting what do you do? Hold him, stroke him, soothe
him – let him know that you are there for him? Well, you are hurting now –
and you need the same thing. It can be really beneficial to receive some positive
sensations in your body again.

## Massage

There are many professional massage therapists who, if you explain your situation, would likely be very caring and sensitive. There are even postnatal massage therapists who specialise in supporting women after birthing. You can tell them you had a traumatic birth and need to feel some good feelings in your body again. Ask for a gentle touch – some women find that postnatally they cannot bear a firm touch in a massage; it's just too much sensation.

Lemise Kassim, a massage therapist who specialises in pregnancy, baby and postnatal massage, says,

> *Touch can be a wonderful way to heal the traumas. Massage can address specific problems associated with the postnatal body, and following stressful birth is a 'must'. A woman can reconnect with her physical body, enabling her to feel less detached, and more accepting. The loving touch of another helps her to feel nurtured and accepted, too. A great time to reflect, release emotions and process all that has gone on. The hour will fly by, but it is a whole hour of self nurturing, very important for regaining self-esteem and as part of the healing process. It is used for all kinds of birth experiences, and an experienced therapist will be adaptable to physical needs.* **Lemise Kassim**

It may seem difficult, at first, to trust someone with your body after a bad birth, and that's okay. Perhaps start with just a head and shoulders massage, or even a massage seated in a chair, if you feel that lying on a massage table 'takes you back'. The important thing is to feel good sensations in your body, and to experience being nurtured.

## Massage as part of therapy

Some counsellors or therapists offer massage or bodywork as part of the healing session or therapy. This approach can be beneficial for a number of reasons including, for some, simply experiencing being on a table without feeling disempowered or traumatised.

> *My counsellor was also a massage therapist and osteopath, and we had sessions 'listening' to my body to see what came up. Once she was gently massaging my belly, and I felt this deep strangled voice bubble up from within and say to her, very loudly, "STOP. STOP IT RIGHT NOW!" It shocked both of us, and she immediately took her hands off. She asked me what it was about,*

*and I realised that her massage took me back to when I was on the operating table during my caesarean, and they were pulling and tugging to get my baby out. I remembered being rocked back and forth, and wanting to grip the sides of the table. It felt so violent; even though I was numb, I could still feel my whole body rocking with the force of the tugging. I'd completely forgotten that. She asked me what I needed, and I said I felt like I need to be held together, that I'd been put back together 'wrong'. So she just held my belly together, gently yet firmly, and it felt so good. Like I was running the show now, and my body was being cared for and I was being listened to. Tears streamed down my face as more healing took place.* **Melissa**

*Another time, my counsellor was massaging my feet when I mentioned to her that ever since my caesarean, I felt like I couldn't 'feel' my feet. It was strange really, like if I stubbed my toe or something, it hurt – but when I was walking around, my feet felt numb. She again asked what I needed, and I said that I just needed my feet massaged. She obliged and as I lay there, I began to recall the horrible feeling when I received my epidural. I remembered that feeling like ice water being poured into my legs, and then that moment when I realised that I couldn't get up and leave – I was paralysed. I remembered the feeling of panic that if something happened, I couldn't just get up and run. I was stuck, and completely at the mercy of strangers. I'd forgotten that too. As my counsellor massaged, I sobbed and told her about my recollections, and we discussed how scary that must have been. She asked a few times if she could stop massaging yet, and I said no – my poor feet felt like they were just coming alive. Eventually I said that was enough, and I could feel my feet again. I really felt some shifts that day.* **Melissa**

## Yoga

Yoga can do wonders for a disconnected body, even if only because you are focused on your body, and nothing else during the session, which is rarely possible in daily life as a mum.

In many cities there are mother and baby postnatal yoga classes available if your little one is still small or regular yoga sessions if your child is old enough to be left with a trusted carer. Even using a Wii or a yoga DVD are options to receive instructions in yoga techniques, without having to leave the house.

Suzanne Swan, Director of *Yogababy.com.au*, says,

> *Yoga means to unite mind and body. It is well understood that*
> *past traumatic experiences are held as memories in the mind/body*
> *and may have been stored away from view for survival. Practising*
> *mind/body centring approaches like yoga can help to unravel*
> *past trauma without having to talk it out. Being asked while in a*
> *yoga posture to direct your attention and breathe into an area of*
> *'tension or numbness' is a gentle approach to healing. Emotions*
> *stored in the body may release slowly as it is given an opportunity*
> *to continue the healing process that was previously interrupted:*
> *you may find yourself close to tears, crying, sweating, shaking,*
> *trembling and even yawning may arise.* **Suzanne Swan**

Jan, whose first birth was traumatic and was attending Yogababy in preparation
for her second birth, shares her experience of being in Suzanne's Active Birth
Yoga session:

> *Almost as soon as we began doing movements focused on the*
> *pelvis, in particular circular movements, I became aware of*
> *how different my two sides felt. I could move easily and freely*
> *through the right side, while the left side felt 'out of bounds'*
> *somehow. There was no pain, just a subtle resistance to 'go there'.*
> *Since the aim of the movement was to free the pelvis, I persisted*
> *and breathed as I rolled into the left side. Almost immediately*
> *tears began to flow uncontrollably and I had flashbacks of*
> *my first birth, the feeling of having been assaulted by medical*
> *intervention. As we continued with the pelvis-focused exercises,*
> *I began to get an image of the cellular memory as being almost*
> *like a sack of fluid that had been tucked away deep in my body.*
> *Once I had opened it, I knew I had to deal with it to enable me*
> *to have a different experience for my second birth. I had a very*
> *powerful healing during the active birth yoga class, which not*
> *only healed my first birth on a deep level, but prepared me to*
> *have a very different and empowering birth experience only a*
> *few weeks later.* **Jan**

## Connecting with nature

After a traumatic birth, we can feel frantic, life can feel hectic, and anxiety levels can be high. All this causes our body to tense up, and we can feel numb, both physically and emotionally. Making contact with the natural world can alleviate these feelings, as you begin to move with nature's rhythms and sounds, which are slower, pleasingly irregular, and soothing. When you are out in nature, you might find using the following tool helps you to become attuned to the world around you.

## Entering the now

Challenge yourself to hear five different sounds around you – there might be the sound of children laughing, a dog barking, a plane flying overhead, the breeze rustling through the trees, some birds calling to each other. The act of focusing on these things brings you into the 'now' and takes you out of your head. You can increase your awareness of some positive things happening right in this moment. You can then expand this exercise to focus on five things happening in your body right now. For example, my tummy is tight, my back is sore, my leg is itchy. This can bring your body into your awareness, and allow for some initial connection when you are feeling more relaxed.

## Some great ways to connect with nature:

- visiting the beach, especially early in the morning and late in the afternoon for a beach walk. You can time your walk to match your baby's tired time, and pop them in a sling or wrap, and just wander along the shoreline.
- going to your local park. If there is a playground or park area where there are lots of trees, just enjoy being outdoors, notice the sky, the way the wind moves the trees, listen to birdlife.
- going for a walk with your baby or child. Just take your time, pop them in a sling or backpack so they can be near you, and begin to notice the feeling of air on your face, how strong your legs are, carrying you along, the feeling of your heart pumping strongly in your chest as you walk, and you might begin to connect with your body's alive-ness and energy.
- sitting in your own backyard and do the *Entering the now* exercise (above). You may be surprised at the goings-on right on your doorstep.

# MAKING PEACE WITH YOUR CAESAREAN SCAR

## Brave Woman

I am so brave
I allowed a stranger
to slice me open
and move my organs
and bring me my child

I lay quietly while
they toyed with my life
my future
my baby

I focused and thought
not of what was occurring
but I got through it
calmly
quietly waiting

I chose to live
Brave Woman

I chose life
genitals intact
scarred belly
alive alive

I can't hear you saying
"so what"

Brave Woman
facing death
facing disfigurement
finding life
and joy
and heartache

Brave Woman
I chose life
I chose to put
my body in the hands
of a gentle
kind stranger

Brave Brave Woman

slice me open
give me my son

and now
life has begun
for two

sacred scar that
heralds your
point of entry

not my badge of failure

my mark of courage
and strength
Brave Woman
I survived
I am alive

*by Melissa Bruijn©2000*

If you had a caesarean, the scar can be a constant reminder of your traumatic experience. It can be hard to look at it, to touch it, and it can become a source of much body-hate. However, the process of making peace with your scar is possible. This acceptance may occur naturally over time if you are undertaking a healing journey with the help of this book. Some women notice that, while working on processing their birth, they have new insights that change the way they think about their whole experience. However, there are some things you can do to specifically focus on facing and embracing this new permanent part of your body.

## Facing your scar

Some women begin making peace with their caesarean scar by simply looking at it in the mirror. For some women, this is intensely painful. If you do try this approach, go easy with yourself. Rather than responding to the emotions that arise, perhaps try just observing them. What feelings come up for you? Sorrow, anger, despair, disgust, distaste, shame, failure, pride, awe, gratitude? All of these feelings are okay, and all of this is really valuable information. It is your starting place for healing.

## Keeping a journal

After facing your scar, perhaps journal about 'what you see' and 'how you feel about what you see'. This might give you some ideas about where your pain lies, and where you need to focus.

For example, one woman's journal might read, "I see a woman cut in half. I see a slur on my previously uncut body. I see a failure". And this can lead to an understanding about why she feels so bad about her scar, and also why these emotions are colouring her life. She could then address these feelings by using the tools we outline in *Self-discovery: what's really going on for me?* (p457) Perhaps she could gain further insights about what's going on for her by completing sentences like:

- My scar is a sign of failure because…
- If my body is cut then that means…
- Then explore what comes up. She may, for example, discover that she feels like she will not be beautiful anymore if she has this scar. She could think about how she can redefine her ideas around beauty, perhaps by looking at how her child sees her 'as she is' and still loves her wholeheartedly. Exposing these emotions can lead to understanding and healing.

## Drawing

You could try using healing art to draw how you see yourself post-caesarean. See the section *Using art as a healing tool* (p461) for more information. Then perhaps try drawing yourself how you'd like to be. This might bring up some insights into what steps you could take to become that person. If that person you would like to be is unattainable (e.g. a woman with no scar who had a two-hour, painless labour), then that needs to be acknowledged and 'let go' so you can move on.

## Caring for your scar

Although you may find your scar hard to look at, and especially difficult to touch, the process of rubbing moisturising cream into it daily can be helpful in a number of ways:

- It keeps the area soft and supple.
- Some women have found it is less inclined to be itchy in the months after the birth when moisturised.
- It encourages a focus on nurturing and kindness towards your physical self.
- It can create an opportunity to connect with the emotions surrounding the experience and to get in touch with the pain.

You can try saying affirmations in your mind as you smooth cream onto your scar, such as:

- "Thank you for allowing my baby to emerge safely."
- "My scar is strong and supple."
- "My scar is a sign of my strength and courage and I acknowledge these in me."

This can all help in the process of making peace with your scar.

Footnote: We wanted to make a comment regarding Melissa's poem about the caesarean scar. This was written in the very early stages of her healing, when she was struggling to accept her caesarean scar. It's important to note that Melissa's line in the poem about her 'intact genitals and scarred belly' is a wry nod to her prenatal fears about tearing in the perineum. When she wrote this poem, she felt having intact genitals in no way made up for the impact of a caesarean. We feel it's important for women to know, also, that undisturbed and well-supported vaginal birth often does not lead to injury to the perineum or vagina. Melissa has gone on, with a whole new set of information and new health carers with a different philosophy of birth, to have two vaginal births, both bigger babies than her caesarean baby, without injury to this area of her body.

Note: Melissa would like to acknowledge the origins of this exercise as coming from suggestions from women of the Homebirth After Caesarean International Caesarean Awareness Network chatlists, as well as Pamela Vireday, who discusses this as a tool in her article, "Emotional Recovery from a Caesarean"

*www.plus-size-pregnancy.org/CSANDVBAC/csemotionalrecov.htm.*

# REDEFINING STRENGTH

Sometimes after a traumatic birth, the last thing a woman feels is that she was strong. She more often feels like a failure, as though she has been 'run over', shocked, confused and vulnerable. Or she might know she was strong, but finds that this strength is not recognised by others, as they are judging her strength by different yardsticks (for example, by whether she had a vaginal birth, or a homebirth, or whether she 'coped' with a caesarean well).

We meet so many incredibly strong women at our *'Healing From Birth'* meetings – women who have been subjected to some extraordinarily challenging situations in their path to meeting their child. Yet they do not feel that they have been strong, when they first attend. During their time with Birthtalk, we have seen them grow to recognise their own strength and courage as they gain knowledge and understanding, and perhaps see themselves in a different light as we hold up a mirror to them and say, "There you are – you were so strong going through all that. We think you are amazing".

## Strength comes in many different forms

'Being strong' in birth can sometimes have little to do with just 'gutsing it out' and not having pain relief. Strength can be illustrated by making difficult decisions in the face of an unexpected situation, and focusing on just getting through the experience. Strength can be seen when a woman is exposed and vulnerable, without her support team, and being asked to consent to a procedure because she is told it will be in her baby's best interest. Strength can be witnessed when seeing a heavily pregnant woman walking into the hospital, terrified, yet still walking, knowing she is having major surgery to meet her baby that day.

## What makes a strong, birthing woman?

In our section *I had a homebirth transfer* (p375) we discuss the issue of the 'Birthing Goddess', and how some women are anticipating being this amazing, strong, birthing woman in their birth. But when the birth takes a vastly different path to that they planned, these plans and ideals can come crashing to the ground.

> *Almost exactly a year after my first child's birth – a traumatic,*
> *long labour, ending in caesarean – some close friends of ours had*
> *their first baby. The new mother called personally, on the day*

*after the birth, and shared with me about her short, drug-free
labour and natural birth. She did so without bragging or boasting
– merely sharing when I asked how the birth went. My head was
reeling with envy and my heart was twisted with grief, and I heard
myself blurt out, "Wow – you are a birthing goddess!" I was
mortified that I had let it slip out like that, and confused by my
response. Because obviously I thought that I wasn't a goddess.
And that was tied in to feeling I'd been weak rather than strong
in my birth, because I'd had a caesarean. Yet, 'til then, I hadn't
realised I felt this way.* **Selina**

If you feel that you have struggled with this issue too, here is adapted text from
what we wrote in *I had a homebirth transfer* (p375):

It can be a big step to reassess what 'being a birthing goddess' means, and
perhaps take the definition wider. It might be beneficial to actually write down
what you believe it means to be a strong birthing woman. It may be that you
believe this woman is someone who births her own child, under her own steam,
without intervention. Well, that's one kind of strong, birthing woman – and
if that's your definition then it would be easy to feel like a failure if things go
differently in your birth. But does it need to be the only definition?

Is there a possibility that a strong, birthing woman is any woman who grows
a baby and does what needs to be done, even at a cost to herself, to see this
child arrive earthside? By this definition, we have met many, many birthing
goddesses. Some have birthed in hospital, some at home, some on the roadside,
some with epidurals on board, some via caesarean, some via caesarean with
general anaesthetic. These strong birthing women are amazing. They may
make incredibly difficult decisions, they may labour long and hard, they may
go through immense pain (physical and emotional) and they are required to
make decisions while completely vulnerable. This, to us, is an amazing, strong,
birthing woman.

## Was I strong?

*So much of how I felt about Leo's arrival and the early
postpartum period with all the feeding problems we had, was
about feeling like a failure and weak, and wondering why was
something everyone else seemed to have no problems with,
so hard for me? What was wrong with me that I found it
overwhelming and felt so desolate? Whereas, now, I see it quite
differently. Instead, I realise how strong I was at that time – strong
to cope with the frightening way Leo arrived, strong to deal with*

> *the aftermath of the surgery both physically and emotionally,
> and strong to cope with the really tough first weeks with feeding
> problems when I felt useless.* **Ciara**

A good exercise for expanding or redefining your perception of what strength in birth is comes from the popular blog *Birth Without Fear*. The blog presents a regular segment where they invite women to submit their stories, beginning with the sentence, "I am strong because…" We love this idea, as it illustrates ways that women are strong in a wide variety of birthing situations, and takes our thinking beyond traditional definitions of strength in birth.

How were you strong in your birth? Were you strong because you endured an induction without emotional support from your carers? Were you strong because you needed a caesarean due to pre-eclampsia and were rushed into theatre without your partner present? Were you strong because you got through a very intense, very fast birth that left you shell-shocked and holding a baby before you really knew what was happening?

Maybe there were steps all along your path to meeting your baby where you were strong. We encourage you to create your own private, "I am strong because…" story. Just start your story, beginning every paragraph with those words, "I am strong because…" and see what comes out. Go to *Birth Without Fear* at *birthwithoutfearblog.com* for inspiration and more ideas.

You may find, like so many women we have met, that you were stronger than you thought. As Kerri, a Birthtalk mum, has said:

> *My feelings of failure have given way to immense pride and inner
> strength. Something I would never have thought possible.* **Kerri**

# Dealing with your family's birth legacy

A part of the healing journey can involve exploring our own definition of birth. This can include getting clear on the ideas about birth we have formed throughout our life.

As part of this, it can be important to visit the experiences of our mothers in birthing us and our siblings. Doing so can also give you clarity, especially if you are feeling unsupported by your mother or have perhaps been clashing with her as you struggle to make your way after a traumatic birth. Understanding her birth legacy and its possible impact may enable you to strengthen your connection.

## Your family stories

Women are often handed down their family's birth history: given in short grabs, and often including horror stories or watered-down abridged versions of stories where the baby 'just popped out'. For most of us, the stories – as well as the unspoken implications – lead us to form a particular perception of birth.

But have you ever really looked closely at what you have been told (and possibly accepted without question) about birth within your family? Do you know what birth was *really* like for your mother? Finding out the answers can be part of understanding, healing and possibly reconnecting with your mum.

## What birth was really like

We meet so many older women still suffering because the importance of birth, or how they felt, has never been acknowledged.

As we note in *Why doesn't anyone get it?* (p129): Many of our mothers are likely to have had miserable births. Women were often left to labour alone, forced to lie on their back unable to move (with no partner attending in the 1960s and 1970s), denied food, treated like naughty children, forbidden from vocalising their pain, and they suffered numerous indignities that were considered routine at the time, such as enemas, pubic shaving and having to birth in stirrups. But if everyone was having births like that, then that must be just how birth is, right?

## Clashing with your mum after your child's birth

When your child's birth was traumatic, it can sometimes be hard to garner support from your own mother. There are ways to move forward and for this road to be smoothed. The first and most important key is to focus on your own healing.

It may be helpful as part of this journey to step back and look at your mother's birthing history. The following points are designed to support you in this process. Perhaps this might be a time to record your discoveries, ideas and answers in a journal to gain clarity and allow further processing. The tricky thing might be finding a way to discuss this with your mum. Could you ask her? If she is not around, can you ask your father, or an aunty or a family friend who knew her at the time? You could say that you want to know because now you have had your own baby, you realise what an enormous thing it is and you'd like to know more about what it was like for her.

## The beginnings

What 'birth history' was your mother given of her own family before she had her first child?

- What was she told about childbirth?
- What was her antenatal education?
- Her Birthtalk Breakdown
- How did your mother feel during her births?
- Could you do a *Birthtalk Breakdown* (p47) with her, even if it's just a spoken one as part of a conversation, rather than written down?

- Just saying things like, "Wow – that must have been so full-on, having to lie down for your whole labour on your back with no pain relief, and not making any sound! I would have felt so scared and helpless if that was me". This might be the very first time someone has acknowledged this with her.

- She might make comments that push aside 'how she felt' such as, "Well, of course I was scared but that's just how birth was in those days. You just got on with it and didn't complain.". That won't lessen the impact of your acknowledgement and validation. It's just what she's used to doing; to push down those feelings. You can just gently say, "I can understand that – you had no choice – but still, that's such a massive experience."

## Rethinking things with your mum

It might not be until later that she allows herself to begin to rethink her births, and this gentle shift into focusing on feelings may give her a way to be able to acknowledge what is happening for you.

You might be the first person to acknowledge the importance of her birth for her. Perhaps by doing so you may enable her to get in touch with her own feelings and, if necessary, finally process or grieve her own births. Or you may just 'plant a seed' of insight or empathy that may enable her to be able to better understand or support you. And if neither of those outcomes occurs, at the very least, you will have gained your own empathy towards her that will hopefully be a positive impact on your relationship with each other.

## Rethinking things about birth

This process may also flag areas where you can see the influences on your own definition of birth. This might be an opportunity to explore this definition, address any 'cloudy' areas where you are unsure of the accuracy of the information you have been given via your mother or family legacy, and to get some evidence-based information, enabling you to re-think how you might approach future births.

This can be a releasing experience as you might begin to be able to see that birth for you does *not* need to be like your mother's was. (See *Birthing again* (p507)*)*

The process of discovering your own birth legacy can also make it easier to understand why people around you don't get it, and it may give you more ways to offer them information about why your birth was traumatic or challenging, and why you are still affected by the experience.

Finally, you can begin to think about the birth legacy that you want to present to your own children. What do you need to do to support their development of a healthy perception of birth? From our experience, taking the healing journey is a vital step, so we encourage you to keep exploring, keep asking questions and continue to be gentle with yourself as you explore this. You can create a new birth legacy based on what you are learning and discovering about yourself, about your child's birth and about the possibilities for an empowering birth.

# *Writing a letter of complaint*

Before taking any steps towards drafting a letter to your health professional or a health complaints entity, we encourage you to read *I'm thinking about making a complaint or taking legal action* (p181). It is really important to be very clear about the reasons for writing a complaint and your expectations, plus thinking about how you will handle their reply. In that section, you can read about the experiences of women who have followed this path of action and we outline ideas for how to write a letter that will be better received than one written in anger or despair.

## How should my letter look?

The more formal and professional your letter appears, the greater the likelihood of them taking you seriously rather than dismissing you. If fear of litigation is their only focus, this will also cause them to take notice.

## What should I write in my letter?

1.  Start by making it clear who you are. Give your name, client number (if known), the date and place of your child's birth and any other relevant details.

    For example:
    *My name is Jane Smith, and I am a previous client. My son was born under your care on August 5, 2014, at the South Estate Hospital.*

2. State the reason for the letter, without getting into specifics. Let them know you have some concerns, rather than saying you have a complaint, as it is a gentler way to start. (It will become evident as the letter proceeds if you are, indeed, complaining.) Consider including an acknowledgement of the health carer's professionalism, presuming pride in their practice and a willingness to respond to feedback.

> For example:
> *I have some concerns about the level of care I received at the time, and I wish to bring them to your attention, as I know that it is only through feedback that you can become aware of experiences such as mine, and that any necessary changes can take place.*

3. Begin with any positives. Follow this with slightly more detail about your reasons for the letter. Remind the Health Carer of 'What Happened'. If you have already completed a Birthtalk Breakdown, this might be helpful for you to use as a guide to recalling the events and their order.

> For example:
> *My son was very healthy at birth, and continues to be to this day, for which my husband and I are truly grateful. However there are some aspects of the labour and birth that have affected our ongoing life as a family, which I believe are a direct result of the care we received during our time in hospital, and under your care. [continue with details about your birth that are relevant – keep it brief]. You did not fully inform me about the reasons or need for a caesarean, after 25 hours in labour, where my baby was not in distress. Instead I was approached while my support team were sleeping, and given information that now know was misleading and incorrect.*

4. Express briefly how you felt when these things happened, and the impact on you, perhaps using the 'How I Felt' column of your Birthtalk Breakdown as a guide. Here you can fill in details of your experience that have fuelled your desire to write this letter: keep it short and concise and choose the key issues to address.

> For example:
> *During my labour I felt frightened and out of control, and without appropriate support. I felt abandoned by my health carer, as you were not present at the time I was most in need of support. You and your team went against my direct and clear wishes regarding pain relief, which resulted in my fear increasing, as I believed this situation would only occur if things were very serious (which they were not). You waited until my support*

*people were asleep to talk to me about a caesarean, which resulted
in a situation where my partner and I were making decisions
without fully understanding our options, as we did not know we
had any. Immediately post-surgery, I struggled to tell the nurses
that I could not breathe, however they were busy discussing
their social life and did not immediately notice. I found this
very frightening, worried that I might die before I properly
met my baby.*

5.  Describe briefly the impact of the birth experience upon areas of your life.

    For example:
    *Unfortunately, the emotional impact of this birth experience on
    myself has been enormous, and has had repercussions for my
    whole family. I have experienced flashbacks of certain aspects
    of the birth, and regularly feel severe anxiety. I have struggled
    to bond with my baby, and found day to day tasks sometimes
    insurmountable, as a result of the high levels of anxiety. I have
    had great difficulty sleeping, beyond the usual newborn issues
    that all women share, and have lost my confidence in social
    settings that previously I felt very comfortable in. I believe these
    symptoms are a direct result of my birth and postnatal experience
    while in your care.*

6.  Refer to the Charter of Healthcare Rights, or the Patient/Consumer Bill of
    Rights or equivalent for your country, if this is appropriate in relation to
    your care (links below).

    For example:
    *I believe that your care violated my rights, according to the
    Australian Charter of Healthcare Rights. According to this charter,
    I have the right "to be informed about services, treatment, and
    options in a clear and open way." This did not occur, as I was
    not informed about any other options in regards to [your unique
    situation]. The Charter also recognises that I "have a right to be
    included in decisions and choices about my care." I do not believe
    you fulfilled your obligation in this instance, as the interventions
    were not offered as choices, but rather as 'must haves' that
    were the only option in my situation, which I know, now, is
    not the case.*

7.   Express what you really needed, in hindsight.

   For example:

   *What I needed, beyond emerging with a healthy child, was a role in this birth, as the lack of this aspect has affected me postnatally and beyond. I needed to be involved in the decision making about my care, just as I would have the opportunity to be in other aspects of health care separate to maternity. I needed to be offered information that would enable me to make choices, rather than feel frightened of not following your plan. I needed accurate information that would make this birth less frightening, as I obviously do not have your expertise, but could have benefited greatly from your sharing of your reasons for wanting to perform some of the interventions I received.*

8.   Then express what you'd like to hear from the carer, or what you'd like to happen as a result of this. You might want an apology, or a change in practice, or even simply an acknowledgement.

   For example:

   *What I'd like to happen as a result of this letter, is for you to review the way you interact with your clients, and be aware of the possible long-term implications of the way you run your practice, on the women in your care. I do not need an apology, or an explanation of your reasons for practicing in the manner you did during the time I had my baby. However, it is my hope that my letter leads you to an acknowledgement of the importance of the woman's emotional experience in the birth of her child, and an understanding of the impact it can have on the postnatal period and beyond. I hope my letter increases your awareness of the great responsibility you have to families: the way you care for mothers can impact very deeply on the way they move forward into their life, and they are trusting you to support them in this, beyond having a healthy baby.*

**Link to the Australian Health Rights Charter:**
*www.safetyandquality.gov.au/national-priorities/charter-of-healthcare-rights/*

**Link to the USA Consumer Bill of Rights:**
*www.nlm.nih.gov/medlineplus/ency/article/001947.htm*

**Link to information about the NHS Constitution for England;**
*www.nhs.uk/choiceintheNHS/Rightsandpledges/NHSConstitution/Pages/Overview.aspx*

# What to do if you're feeling stuck

To make the writing process a little easier, below is a sample letter. It is just one example of wide variety of letters that could be written.

# Receiving a response

It is important to think about how you will handle a reply to your letter of complaint. In our section *I'm thinking about making a complaint or taking legal action* (p181) we share the stories of women who have taken various forms of action, with a variety of responses received. These different responses were due to influences such as the nature of the person responding and the individual circumstances surrounding each case. It is important, therefore, to remember that your letter will also be subject to these influences, and there are no guarantees that you will receive a particular response or outcome.

In that same section, we suggested getting to a stage in your healing where you are not reliant on a particular reply. We highly recommend taking this journey towards healing first. You may still, however, find that reading through a response to your letter of complaint requires a high level of emotional support. For this reason, you may find it helpful to have your partner, your counsellor, or a trusted friend with you when you read any response received.

*07/01/2015*

*Attention Kathy Jones:*
*Eastville Hospital Midwifery Unit*
*PO BOX 123 Eastville*

*Dear Kathy Jones,*

*My name is Jane Smith (Hospital number: 123456) and my son was born under the care of the maternity staff at Eastville Hospital on 21 June 2011. I would like to share some concerns I have held about the care I received during the birth of my son, as I understand that it is only through feedback that changes can be made.*

*I was admitted to the maternity ward on suspicion of possible pre-eclampsia following some higher blood pressure readings at a routine check at 35-weeks pregnant. What followed was a stressful and confusing week-long hospital stay, during which I had Dr J. Bloggs and Dr N. Smith tell me different diagnoses and conflicting treatment plans on each morning and afternoon shift. The conflicting information that I received regarding my condition, my diagnosis, my baby's condition and potential condition if induced, and even the information regarding my options of induction, was confusing and caused a great deal of stress. I was told by the nursing staff to 'calm down' and 'just let the doctors do their job 'and 'don't stress yourself out as it will make your blood pressure go up'. Comments like this were not supportive and did not assist me in making an informed decision.*

*Six days later, I had had enough of feeling pressured – I 'gave up' and agreed to induction. 24-hours later, Nurse B. Jones said she needed to perform an internal and stretch and sweep. I was in a lot of pain while she performed this procedure and I asked her to stop. She told me, "No, I'm almost done" and kept going. It hurt so much that I screamed to my husband, "Make her stop, now!" and tried to get off the bed. She ignored my request to stop, and when she finished, she joked about how little that pain that was compared to what I would go through once in labour. I asked to speak to you, as the person in charge, and I requested that she not be allowed back into my room again. I am grateful that this request was listened to and she was replaced with a different midwife to care for me.*

*This was a very traumatising experience and its impact led to me being diagnosed with Post-Traumatic Stress Disorder, as I continued to have flashbacks for over two years post-birth. I would not like other women to go through the trauma that I have had to process following that examination, and that is why I am sharing this today.*

*Another incident that has led to me filing of this letter to you involves the lack of informed consent around the use of various interventions during my labour. I was administered pethidine, despite my birth plan clearly stating I did not want this intervention, and the midwife initially agreeing to this birth plan. I was 6 cm dilated at the time, and I declined the pethidine repeatedly; however, the midwife told me it would still be a long time until the birth so, "I should definitely have it so I could get some sleep", even though I had only been in labour for four hours. She then tried to convince my husband that it was in my best interest, and I eventually gave in and let her administer it. My baby was born within 30 minutes of having the pethidine* and was affected by it accordingly. My eventual reluctant consent to receiving the pethidine was not an informed decision, as I was only told after the pethidine was administered that I now needed to have a foetal scalp monitor on the baby. Had I been told that, I would have even more strongly refused it.

The placement of the foetal scalp monitor was extremely upsetting and traumatic. The first attempt ended with it being attached to the wall of my vagina instead of the baby's head. On the next attempt, it was attached to the baby's head, but then the doctor pulled too hard while adjusting, and it came out with a clump of skin and hair on it. This was the cause of my husband's PTSD, and has caused ongoing issues for him ever since.

The experience of the internal examination, feeling coerced into having the pethidine, the lack of informed consent and the subsequent issues with the foetal scalp monitor, add to other factors that have left me with ongoing emotional fall out from this birth. My confusion on the day I was admitted, brushing-off my symptoms, questions and concerns throughout my stay, the procedures done to both me and my baby without my expressed consent, and the lack of support following the birth, all resulted in not just Post-Traumatic Stress Disorder, but also impacted the bond that I struggled to form with my son. Our breastfeeding journey was also affected. I have had flashbacks, insomnia and trouble sleeping, anxiety attacks, and began my life as a parent with absolutely no confidence in myself as a mother. I became so hyper-vigilant from a need to protect my son that it affected all facets of my life. I was unable to leave my son, unable to sleep, unable to let other people hold him. I wouldn't let anyone assist me and felt a need to 'make up' for everything that happened.

My husband also suffered from the impact of the care we received and was diagnosed with depression and anxiety following the birth of our son. The events that occurred during the labour and in the first hours after the birth were extremely stressful and daunting for him.

There were many other incidents of both misinformation, manipulation with fear and my wishes being ignored during my birth as well, and I am open to discussing these further with you. I now understand that the care I received violated my rights, according to the Australian Charter of Healthcare Rights. According to this Charter, I have the right, "to be informed about *services, treatment, and options in a clear and open way". This did not occur, as I was given different information about the treatment and diagnosis each time I spoke to a different doctor, which was not clear or open. The Charter recognises that I, "have a right to be included in decisions and choices about my care". I do not believe you fulfilled your obligation in this instance as the interventions were not offered as choices, but rather as 'must haves' that were the only option in my situation, which I know now is not the case.*

*What I needed in my situation was to be respected as a patient, as a woman, and as a mother. I needed to be involved in the decision making and allowed to make informed decisions without fear of judgement or chastisement. I needed to feel supported by the medical team and to feel they had me and my son's best interests in mind. I needed to be encouraged and supported.*

*What I would like to happen as a result of this letter is for the midwives and doctors who played a role in my care, to be made aware of the long-term impact they can have on women in their care. I do not need an explanation or reasoning for why I was treated this way. However, it is my hope that this letter will lead to a greater understanding of the implications for women and babies who suffer traumatising situations during birth and the importance of the voice of the woman and her family. I would like for this letter to be shared with Nurse B. Jones, as the impact that she had on my birth still haunts me today in many ways, I would like her to be made aware of how much damage it is possible to cause in just a few moments of disrespect for a woman's needs or boundaries. Birthing goes beyond 'healthy baby, healthy mum' and while I am grateful for the health of my child, the support of the carers around me was what I really needed to ensure I could care for him to the best of my abilities after I left the hospital.*

*I appreciate the attention that I know you will give this matter. You can reach me at 0433 123 456, or via email at jsmith@hotmail.com.*

*Regards,*

*Jane Smith*

# PART FOUR: THE CONTINUING JOURNEY

# Birthing again

## HOW TO HAVE A BETTER BIRTH NEXT TIME

*There is much more I could say in regards to my son's birth but, ultimately, I was left feeling powerless, empty, traumatised, guilty, ripped off. I knew deep down that this was not what birth should be. I vowed that next time it would be different. By the time I fell pregnant with my daughter, I felt that I had healed from my son's birth but went to a Birthtalk 'Healing From Birth' evening to 'clear the slate'. To my, surprise the evening evoked a lot of unresolved emotions for me and I knew that I had inner work to do to ensure my daughter's birth would not only be different, but would be her own.* **Kirsten**

*The birth of my second child was so different to that of my firstborn. It was certainly not your textbook birth, but through all that I had learned at the Birthtalk meetings I was able to trust my body and question the doctors when they did not [trust it]. I think this is the biggest thing about the birth of my children that I will carry with me for the rest of my life – not to take the first advice that is given, explore your options, trust your instincts and seek a second opinion, do the research and make educated decisions. It has brought my husband and I closer; he was so proud in the delivery room instead of being scared like he was at the first. Funnily enough, the birth of my second child has brought me closer to both of my children. I have been able to bond with both of them, feeling competent and strong about my capabilities as a mother. Breastfeeding was a breeze the second time around. Don't get me wrong, it has been hard work, but my outlook on it has changed. Instead of feeling frightened when something comes up that I don't know how to handle, I get the information I need and deal with it.* **Trudy**

*Working through the feelings of my first birth helped me to face my second pregnancy and birth very positively. A massive amount of emotion, fear and anxiety would have cropped up in my second pregnancy if I had not faced it. When I did get anxious or fearful I understood why and could work through it and move on. I felt like I had the tools to make my decisions out of knowledge, not fear or anxiety. And that was a saviour after my first experience!* **Kerri**

*Importantly I realised that this second birth was not about righting a wrong – it was about clearing away my fears and emotional blocks to ensure this baby was born according to its own destiny. It was about me doing everything I could to inform myself and set up a safe passage for my babe, but then emotionally stepping out of the way and handing the outcome over to faith, confident that I had done everything I could. I came to trust birth, trust my body, and trust that the baby knew how to be born.* **Kirsten**

## I can't go through that again

The feelings of apprehension, of dread, of being out-of-control or downright fear that can arise when thinking about birthing again can lead a woman to an understanding that she might need to process her last birth. If she is already pregnant, there can be a feeling of desperation, of the 'clock ticking', as she struggles to heal from the last birth, while knowing she absolutely wants a different experience with the upcoming one, but not knowing how to get it.

Other women know immediately that they have been traumatised, and perhaps initially vow never to 'do that again'. Then as time passes, they realise they want more children – yet feel helpless to explain their feelings of trepidation and a myriad of concerns. They want to know, firstly, whether birth can be different for them next time around. They also want to know where to find support and information to plan for this better experience of birth – and often they don't know where to start.

# Gifts from the healing journey

The good news is that taking the journey through the healing process can give you enormous gifts of knowledge, self-awareness and insights that will support you in working towards a better birth. In taking the healing path, you can potentially reveal to yourself so many insights that will be beneficial in your planning. By working through the various sections of this book, you may find exciting discoveries about issues such as:

- what you want when birthing
- what you *don't* want when birthing
- what's important to you to feel emotionally and physically safe in birth
- what attributes are important for your health carer to have
- what attributes are important for your health carer to *not* have
- what information you wish you had access to last time
- what particular issues you may have this time, based on what happened last time, that you want to get sorted before you are birthing
- which people are important for you to have around you when birthing
- which people are important for you to *not* have around you when birthing.

One major new understanding many women find they gain from taking the healing journey is that *the emotional journey towards birth is just as important as the physical journey.* They learn that pregnancy and birth can be special opportunities to grow in self-knowledge, to gain new emotional clarity and strength, and to prepare for the challenges of mothering. This topic is often not understood or shared before women first give birth. So this is a beautiful opportunity to prepare yourself to expand your mind and your heart, as you prepare for an empowering birth.

There are complete books written about this topic, some of which can be found in *Appendix A*, under the heading, "Suggested reading for birthing again". We will keep our focus here on preparing for an empowering experience using the Birthtalk philosophy that you read about in *The foundations of your healing journey* (p37). This information will give you an outline and framework in which to begin preparations for a much better pregnancy and birth, including negotiating your path towards this birth, accessing relevant information and finding and facilitating optimal care.

## The good news

The good news is that almost *any* birth can be an empowering, positive birth. That's regardless of whether it is a natural birth, or a caesarean, or a surprise situation arising during labour, or a birth where a detour is taken from your preferred plan. Why? Because it is the *feelings* that we have *during* labour that can affect how we feel and respond to things *after labour*. Remember this table from the section, *What is a traumatic or bad birth anyway?* (p42)

| Type of feelings during birth | Results for parents postnatally and beyond |
|---|---|
| Empowered, safe, supported, respected, nurtured and able to ask questions. | Positive, confident, strong, instinctive, able to cope, good bonding. |
| Powerless, confused, fearful, isolated or abandoned, unacknowledged or unheard. | A negative impact can occur on all areas of life and it can be difficult to move forward, can include panic attacks, vivid flashbacks, hypervigilance, or a feeling of emptiness. |

To reiterate from that section: If we feel *good feelings*, we take them and their happy consequences into parenthood. If we feel *bad feelings*, then we take them and their negative consequences into parenthood. Any path to birth can be good if you have the right information and support so that you can experience those good feelings.

So, that might make it easier already! Now you know that you are planning a birth where you feel empowered, safe, supported, respected, nurtured, and able to ask questions. What that birth looks like will be different for every woman.

# The way forward – questions to ask yourself

Now that you are planning this next (more empowering) birth, you need to ask yourself some questions to enable you to fully explore your options. These are the 'where, who and what' of empowered birth.

## Where

- What type of birth setting is going to be right for me and my baby? Which birth setting (public hospital, private hospital, birth centre or homebirth) is going to be able to meet my emotional and physical needs?

## Who

- What type of health carer is going to be right for me and my baby? For example, midwifery care (hospital based, in private practice or homebirth) obstetrician-led care (public or private) or shared care between my midwife or GP and the hospital I'm birthing at. What are the philosophies of these different health carers, and how will that affect my decisions? To get more information about different models of care, see *www.maternitychoices.org.au/uploads/1/5/1/4/15149676/infosheet_model.pdf*.

- Who will my support people be (partner, doula, mother, friend)? What are my expectations of them? What did my last experience tell me about my needs for support?

## What

- What information do I feel was lacking in my antenatal education last time? Where can I find balanced and trusted information to fill in the gaps? We offer some recommendations of areas and sources for women to expand their understanding of birth in the next section *The pitfalls of going with the flow in birth* (p513). You can also find some great information about how our bodies are designed to support us in birth in *Why wouldn't my body work in labour?* (p230)

These questions will set you off on a new path. You may find that even your pregnancy is different this time around, as you may ask different questions of your health carers. You may perhaps even carry yourself differently when you know that a positive birth is possible, and know what you need to get there. This confidence may come from knowing that you are an informed consumer rather than a passive recipient in the traditional role of a patient.

Working towards maximising the feelings from a good birth, as listed in our definition of a good birth in *Why does it matter? And isn't a live birth a good birth?* (p40) is the single most important factor in having a positive birth experience. Maximising the good feelings will impact directly on how you feel about the experience and the consequences that will follow postnatally. These good feelings are essential for you to fully access the hormonal support your body has to offer and are important to enhance the safety and wellbeing of yourself and your baby.

We have seen many women go on to have wonderful births, even if they were unpredictable and not smooth-sailing, after exploring the issues we present in this book, and asking the questions, as we have suggested above. Their stories are on our Birthtalk Website and Birthtalk Blog and we encourage you to take these stories in, pull them apart, and see yourself in their place. If you need some guidance, see *Appendix A* for some wonderful people and groups that can support you in that journey.

# THE PITFALLS OF GOING WITH THE FLOW IN BIRTH

**(An article from our blog, *Birth Trauma Truths*)**

So many of us aim to 'just go with the flow' as our birth plan. But could the gentle flow of birth we envisage actually be undermined with this approach? Could 'going with the flow' ever be detrimental to a positive start to life for your new family?

Kelly is thirty-nine weeks pregnant with her first child – round, radiant, and ready. Her belly precedes her as she enters the café, kisses her friends hello, and lowers herself carefully onto the chair. After they joke and jostle over the menu, all eyes turn to Kelly and the question is asked, "So," says one friend, "Are you scared about the birth?" "Oh," replies Kelly casually, "I'd really like a natural birth, and I don't really want any drugs, but I'm just going to go with the flow and see what happens". One-and-a-half weeks later, Kelly is lying on an operating table, after an induction, some pethidine, an epidural and twenty-eight hours of labour. She is exhausted, frightened, concerned for her baby, and in shock at the happenings of the last day and night. And now she is meeting her baby via abdominal surgery.

## Necessary or not?

Many people would look at this scenario above and express relief that Kelly was able to access the care she and her baby apparently needed. They would understandably assume that some dangerous and unexpected complication had arisen that necessitated the interventions, and ultimately the caesarean, in her labour. This is certainly a possibility and of course does occur. But what if this situation was merely the end result of going with the flow?

This possibility can be difficult to embrace. As Melissa from Birthtalk shares, "I know that when this was suggested to me after my own caesarean, my emotions shifted from immediate denial, ("No! I was *told* it was necessary!"), to disbelief ("I *do not* want to hear that the pain and side effects of major surgery may have been avoided!"), to intrigue ("You mean – maybe I *could have* birthed normally?"), to anger ("I can't *believe* no one told me this could happen!"), to grief ("I am *devastated* for what I missed out on.") to an exploration of a whole side to birth that I had never known existed.

"I discovered that my own antenatal education was sorely lacking, even though I did the hospital's antenatal course, and a private Active Birth course. No one told me that just going with the flow could possibly be setting me on a trajectory to an outcome I did not want – and very possibly did not need."

## Why we decide to 'go with the flow'

Going with the flow is an oft-used expression many women turn to when asked about their impending birth. For some of us, it takes the pressure off us to perform and have the perfect birth. It suggests we are fairly relaxed about the whole deal.

What else can we say when we don't know how things will turn out? We may not have road-tested our bodies for this sort of thing before. Most of us have never seen a baby being born, unless you count watching our favourite characters in sitcoms – which most of us acknowledge aren't very realistic birthing moments.

What else can we say, when we have been bombarded with horror stories of birth from friends, family and people in line at the bank? How else do we quell the nervous ache in the pit of our (sizeable) belly, except by acknowledging and accepting the unpredictability of birth? And where do we find the good stories, the happy stories about babies being born? We certainly don't hear them in the street or at parties. Unless you count those women who see birth as a sporting event, and define their births in terms of velocity, which just ups the ante for those of us who are already feeling pressured to perform.

## Out of our control

Going with the flow can be a safe way of saying, "I have no idea. I am scared stiff. All I hear are descriptions of excruciating pain and watermelons coming out of places they shouldn't. I am just going to put myself in the hands of the experts, and hope I am fine". Women may be inclined to turn to this approach as a form of default, not knowing any other way, and as an acknowledgement that childbirth is out of their control. This is an understandable justification, and these are understandable fears when you look at the way our culture views birth – as an event that must be endured to extract an offspring. No wonder many of us become frozen in our tracks, looking for guidance. But the act of going with the flow can contain inherent pitfalls unknown to most women who follow that plan of action. Unfortunately, the question is not, "Are you going to go with the flow?" In our current birthing climate, the real question is, "Just whose flow are you going with?"

## Healthy mother, healthy baby?

'The flow' implies a natural unfolding of events, where mother and baby's wellbeing is paramount and central to the occasion. It suggests a gentle meander from stage to stage of the birthing process, veering smoothly to a different course if the current path seems unviable. It implies that all paths of the flow lead to the same outcome: a healthy mother and healthy child.

Healthy mother and child. If we pause for a moment and really consider this over-used phrase, we need to look at what defines 'healthy'. When we look at safety in birth, we tend to only think of physical safety, that is, getting both parties out of the experience alive. But doing so without attending to a woman's mental wellbeing seems to have shocking implications for women, their babies, and their whole family after the birth.

Debby (from Birthtalk) says, "Every week we talk with women whose birth plan was to just 'go with the flow'. Unfortunately, many have experienced their birth as traumatic and are contacting us for support". Debby describes these women as expressing feelings of sadness, confusion and often, anger. "The effects are more far-reaching than most of us realise. These emotions can spill over and impact on how women parent, how they relate with their partners, and even how they feel about themselves".

Most women's interpretation of going with the flow is to put ourselves in the hands of health carers, and accept the interventions they suggest as inevitable, and unquestionable and always in our best interests. However, as Debby is finding at Birthtalk, it seems that this approach may not only offer us few benefits for the actual birth, it may also put us at a disadvantage in parenting our new babies and how we experience our entire postnatal phase.

## What is the hospital's definition of healthy?

Miranda, a thirty-eight year old mother of two tells of her realisation that her definition of the 'healthy mum and bub' and her hospital's definition were eons apart.

> I could not fathom that any decision would be made that was not solely in my best interest. I did not think for a moment that we weren't all working towards the same goal. I was going with the flow. But their flow took me to a place I never wanted to be, and I am still paying the price. And it wasn't because their way was safer. It was because it suited their institution better. **Miranda**

This is where the real flow can rear its sometimes ugly, institutionalised head. Although our health carers are there to ensure physical safety, and many would like to be able to support women emotionally through birth, they are often stymied by the very system they work in. The birthing journey consists of many twists and turns, and some of these turning points may require decision making. As an institution, the hospital has certain protocols and policies in place to enhance the smooth running of an enormous organisation. While some of these policies are designed with the woman as the main focus, many other regulations were created to also meet the hospital's needs. So, every decision made about a woman during birth must take into account not just the woman and her baby, but issues such as litigation, liability, staffing, costing, and more. We generally assume that all flows will arrive at the same result of healthy mother and baby. But what is the hospital's definition of healthy? And indeed, what is the doctor's definition of healthy?

Debby witnesses over and over again that physically healthy is not enough. "The goal of emerging from birth with your body and baby intact is a bit of a no-brainer, really," she says. "Of course we are all working towards that. However, what many health providers fail to recognise is that prioritising supporting a woman to birth a child so she feels mentally healthy afterwards is completely possible, without compromising safety in any way."

Maternity care needs to go beyond the physical care of the woman and perfunctory acknowledgement of her involvement of the process and be taken to a new level of opportunity for the woman's participation in her own birth.

Debby believes that the key areas for health carers to address are enabling women with support and information to be involved in decision making in their births, and acknowledging women's expert insights into their own bodies. She acknowledges that it can be challenging for health carers in busy hospitals to build relationships of understanding and trust with birthing women they may have never met before. However, taking steps in this direction in fact enhances safety and women's long-term emotional wellbeing.

## Is there another way to approach birth?

Going with the flow just doesn't seem to have worked for women such as Miranda and many of the women who contact Birthtalk. Sadly, they are not alone. Research shows that one in three women identified their birth as being a traumatic event.[254] Many more are disappointed or view their birth experience

---

254   Creedy, D. K., Shochet, I. M., & Horsfall, J. (2000). Childbirth and the development of acute trauma symptoms: Incidence and contributing factors. *Birth, 27*, 104–111.

negatively. But is this because birth is horrible? Or is it more the culture of care being provided that causes problems? Are we helpless pawns in the machinations of the maternal health system?

Debby believes there is much we can do to birth safely and experience the actual birth as an enriching, positive event. She offers some practical advice on a different approach to labour and birth, tried and tested by hundreds of women attending Birthtalk, explored below. Firstly, though, does it really matter? Is it important that the birth is a positive experience for the mother, as well as a safe experience for mother and child?

## Does birth matter?

Contrary to popular belief, birth is not just one day in your life. Why? Because we don't just leave our feelings about birth at the hospital. The feelings we bring home about the birth can affect our experience of parenting our new babies. If we bring home feelings of confidence, joy and strength, our instinctive bonding is promoted with our babies. Our confidence in all aspects of life can soar and we can connect at a new level with our partners. Conversely, if we are bringing home feelings of fear, isolation and confusion, bonding with our beautiful babies can be difficult and feelings of failure can result. Our confidence can plummet, and relationships with partners can suffer. These feelings can infiltrate all areas of our lives as a new family.

Birth *does* matter, because how we experience it can affect every single thing that occurs after it. For this reason, just going with the flow can be risky, as it often entails giving your birth over to the experts, and following their flow as they advise you throughout. What this process can fail to provide for a woman and her partner, is the opportunity to ask questions, provide insights, and make decisions as part of a team. Being involved in decision making is a key aspect of emerging empowered from birth. Even if you make the same decision as your health carer advises, it is still *your* decision if made from a place of knowledge, rather than fear.

To make that clear – we are not advising ignoring your health carer's suggestions and advice. We are, however, sharing the benefits to be gained from taking an active role in the decisions made and entering this process with a wealth of information rarely offered in regular antenatal courses, to optimise your chances of emerging empowered and ready for parenting.

# A birth that is safe *and* positive

Debby suggests, firstly, to look further afield for birth information and knowledge than the regular hospital antenatal classes and mainstream pregnancy books. "There is often a huge gap in women's antenatal education," she says. "Women are encouraged to just go with the flow, and then are naturally surprised and disappointed when their outcome is so different from what the books and classes told them to expect." Debby recommends that women expand their understanding of birth to include education in a few key areas:

### Knowing how women's bodies work best.

Finding out what our bodies need to be able to access their innate ability to do their job is strongly recommended. Influences such as sound levels (quiet allows focus), obtrusive interruptions during contractions (avoid), lighting (low is best), privacy, and feeling safe and supported are often important factors in determining our body's optimal physiological ability to birth. "By knowing what our bodies need, we can ascertain if these needs will be met by purely following the hospital's flow. If not, we can take steps to ensure our needs are met," explains Debby. We recommend reading our sections *Why wouldn't my body work in labour* (p230) and *I don't feel bonded to my child* (p218), as they contain some vital information about what our bodies need. We also suggest reading the work of Dr Sarah Buckley, an obstetric GP, mother of four, and author of *Gentle Birth, Gentle Mothering*.[255] Dr Sarah Buckley's work can be found at *www.sarahbuckley.com*. This information can be helpful to us in understanding and supporting the birthing process and in our decision making along the path to birth.

### Understanding how our health system works.

"To birth in our system and emerge emotionally healthy, women may need to buoy themselves with knowledge in how decisions are made about their provision of care," says Debby. Knowing how and why the hospital usually arrive at their flow, decisions can make it easier to negotiate (if necessary) to get your own needs met, often in a positive way for both you and your health carer. See *Appendix A* for links to professionals, organisations and information that could help.

---

255    *Gentle Birth, Gentle Mothering: A Doctor's Guide to Natural Childbirth and Gentle Early Parenting Choices* (Sarah J Buckley, Celestial Arts, Berkeley CA, 2009)

## Support, support, support.

Most of us expect to have our partners at the birth of our child. It is worth considering the research that suggests the presence of another support person who understands birth can greatly enhance the experience for everyone. This leads many women to consider hiring a doula (a professional birth support person). Some partners are reluctant to share the birth with an outsider, and worry they will be made redundant in the birthing room if there is someone else there in a support role. But talking to couples after the baby is born, this doesn't seem to be the case. For many couples the actual experience of having extra support is usually a blessing, and a part of their positive view of their birth and their role within it.

Research indicates that continuous caregiver support during childbirth has a number of benefits. A review of twenty-two trials involving 15 288 women found that women who received continuous labour support were more likely to give birth 'spontaneously', that is, with neither caesarean, vacuum nor forceps, less likely to use pain medications, were less likely to be dissatisfied and had slightly shorter labours. Another benefit was that their babies were also less likely to have low five-minute Apgar scores.[256]

This research makes sense to us, from our own experiences with Birthtalk women. If a woman feels safe, supported, acknowledged, cared for, then her body usually works as it is designed to, with the birth hormones combining to enhance the safety and ease of birthing. Obviously in this scenario she is going to also have high levels of satisfaction. We have written this article: '*Do I Need a Doula*', available on our website, to assist you in further exploring this option.

Catherine, a mother of two young children, wishes she knew about professional support before her first child was born.

> *I didn't think I would need any support, as I knew exactly how things were planned to go. I so wish I had someone to advocate for me, and explain my options in more details, and offer me the continuous care I know I needed. I could see the birth just getting away from me, and I didn't know where to turn.* **Catherine**

So who is going to provide this continuous presence throughout the labour if it is so beneficial? Usually not the obstetricians – they are generally only called in towards the end of the labour or if there are any concerns. Traditionally, this support has been provided by midwives, but as we have seen, our health care system places many limitations on our health carers. This is especially true of midwives. In our hospitals, midwives are generally unable to really get to know

---

256    Hodnett, E.D., Gates, S., Hofmeyr, G.J., & Sakala, C. (2012). Continuous support for women during childbirth. *Cochrane Database of Systematic Reviews*, 10. Art.

women prior to their birth. So they are unlikely to be aware of your particular needs, and the flow of birth you are looking for, and are often unable (due to hospital policies) to remain with a woman for her entire labour.

Many women are now seeking the services of models of care offering continual care from a known carer or a professional support person who see their job as supporting both partners as they enter this new phase of life. A doula can stay with the woman at all times, as well as act as an advocate for her, to work with the midwife to ensure that, as much as possible, her birth is a positive event. Kay, thirty-seven, is a mum who experienced a vaginal birth after caesarean, and hired a doula to support herself and husband Jake.

> *Having experienced hospital policy with the birth of my first child, which culminated in a possibly unnecessary emergency caesarean, I could not imagine giving birth in the hospital environment without the support of a doula. To know that I was going to take a doula second time round probably gave me the confidence to proceed with falling pregnant.* **Kay**

This confidence extended to Kay's birthing experience, as she recalls, "The step into motherhood following a well supported birth has been streets ahead of the step into motherhood following [my previous unsupported] birth where I felt a failure".

### Being involved in decision making.

This tip from Debby comes with an assurance that, "We don't all need to be midwives and know every possible thing about birth to be able to birth well in our system". Rather, it means knowing which questions to ask so you can weigh up each situation. Many issues that arise during birth can be resolved a number of ways – there is often no set path that must be followed. The hospital may not volunteer the fact that you have choices – as they may have what they consider to be the best path to meet your needs (as they perceive them), as well as the needs of their establishment. Once you know there may be options, the trick is determining which option is right for you and your family in your situation. How do we choose, when we are not doctors or midwives ourselves? Debby says, "Once women have attained the information about how their bodies work, they will have a better idea of what will support them in birth. We suggest beginning by using the acronym of BRAN to help to get enough information from care givers that will enable you to choose from different options to meet your individual needs." By asking about BRAN, as detailed below, you can get a wealth of information to enhance your decision-making abilities.

**BRAN:**

*Benefits:* What are the benefits of this intervention?

*Risks:* What are the risks of this intervention?

*Alternatives:* Are there any alternatives to this procedure?

*Nothing:* What would happen if we did nothing? (Or do we have to act now?)

## Why didn't anyone tell me?

Remember Kelly, who we met at the beginning of this article, as she was about to undergo an unplanned caesarean? Kelly knew she couldn't control childbirth. She decided to go with the flow. But no one told her that in doing so she was potentially giving up her chance to be involved in one of the most amazing, empowering experiences life offers us. A few months later, she is still upset, confused and affected by her experience.

> *What tears me up the most is that I am really questioning whether my caesarean was even necessary. Right from the induction onwards, no one let me know I had any options. I didn't know if decisions were being made because my baby was at risk, or because the hospital's timetable was at risk, or some other reason. I didn't know that every intervention could have repercussions for the natural labour I envisaged. Now I am finding out about the choices I could have had. I am so upset. Why didn't anyone tell me?* **Kelly**

## So, when *is* it *okay* to go with the flow?

While we can't control childbirth, we certainly can have a level of control over the environment we are birthing in, made possible by the knowledge we bring to the birth, the support we have around us, and the ability to ask the right questions. When these things are in place, it becomes time to go with the flow – although with a different focus. When a woman has this additional information and support, it becomes the flow of *birth* we are going with, not the flow of birth as dictated by an institution or a particular carer. It is then possible to surrender to the power of your birthing body, to follow the flow of this birth, knowing that you have set in place the people and the environment to support you in meeting your goal of empowered healthy mother, and healthy baby, no matter what path your birth follows.

And by giving ourselves the gift of an informed, empowering birth, we are giving our new little family the gift of a strong, confident mother, who has the ability to create a gentle flow of family life based on what is best for herself, her child and her family.

Note: You may want to go to the original blog post on our blog, '*Birth Trauma Truths*' at *birthtraumatruths.wordpress.com* to see the interesting and spirited discussion in the comments.

# *A final note*

## A FINAL NOTE TO WOMEN

Thank you. Thank you for trusting us enough to read our book. Thank you for gathering the immense courage we know it took to draw a deep breath, open the front cover and face your experience. Thank you for giving us the opportunity to support you on your journey towards healing. Thank you for opening yourself to the possibility of moving on.

We know so many women like you who have been on this rocky path, stumbled, fallen and got back up again as they traverse this territory. You are amazing, and you are so important. We honour your strength as you walk your own path to healing. And we know you can do this.

Thank you and many blessings as you continue on your journey to make sense, make peace and move on.

*Melissa and Deb*

# A FINAL NOTE TO PARTNERS, HEALTH WORKERS, GRANDPARENTS AND OTHERS WHO WANT TO HELP

At the beginning of this book, we shared how the best thing you can do in an effort to support a woman through the aftermath of a traumatic birth is to *read this book* and then *listen*. The following poem is to reiterate 'where to look' in an effort to really hear a woman's pain, and to be able to offer genuine validation and understanding. We leave you with this as a message to carry with you.
On behalf of any woman you may support, we thank you for reading. We thank you for caring. And we honour your own journey.

## Don't Ask Me

> My birth was traumatic
> Don't ask me why
> I may not be able to tell you
> I've asked myself the same question
> And still can't come up with a reply
> Or when I do it sounds hollow
> And unimportant
> And an inadequate way to express my pain
>
> My birth was traumatic
> Don't ask me what happened
> That won't tell you why I'm traumatised
> And I will just feel more like a fraud
> As I read your expression of, "But other women have that happen
> and they are fine"
> What happened is only part of the story
> And I don't know what the other part is
> Only that it's there inside me
> Like a block over my heart

My birth was traumatic
Don't ask me to explain the process
You won't get it
My pain is not in the process
It's in the spaces in between
It's in the unsaid
My pain is in what didn't happen
As much as in what did happen

My birth was traumatic
Just hear me
But don't listen to what I say
Hear what I am begging for
Hear what I so desperately need from you
That I can't ask for because
I don't know I want it

Ask me how I feel now
Ask me how I felt in the birth
Ask me how 'what happened' felt

It wasn't so much the procedure
It was the fear and the confusion and the isolation

It wasn't so much the pain
But the bearing of that pain without love, reassurance, respect

It wasn't so much what was happening
But the swirling, whirling emotions ripping through me
Was I okay?
Was I safe?
I was at my peak moment of vulnerability
Where was my port in this storm?
If I can't find it – I must face this tempest alone
Unacknowledged
Unheard

Don't ask me what happened
Just hear how I felt when it happened
That is your key to my pain
And that is my key to being understood
And validated
And being able to begin the journey to healing

Ask me
And I will tell you

**by Melissa Bruijn©2008**

# *Appendix A: Resources & links*

Note: The information provided by these resources may provide a starting point for further information or support. However, we cannot guarantee that members of these different organisations are aligned with our own philosophy. It is important that you are discerning in your choice of support, and it is our hope that this book enables you to be more confident with understanding and communicating your own needs. We recommend connecting with health carers who understand both birth and the possible impact of birth, who are empathetic and embracing of wherever you are on your healing journey.

## IF YOU HAVE HAD A TRAUMATIC BIRTH

### Our blog: Birth Trauma Truths

The Truth About Traumatic Birth: what you need to know on the healing journey. An archive of articles by Birthtalk about birth trauma and healing from a difficult, disappointing or challenging birth. Explored common myths and misperceptions about birth trauma and provides validation and information for those on the journey to healing.
*http://birthtraumatruths.wordpress.com*

### Birth Crisis Network

The Birth Crisis Network is a helpline in Britain, founded by Sheila Kitzinger, that women can ring if they want to talk about a traumatic birth.
See *www.sheilakitzinger.com/birthcrisis.htm* for the most up-to-date contact information or *birthcrisis@sheilakitzinger.com*

## Solace for Mothers

Solace for Mothers is an organisation designed for the sole purpose of providing and creating support for women who have experienced childbirth as traumatic. They also have a list of professionals in the US who have identified themselves as working with mothers who have experienced birth trauma.

*www.solaceformothers.org*
*www.solaceformothers.org/professionals.html*

## Trauma and Birth Stress (TABS)

A New Zealand-based website with information about childbirth-related Post-Traumatic Stress Disorder, articles and links, and list of support contacts in New Zealand

*www.tabs.org.nz/*
*www.tabs.org.nz/tabscontacts.htm*

## Birth Trauma Association (UK)

The Birth Trauma Association supports all women who have had a traumatic birth experience. They want women to know that they are not alone. On these pages, they offer emotional and practical support to women and also their families.

*www.birthtraumaassociation.org.uk/*

## Prevention and Treatment of Traumatic Birth (PATTCh)

PATTCh is a collective of birth and mental health experts dedicated to the prevention and treatment of traumatic childbirth.

*http://pattch.org*

## Birthing From Within

Birthing From Within is an organisation evolved from the popular book by the same name. The book's author, Pam England and co-owner, Virginia Bobro provide a number of services to support women preparing to birth, including birth classes, workshops and professional training. Birthing From Within's mission includes inspiring and teaching expectant and new parents, and those who work with them, to prepare for birth as a Rite of Passage; to build a foundation for birthing in awareness in our birth culture, whatever the birth location or outcome or events of the birth; to prevent or minimise emotionally difficult births (for parents and professionals) through compassionate, honest preparation; and to honor and use the power of Birth Storytelling and listening. There is also a listing of official Birthing From Within Mentors and doulas throughout the world.

*http://birthingfromwithin.com*

# CRISIS SUPPORT

## Australia

### Beyondblue

Beyondblue is working to reduce the impact of anxiety, depression and suicide in the community by raising awareness and understanding, empowering people to seek help, and supporting recovery, management and resilience.
Online chat: 3pm – 12am AEST
*www.beyondblue.org.au/get-support/get-immediate-support*
Phone: Call 24 hours a day, 7 days a week: 1300 22 4636

### Lifeline

Lifeline is a national charity providing all Australians experiencing a personal crisis with access to 24 hour crisis support and suicide prevention services.
Phone support 24-hours-a-day
Online Crisis Chat 8pm – 4am (AEST) 7 days:
*www.lifeline.org.au/Get-Help/Online-Services/crisis-chat*
Phone: 13 11 14

### Suicide Call Back Service

The Suicide Call Back Service provides free nationwide professional telephone and online counselling for anyone affected by suicide.
24-hours-a-day, 7-days-a-week
1300 659 467

## New Zealand

### Lifeline NZ

Mission: To provide safe, effective and innovative services that support the emotional and mental wellbeing of our communities. Lifeline NZ It always helps to talk. At Lifeline, we're here to listen.
24hour telephone counselling
Within Auckland: 09 5222 999
Outside Auckland: 0800 543 354

# UK

### Samaritans

If something's troubling you, then get in touch. Talk to them any time you like, in your own way, and off the record – about whatever's getting to you.
24-hour helpline
*www.samaritans.org*
UK: 08457 909090 or ROI: 116 123

### SANEline

Their mental health support services are completely confidential. Whatever your problems or concerns, you will receive non-judgemental emotional support. Their professional staff and trained volunteers have specialist mental health knowledge; they can help you consider options for support that address your individual circumstances.
*www.sane.org.uk*
0845 767 8000

### Some more info via Birth Trauma Association UK:

You can also call your GP surgery for advice, during out-of-hours you should hear a recorded message giving advice as to who to call.
NHS Direct is available 24-hours-a-day
NHS Direct: 0845 4647

---

# USA

### The National Suicide Prevention Lifeline

A 24-hour Helpline for people in emotional distress: provides free and confidential emotional support to people in suicidal crisis or emotional distress 24-hours a day, 7 days a week. Your state's crisis prevention helplines can be accessed by contacting the 24-hour helpline, which links to local crisis centres.
1-800-273-8255

---

# Canada

### Canadian Association for Suicide Prevention (CASP)

CASP's ultimate purpose is to reduce the suicide rate and minimise the harmful consequences of suicidal behaviour.
*http://suicideprevention.ca*

---

# Worldwide

## Befrienders Worldwide

Network of 349 emotional support centres in 32 countries, spanning five continents. Befrienders Worldwide centres provide an open space for those in distress to talk and be heard. This is via telephone helplines, SMS messaging, face to face, internet chat, outreach and local partnerships.
*www.befrienders.org*

## International Association for Suicide Prevention

Has a list of crisis centres worldwide
*www.iasp.info/resources/Crisis_Centres*:

---

# IF YOU HAVE HAD A CAESAREAN

## International Caesarean Awareness Network (ICAN):

ICAN is a nonprofit organisation whose mission is to improve maternal-child health by preventing unnecessary cesareans through education, providing support for cesarean recovery, and promoting Vaginal Birth After Cesarean (VBAC).
*http://ican-online.org*

## Caesarean Awareness Network Australia (CANA)

Caesarean Awareness Network Australia is the vision of three Australian mothers who saw a need to provide a public voice on behalf of women who have had caesareans, women who are considering having a baby by caesarean and women planning to have a vaginal birth after caesarean.
*www.canaustralia.net*

## Caesarean Awareness Recovery Education Support – South Australia

(but a source of good info wherever you are) (CARES SA)
CARES is a South Australian, not-for-profit organisation made up of women who have all experienced birth by caesarean and at some point themselves have sought support from CARES.
*www.caresinc.org.au*

### Birthrites – Healing After Caesarean – Western Australia

(but a source of good info wherever you are)

Birthrites: Healing After Caesarean aims to provide a support network for women who've had a previous caesarean/s, and to increase the awareness of these women's needs to their health-carers within the medical profession. *www.birthrites.org*

### Homebirth Cesarean International

Courtney Jarecki, along with Ann Jamison co-founded the non-profit organisation called Homebirth Cesarean International. "Our mission is to promote healing and support for women whose planned out-of-hospital births ended in the operating room. HBCI envisions a world where women birth their children with dignity and power, even on the operating table."

They accomplish their mission through:

- providing families with peer support and research-based information about the homebirth cesarean experience
- educating birth professionals and care providers on best practices and research-based methodologies that can help mitigate the potential trauma of an unplanned caesarean
- developing postpartum care protocols to facilitate the mental and physical healing process.

*http://homebirthcesarean.org/*

---

## IF YOUR BABY WAS PREMATURE

## Australia

### National Premmie Foundation (NPF)

The National Premmie Foundation (NPF) is a peak national organisation in Australia for parents who experience premature birth or neonatal loss. The NPF works to raise awareness of premature birth and neonatal loss. Its aim is to ensure that all prem parents receive the information, care and support they need to make an extremely difficult time just that little bit easier. The majority of members are parents who have experienced premature birth or neonatal loss. *www.prembaby.org.au*

---

## New Zealand

### Early Buds

Early Buds provides current and useful information, personal stories and product samples specifically for premature babies and their parents in their prem packs.

*www.earlybuds.org.nz*

## UK

### Bliss UK – for babies born too soon, too small, too sick

Bliss offers a wide range of family support services that provide confidential advice, information and support to the families of premature and sick babies. These services are free of charge and are available to help and support the whole family.

*www.bliss.org.uk/*

0500 618140 Helpline available Monday to Friday, between 9 a.m. and 9 p.m.

## USA

### Graham's Foundation

Graham's Foundation offers resources, programs, and connections so parents are supported, empowered and hopeful throughout their journey. Graham's Foundation is committed to a world where no parent goes through the journey of prematurity alone.

*www.grahamsfoundation.org*

## Canada

### Canadian Premature Babies Foundation

Their purpose is to prevent pre-term birth through education and research, supporting the best standards of care for premature babies and give premature babies and their families a voice across Canada.

*http://cpbf-fbpc.org*

# POST AND ANTENATAL DEPRESSION SUPPORT

## Australia

### Perinatal Anxiety and Depression Australia (PANDA)
### (formerly Post and Antenatal Depression Association)

PANDA is committed to a community where perinatal depression and anxiety are recognised and the impact on women, men and their families are minimised through acknowledgement, support and education.

*www.panda.org.au*

PANDA National Helpline: 1300 726 306

(open Monday to Friday, 10 a.m. – 5 p.m.)

---

## International

### Postpartum Support International

Postpartum Support International is dedicated to helping women suffering from perinatal mood and anxiety disorders, including postpartum depression, the most common complication of childbirth. We also work to educate family, friends and healthcare providers so that moms and moms-to-be can get the support they need and recover.

*www.postpartum.net*

---

# IF YOU HAVE SUFFERED THE LOSS OF YOUR BABY

## Australia

### SANDS (Miscarriage, Stillbirth and Newborn Death Support)

24hr confidential telephone support

*www.sands.org.au*

1300 0 sands (1300 0 72637)

### National Premmie Foundation (NPF)

The National Premmie Foundation (NPF) is the peak national organisation in Australia for parents who experience premature birth or neonatal loss. The NPF works to raise awareness of premature birth and neonatal loss. Its aim is to ensure that all prem parents receive the information, care and support they need

to make an extremely difficult time just that little bit easier. The majority of members are parents who have experienced premature birth or neonatal loss.
*www.prembaby.org.au*

### Compassionate Friends

The Compassionate Friends in Australia have been set up as state-based organisations for the delivery of services to grieving parents and families. The role of TCF Australia is to provide coordination and communication support to the state-based organisations.
*www.thecompassionatefriends.org.au/*

## New Zealand

### SANDS NZ

A voluntary, parent-run, non-profit organisation set up to support parents and families who have experienced the death of a baby at any stage during pregnancy, as a baby or infant.
*www.sands.org.nz*

## USA

### First Candle

Grief Counsellors are available 24-hours a day, 7 days a week
*www.firstcandle.org*
1 800 221 7437

### Compassionate Friends

The Compassionate Friends offers more than 660 meeting locations around the country
*www.compassionatefriends.org/*

## UK

### UK SANDS (Stillbirth and Neonatal Death)

The helpline is open: Monday to Friday: 9.30 a.m. – 5.30 p.m.
Tuesday and Thursday evenings: 6 p.m. – 10 p.m.
*www.uk-sands.org/*
020 7436 5881

## Canada

### Pregnancy and Infant Loss Network (PAIL)

Pregnancy and Infant Loss Network is a registered Canadian charity committed to making a positive difference to those affected by pregnancy and infant loss.
*www.pailnetwork.ca*

---

## DOULAS

## Southeast Queensland

To find a doula in Southeast Queensland, contact us at Birthtalk.org
*Birthtalk.org*

---

## Australia

### Find a Doula

*http://findadoula.com.au/*

---

## Worldwide

### DONA International

*www.dona.org/*

---

## INDEPENDENT MIDWIVES

## Australia

### Midwives Australia

To find a registered midwife practising under the Medicare framework in your area
*www.midwivesaustralia.com.au/?page_id=68*

### Homebirth Australia (HBA)

Homebirth Australia is the peak national body for homebirth in Australia. For over thirty years, HBA has worked to support consumers and midwives who choose homebirth. The organisation is run by volunteers – consumers and midwives and includes a 'Find a Midwife' tool.
*http://homebirthaustralia.org*

## New Zealand

### Find Your Midwife New Zealand

The Find your Midwife website was created by the New Zealand College of Midwives to help women to find and choose a midwife that they can work with best. All midwives who are members of the New Zealand College of Midwives are able to have their details listed on this website.
*www.findyourmidwife.co.nz*

## UK

### Independent Midwives UK

Independent Midwives are fully qualified midwives who have chosen to work outside the NHS in a self-employed capacity. They have a 'Find a Midwife' tool on their website.
*www.independentmidwives.org.uk/?node=722*

## USA

### Mothers Naturally USA

Mothers Naturally provides names to help you locate a midwife in your area. The midwives listed here are members of the Midwives Alliance of North America who choose to release their names for referral.
*http://mothersnaturally.org/midwives/findAMidwife.php*

## Canada

### Canadian Association of Midwives (CAM)

The Canadian Association of Midwives is the national organisation representing midwives and the profession of midwifery in Canada. They have a 'Find a Midwife' tool on their website.
*www.canadianmidwives.org/*

# FURTHER RESOURCES FOR BIRTHING AGAIN

## General

### Debby Gould from Birthtalk.org

Contact Debby Gould (co-author of this book and co-founder of Birthtalk.org) for a private consultation, in real life if you are local to Brisbane, Australia, or via phone/Skype. Learn more about how to support your birthing body and how our health system makes its decisions about your birth.
*http://debbygould.wordpress.com/*

### Childbirth Connection

Evidence-based information about Vaginal Birth After Caesarean vs Repeat Caesarean and other concerns. We highly recommend this site as a good source of information. It is a core program of the US National Partnership for Women & Families.
*http://childbirthconnection.com*

### Dr Sarah Buckley's eBook

Pain in Labour: your hormones are your helpers
*www.sarahbuckley.com/pain-in-labour-your-hormones-are-your-helpers/*

---

## Australia

### My Birth

Australian website with information about your rights as a birthing woman, hospital stats for various states of Australia, and some great information designed to empower you.
*www.mybirth.com.au*

### Maternity Choices Australia (formerly Maternity Coalition)

A national (Australian) consumer advocacy organisation made up of individuals and groups who share a commitment to improving the care of women in pregnancy, birth and the postnatal period. They provide excellent birthing and babies support groups and Choices in Childbirth education sessions in Australia.
*www.maternitycoalition.org.au/what-we-do.html*

### Maternity Choices Infosheets

Well-written and researched infosheets on a range of topics including birth after caesarean, induction, pre-labour rupture of membranes.
*www.maternitycoalition.org.au/info-sheets.html*

# UK

## Association for Improvements in the Maternity Services (AIMS – UK)

Working towards normal birth, providing independent support and information about maternity choices, raising awareness of current research on childbirth and related issues, protecting women's human rights in childbirth.
*www.aims.org.uk*

## Birthing From Within

Birthing From Within is an organisation that has evolved from the popular book by the same name. With the book's author, Pam England, and co-owner, Virginia Bobro, at the helm, Birthing From Within provides a number of services to support women preparing to birth, including birth classes, workshops and professional training. Birthing From Within's mission includes inspiring and teaching expectant and new parents, and those who work with them, to prepare for birth as a Rite of Passage; to build a foundation for birthing in awareness in our birth culture, whatever the birth location or outcome or events of the birth; to prevent or minimise emotionally difficult births (for parents and professionals) through compassionate, honest preparation; and to honor and use the power of Birth Storytelling and listening. There is also a listing of official Birthing From Within Mentors and doulas throughout the world.
*www.birthingfromwithin.com*

---

# OTHER CONDITIONS YOU MAY BE SEEKING HELP FOR:

# Postpartum Psychosis

Although relatively rare, Postpartum Psychosis is considered to be a psychiatric emergency, as the safety of the mother and her infant may be at risk.

For more information see:
*www.postpartum.net/Get-the-Facts/Postpartum-Psychosis.aspx*

## PIA Australia Inc.
## (Formerly Pelvic Instability Association)

PIA Australia is a women's not-for-profit organisation that aims to provide support and information to women and families affected by pelvic girdle pain (PGP), and previously known as pelvic instability, and raise awareness of PGP in the community and among health professionals.
*www.piaaustralia.com*

---

## Suggested reading for birthing again

Buckley, S.J. (2009). *Gentle Birth, Gentle Mothering: A Doctor's Guide to Natural Childbirth and Gentle Early Parenting Choices.* Berkeley, CA: Celestial Arts.

Dempsey, R. (2013). *Birth With Confidence: Savvy choices for normal birth.* Melbourne: Boathouse Press.

England, P., & Horowitz, R. (1998). *Birthing from Within.* New Mexico: Partera Press

Goer, H. (1999). *The Thinking Woman's Guide to a Better Birth.* New York: Perigee Books, Berkley publishing group.

Kitzinger, S. (2001). *Rediscovering Birth.* New York: Atria, Simon and Schuster.

Kitzinger, S. (1992). *Ourselves as Mothers: the universal experience of motherhood,* London: Transworld Publishers

MacDonald, L. (2011). *Birth Journeys: positive birth stories to encourage and inspire.* Canberra: Star Class.

Odent, M. (1994). *Birth Reborn.* United Kingdom: Souvenir Press Ltd.

# *Appendix B*

## Disclaimer

*This appendix comprises general information about legal matters. The appendix is not comprehensive about possible legal options and is not legal advice. You must not rely on the information in this appendix as an alternative to seeking legal advice from a lawyer. If you have specific questions about any legal matter you should consult a lawyer. You should never delay seeking legal advice, disregard legal advice, or commence or discontinue any legal action because of information in this appendix. Birthtalk makes no representations or warranties in relation to the legal information in this appendix.*

## Potential Legal Claims

It is sometimes possible to bring a legal action about inadequate maternity care. Legal action can be expensive, time-consuming and stressful and success cannot be guaranteed.

The following is a summary of potential legal claims. This summary refers to the Australian legal system. The law in the United Kingdom, United States of America, Canada and New Zealand is broadly similar, although legal claims for compensation are barred in New Zealand if the injuries are covered under the accident compensation scheme (ACC).

For individualised advice about potential legal claims, please consult a local solicitor who specialises in personal injury litigation or health law.

1. **Negligence**

    The law requires that health care providers adhere to Australian standards of practice.

    You could bring a claim in negligence if a health care provider did not provide care to the standard expected in Australia. For example:

- if there was inadequate monitoring of the safety of you and your baby in labour;
- if a problem arose and was not acted on sufficiently promptly;
- if a medical condition was not diagnosed or not diagnosed sufficiently promptly; or
- if you were not given appropriate post-operative care.

    The details vary between states and territories but as a general rule, it is a defence for the health care provider to prove that a respectable body of their colleagues would have acted in the same way.

    You may also bring a claim in negligence if a heath care provider did not properly advise you as to the risks associated with a medical procedure, and the risk in question eventuates.

    When considering treatment options, the law requires the health care provider to inform you about both risks that most people would consider significant and risks that they know would be significant to you.

    In order to succeed in a negligence action, you would need to prove that the negligence caused injury or loss to you or your baby and that this was foreseeable.

    You can potentially claim compensation for:

- pain and suffering or loss of enjoyment of life;
- costs of medical or other appointments;
- costs of care for you or your baby;
- loss of earnings;
- psychological damage.

2. **Trespass to the person/battery**

> Your consent is legally required every time a health provider performs a procedure on you, even a relatively minor procedure such as a vaginal examination.
>
> If you were treated without your consent, you may be able to bring a claim in the law of trespass to the person or battery.
>
> There is a limited exception for emergencies if you were unconscious or otherwise incapable of consenting, and nobody else had legal authority (for instance via a power of attorney or guardianship order) to consent on your behalf.
>
> It is no defence to a battery claim to prove that the treatment was clinically appropriate.
>
> It can sometimes be difficult to prove injury or loss in a battery claim. However, it may be possible to claim vindicatory or punitive damages due to the fact that the battery has occurred.

3. **Assault or indecent assault**

> In a really strong case there may be the basis for complaint to the police for assault or indecent assault if a procedure was performed without consent.

4. **Breach of human rights**

> Public authorities such as public hospitals and their employees are legally obliged to act in a way that is consistent with your human rights. In Victoria and the Australian Capital Territory, you may potentially make a legal claim for a breach of human rights law.
>
> In Europe, the right to respect for privacy and family life has been found to cover the right of a woman to exercise autonomy over the place she gives birth. However, the potential for human rights law claims related to childbirth is currently not well articulated in Australian law.

You cannot claim monetary damages for a breach of human rights.

***Thank you to Dr Rhonda Powell, School of Law, University of Canterbury, for her assistance in drafting this appendix.***

# Contact us

## How to contact us at Birthtalk.org

We would love to hear from you!

Email is the easiest way to contact us: *info@birthtalk.org.*
For further contact details see our website at *www.birthtalk.org.*

# Thank you

Thank you so much to our editing team, who each took us to a new phase of the project, and gave us encouragement and clarity as we progressed: Melissa Fox, who sat with us every weekend during the winter of 2013 and gently helped us as we formulated a final manuscript from our many drafts; Rachelle Page, who volunteered to completely edit the manuscript and corrected a lot of our early mistakes; Idoya Torres, who also gave constructive feedback of the early manuscript; Nicole Holyer, who presented us with our first professional edit; Justine Gannon, who took us to the next level after we overhauled the manuscript and gave us a complete final edit; and Caylie Jeffery, who brought us over the line with her remarkable editorial assistance in the final months.

We are incredibly grateful to Dr Sarah Buckley for her ongoing encouragement and support, her availability to chat about our concerns, and especially for reading an early draft and providing invaluable feedback that meant we wrote an additional chapter! Thanks to Jennie Elston, who offered us both invaluable support at various stages throughout this process. Our gratitude goes to all the wonderful women and student midwives who have supported us through research assistance, offering feedback of drafts, preparing additional material, and just being a sounding board for our many questions.

Thank you also to the women and men who completed initial questionnaires for us in 2010, and everyone who has answered our (often highly personal) questions about how they dealt with aspects of a traumatic birth since then. We are not mentioning your names here as some of you want to remain anonymous, but please know that your contribution to the book has been invaluable. Your stories offer deep insight and paint a very personal picture of what the aftermath of a traumatic birth can be like. These stories need to be heard, and our book would be poorer without them. Thank you so very much.

We want to thank Leonie MacDonald, Editor of *Birth Journeys : Positive birth stories to encourage and inspire* and her husband Michael, for their invaluable input in the area of self-publishing. They were so forthcoming in information as well as support, providing detailed answers to our many questions that really supported that part of our early process towards publication.

Jesse Richardson has been an incredible support to us, as Art Director of our book cover, our website, our brochures, and everything to do with the 'look' of our book. We are so grateful. He has given us hours of his time plus his creative insights and suggestions, leading us ever-so-patiently to our beautiful final book cover. Thank you so much Jesse!

Thank you to Jen Shipston from The He{ART} of Motherhood for the fabulous photography – providing us with the incredible image for our cover photo, and taking our head shots for the book and website, while encouraging us to be natural in a setting where we felt less-than-comfortable. You did a great job, Jen.

Melissa would like to give a special thank you to the women of the HBAC Yahoo list she was a member of in the early days of her healing, including Jenny Griebenow, Gretchen Humphries, Pam Kleingers, Victoria Brigham, and Pamela Vireday from the ICAN Yahoo list.

We would both like thank our beautiful midwives, who supported us as we brought our children into the world, and who willingly shared many chats about birth and its impact with us as we prepared to meet our babies: Lynne Staff, Lisca Hoy, Andrea Anderson and Tania Nairn.

Thanks and hugs go to Karen Hofman, who started Birthtalk with us back in 2002, and was an integral part of Birthtalk's original format and philosophy. Thank you, Karen for your dedication to the formation of Birthtalk, so that women and families could begin to receive support and information previously difficult to find.

We want to thank our friends and colleagues for their encouragement and support and patience as they have ridden the waves of emotion that the writing of this book entailed over the many years of work. Thank you for sticking with us, always being positive, and lifting us up when we've struggled. All those messages and enthusiasm and hugs have meant more than you could know.

We want to thank our families, who have not only been extremely patient as we have worked on this book for the past seven years, but have also been sharing us with Birthtalk since 2002. It has not been easy on husbands, children and grandparents, who have all stepped up to help us get this book over the line. Thanks also to our siblings who have offered their support and encouragement throughout the years. We are grateful, and we love you.

And to the women and men who have been to Birthtalk, or emailed us, or phoned us, and especially those who have shared their stories in the pages of this book – thank you. You have inspired us with your courage, your tenacity, and your willingness to 'go there' and be vulnerable in order to move on. It's because of you that we have been able to keep going, and we thank you.